SCRIBNER READING SERIES

# FIND YOUR WAY

*Jack Cassidy*

*Doris Roettger* *Karen K. Wixson*

SCRIBNER EDUCATIONAL PUBLISHERS

New York

ACKNOWLEDGMENTS

"The Beach" is abridged and adapted from pp. 5, 11-19 in BORN TO DANCE SAMBA by Miriam Cohen.   Copyright © 1984 by Miriam Cohen. Reprinted by permission of Harper & Row, Publishers, Inc.

"The Best Town in the World" is adapted from the text THE BEST TOWN IN THE WORLD by Byrd Baylor. Text copyright © 1982 Byrd Baylor. Reprinted by permission of Charles Scribner's Sons.

"Breeds of Dogs" is from "Breeds of Dogs" by Simon J. B. Davis which appeared originally in *Cricket* magazine. Copyright © 1984 by Simon J. B. Davis and reprinted with permission of the author.

"Chinese Writing" is from CHINESE WRITING, An Introduction by Diane Wolff with calligraphy by Jeanette Chien. Copyright © 1975 by Diane Wolff. Reprinted by permission of Henry Holt & Company.

"Cindy, A Hearing Ear Dog" is an adaptation of CINDY, A HEARING EAR DOG by Patricia Curtis, photos by David Cupp. Text copyright © 1981 by Patricia Curtis. Illustrations copyright © 1981 by David Cupp. Reprinted by permission of the publisher, E. P. Dutton, a Division of New American Library and by permission also of McIntosh & Otis, Inc.

"City" by Langston Hughes is from THE LANGSTON HUGHES READER. Copyright © 1958 by Langston Hughes. Copyright renewed 1986 by George Houston Bass. Reprinted by permission of Harold Ober Associates Incorporated.

"Code in the Mailbox" is from "Code in the Mailbox" by Kathy Kennedy Tapp and appeared originally in *Cricket* Magazine. Copyright © 1984 by Kathy Kennedy Tapp and reprinted with her permission.

"The Crane Maiden" is adapted from THE CRANE MAIDEN by Miyoko Matsutani, English version by Alvin Tresselt. Copyright © 1968 by Parents Magazine Press. Reprinted by permission of Scholastic Inc.

"The Day After Thanksgiving" is from "The Day After Thanksgiving" by Maureen Ash and appeared originally in *Cricket* Magazine. Copyright © 1984 by Maureen Ash and reprinted with her permission.

"The Day Out" is from MARY POPPINS and MARY POPPINS COMES BACK both by P.L. Travers and illustrated by Mary Shepard. Copyright 1934, 1935, 1962, 1963 by P.L. Travers. Reprinted by permission of Harcourt Brace Jovanovich, Inc. © Text P.L. Travers 1982, © Illustrations Mary Shepard 1982, published by Collins.

(Acknowledgments continued on page 573)

SCRIBNER EDUCATIONAL PUBLISHERS
866 Third Avenue
New York, NY 10022
Collier Macmillan Publishers, London
Collier Macmillan Canada, Inc.

Printed in the United States of America
ISBN 0-02-256110-2
9 8 7 6 5 4 3

# FIND
# YOUR WAY

# Contents

# STRATEGIES
## TO USE WHEN YOU MEET A NEW WORD

### PRONOUNCE THE WORD

Is it a word you know?
Is it a word you have heard other people use?

### EXAMINE THE WORD

Is it a compound word? Do you know the meanings of the
smaller words?
Are any parts of the word like another word you know? Does
it have a familiar base word? Does it have a familiar prefix
or suffix?

### EXAMINE THE SENTENCE IN WHICH THE WORD
### APPEARS

Are there any clues that help you understand the meaning of
the new word?

If you are still not sure what the word means, look it up in the
glossary or a dictionary to find out its meaning.

# STRATEGIES
## TO USE WHEN YOU WRITE

**PREWRITING**—Before you write,

- choose a topic.
- consider your purpose and audience.
- take notes and make an outline.

**WRITING**—When you write your first draft,

- use your notes.
- compose a topic sentence.
- compose detail sentences that support your topic.
- vary sentence length and structure for interest.

**REVISING**—When you revise,

- edit your first draft. Be sure you have kept to your topic, arranged your sentences in the best order, used vivid words, and achieved your purpose for writing.
- proofread. Be sure the punctuation, spelling, and grammar you have used are correct.

| Use these marks when you edit and proofread. | ¶ | Start new paragraph |
| | ∧ | Add this |
| | ℒ | Delete this |
| lowercase | | Make this lowercase |
| capital | | Make this uppercase |

- copy your revised draft neatly on a clean sheet of paper.

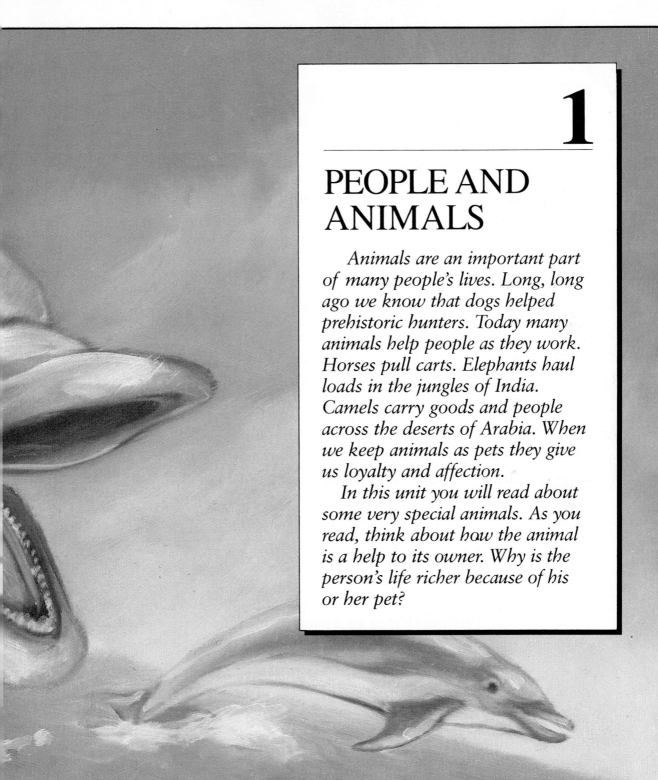

# 1

# PEOPLE AND ANIMALS

Animals are an important part of many people's lives. Long, long ago we know that dogs helped prehistoric hunters. Today many animals help people as they work. Horses pull carts. Elephants haul loads in the jungles of India. Camels carry goods and people across the deserts of Arabia. When we keep animals as pets they give us loyalty and affection.

In this unit you will read about some very special animals. As you read, think about how the animal is a help to its owner. Why is the person's life richer because of his or her pet?

# The Three Mr. P's

by COLIN THIELE

Animals and humans can form strong friendships. Animals often return the kindness shown them by humans with loyalty. In this story, Storm Boy, who lives with his father on an island off the coast of Australia, rescues three pelicans.

How was the pelican nest destroyed? What happens after Storm Boy and his father bring the pelicans back to the sanctuary?

When Storm Boy went walking along the beach, or over the sand hills, or in the sanctuary, the birds were not afraid. They knew he was a friend. The pelicans sat in a row and rattled their beaks drily in greeting. The moorhens fussed and chattered. The ibises cut the air into strips as they jerked their curved beaks up and down. The blue crane stood in silent dignity like a tall, thin statue as Storm Boy went past.

But one morning Storm Boy found everything in uproar and confusion. Three or four young men had gone into the sanctuary. They had found some pelican nests—wide, rough nests of sticks, grass, and pelican feathers as big as turkey quills—and they had killed two of the big birds nesting there. After that they had scattered everything wildly with their boots, kicking and shouting and picking up the white eggs and throwing them about until they were all broken. Then they had gone off laughing.

Storm Boy crept forward in fear and anger. He looked around sadly at the ruin and destruction. Then he heard a faint rustling and crying. There, under the sticks and grass of the broken nests, were three tiny pelicans—still alive. Storm Boy picked them up carefully and hurried back to Hideaway with them.

Two of the baby pelicans were fairly strong, but the third was gravely ill. He was bruised and hurt and helpless. He was so weak that he couldn't even hold up his head to be fed. He just let it drop back flat on the ground as soon as Storm Boy or Hideaway let go of it.

"I don't think he'll live," said Hideaway. "He's too small and sick."

"He mustn't die," Storm Boy said desperately. "He mustn't! He mustn't!"

He wrapped up the tiny bruised body in one of Hideaway's scarves and put it by the fire. All day long he watched it lying there, sometimes moving feebly or opening its beak to give a noiseless cry. Every now and then Storm Boy poured out a drop of cod-liver oil from the bottle that Hideaway had once bought for him. He tried to trickle it down the baby bird's throat.

Night came on, and still Storm Boy couldn't sleep. Again and again through the night he slipped out of bed and tiptoed across the dirt floor to the fireplace to make sure the baby pelican was warm enough.

And in the morning it was still living.

It was three days before the baby pelican was well enough to sit up and ask for food. By then his two brothers had their beaks open hungrily all the time, although of course they were still too young for their skin pouches to be ready.

"Anyone would think that I was Grandfather Pelican," said Hideaway, "by the way they always turn to me for food."

"You'll have to be," Storm Boy told him, "because their own father and mother are dead."

"Well, they needn't think I can spend all my time catching fish for them. Look at that fellow sitting up as if he owns the place."

"Oh, that's Mr. Proud," said Storm Boy.

"How do you do, Mr. Proud?" Hideaway bowed and scratched the top of the pelican's head. "And what's your brother's name?"

"That's Mr. Ponder," Storm Boy said. "He's very wise and serious."

"And what about the tiny fellow?" asked Hideaway. "Is he Mr. Peep?"

"No, he's Mr. Percival." Storm Boy picked up the bird gently in the scarf and held him on his lap. "He's been very sick."

"Welcome," said Hideaway. "And now Grandfather Pelican had better go and catch some fish or there won't be any supper for the three Mr. P's." And he went off down to his boat.

And that was how Mr. Proud, Mr. Ponder, and Mr. Percival came to live with Storm Boy.

Before long, the three pelicans were big and strong. Their white necks curved up cleanly, their skin pouches grew, and their upper beaks shone like pink pearl shell. Every morning they spread their great white wings with the black edges and flew three or four times around the shack and the beach nearby to make sure that everything was in order for the new day. By then they thought it was time for breakfast, so they landed heavily beside the shack, took a few dignified steps forward, and lined up at the back door.

If Hideaway and Storm Boy were still in bed, the three birds stood politely for a little while, waiting for some sign of movement or greeting. But if nothing happened, Mr. Proud and Mr. Ponder began to get impatient after five or ten minutes. They

started rattling their beaks in disapproval—a snippery-snappery, snickery-snackery sort of sound like dry reeds crackling—until someone woke up.

"All right! All right!" Storm Boy would say sleepily. "I can hear you, Mr. Proud!"

He would sit up and look at the three gentlemen standing there on parade.

"I know what you're thinking, Mr. Ponder. Time for respectable people to be up."

"Time for respectable pelicans to get their *own* breakfast," Hideaway grumbled, "instead of begging from their friends."

And as time went on, he really meant what he said.

At last Hideaway spoke sternly to Storm Boy.

"Mr. Proud, Mr. Ponder, and Mr. Percival will have to go back to the sanctuary where they came from. We just can't afford to feed them anymore."

Storm Boy was sad, but he always knew when his father had made up his mind. "Yes, Dad," he said.

"We'll put them in the big fish baskets," said Hideaway, "and take them in the boat."

"Yes, Dad," said Storm Boy, hanging his head.

So they caught Mr. Proud first, and then Mr. Ponder. They held their wings against their sides, and put them firmly in the fish baskets. Neither Mr. Proud nor Mr. Ponder thought much of the idea. They snackered noisily at Hideaway, raked their ruffled feathers crossly, and glared out through the wickerwork with their yellow eyes.

"Huh!" Hideaway laughed. "We've offended the two gentlemen. Never mind, it's for their own good." And he bowed first to Mr. Proud and then to Mr. Ponder.

But when it came to Mr. Percival's turn, Storm Boy couldn't bear to see him shut up, too. Ever since the miracle of Mr. Percival's rescue, he had been Storm Boy's favorite. He was always quieter, more gentle, and more trusting than his two brothers. Storm Boy picked him up, smoothed his wings, and held him close. "Poor Mr. Percival," he said gently. He looked up at his father. "I'll hold Mr. Percival," he said. "Can I, Dad?"

"Oh, all right," Hideaway said, taking up the two baskets. "Come on, it's time we started."

Hideaway sailed for five miles up the sanctuary before he stopped the boat.

"Here we are," he said at last.

Then he opened the two baskets and took out Mr. Proud and Mr. Ponder.

"Off you go," he said. "Now you'll have to look after yourselves." Then he pushed them off. They flew away in a high wide arc and made for the shore.

"Now Mr. Percival," he said.

Storm Boy pressed his head against Mr. Percival and gave his friend a last soft squeeze. "Good-by, Mr. Percival," he said. He had to pause for a second to clear his throat. "Be a . . . be a good pelican,

21

Mr. Percival, and look after yourself."

He lifted him over the side of the boat and put him down on the water as if he were a big rubber duck. Mr. Percival looked surprised and pained for a minute and floated up and down on the ripples. Then he lifted his big wings, pedaled strongly, and rose slowly up over the water.

Storm Boy brushed at his eye with his knuckles and looked away. He didn't want to let his father see his face.

Hideaway and Storm Boy spent the day fishing. It was fine and sunny, but somehow it seemed cold. Most of the time they just sat in the bobbing boat without talking. Storm Boy knew that his father knew what he was thinking. Sometimes Hideaway looked at him strangely. Once he even cleared his throat carefully, gazed out across the water, and said in an unhappy, bright voice, "Well, I wonder how the three Mr. P's are feeling. Happy to be home, I'll bet!" He looked rather miserably at Storm Boy and went on with his fishing.

Toward evening they packed up and set off for home. The sun was flinging a million golden mirrors in a lane across the water. It glowed on the bare patches of the sand hills and lit up the bushes till every stem and twig shone with rosy fire. The little boat came gliding in to shore through the chuckle of the ripples.

Suddenly Storm Boy looked up.

"Look, Dad, look!" cried Storm Boy.

Hideaway beached the boat and looked up to where Storm Boy was pointing. "What?"

"Look! Look!" cried Storm Boy.

High against the sky on the big sand hill stood the tall Lookout Post that Hideaway had put up years before. And right on top of the post was a big shape. It was quite still, a statue on a column, a bird of stone.

23

Then, as if hearing Storm Boy's startled voice, it suddenly spread out two big wings and launched itself into the air. As it banked against the western sun, its beak and black-tipped wings glowed in the shooting beams of light. For an instant it looked like a magic bird. Storm Boy ran ahead, craning upward, yelling and waving.

"Mr. Percival! It's Mr. Percival! Mr. Percival has come back home!"

*Hideaway agreed to let Mr. Percival stay, so long as Mr. Proud and Mr. Ponder didn't return as well. Although the two other birds sometimes flew overhead or landed on the beach near Storm Boy and Hideaway's house, they always went back to the sanctuary. But not Mr. Percival. He refused even to leave Storm Boy's side.*

## CHECK FOR UNDERSTANDING

1. How was the pelican nest destroyed?
2. Which of the pelicans was the weakest and the most seriously hurt when Storm Boy found them?
3. Why did Storm Boy call one of the pelicans Mr. Proud? Why did he call another one Mr. Ponder?
4. In what ways was Mr. Percival different from Mr. Proud and Mr. Ponder?
5. Why did Hideaway decide that the pelicans had to go back to the sanctuary?
6. What happened after Storm Boy and his father brought the pelicans back to the sanctuary? Why do you think this happened?

**WRITE ABOUT** *"The Three Mr. P's"*

Bird sanctuaries are places where birds are supposed to be protected from being harmed by animals and humans. The pelicans in this story, however, were attacked by humans in the sanctuary. Imagine that you were in charge of the sanctuary. How would you prevent something like this from happening again? Write a paragraph explaining what you would do to ensure the safety of the birds in the sanctuary.

# VOCABULARY • LANGUAGE

## Context Clues

In "The Three Mr. P's," you learned that

> When Storm Boy went walking along the beach
> . . .the birds were not afraid. . . . The pelicans sat in a
> row and rattled their beaks drily in greeting. The
> moorhens fussed and chattered.

Look at the word *moorhens* in the passage above.
Were you familiar with this word before you read the
story? Probably not. But you can figure out its meaning
by looking at the **context**. This means the words and
sentences around the word. **Context clues** will help you
find the word's meaning.

For example, the writer states that "The *birds* were not
afraid. . . . The *pelicans* sat in a row. . . . The *moorhens*
fussed. . . ." The words *birds* and *pelicans* are context
clues. They suggest that *moorhens* are birds.

Storm Boy discovered that one of the pelicans

> . . .was *gravely* ill. He was bruised and hurt and help-
> less. He was so weak that he couldn't even hold up
> his head.

By using context clues, you should be able to figure
out the meaning of *gravely*. Does *gravely* mean
"cheerfully," "seriously," or "smoothly"? What clues helped
you figure out the answer?

You may remember that Storm Boy named one of the
pelicans Mr. Proud because he used to sit up proudly, as

if he owned the place. Storm Boy named another pelican Mr. Ponder.

"That's Mr. Ponder," Storm Boy said. "He's very wise and serious."

Does *ponder* mean "think about carefully," "feel very sad," or "act foolishly"? What clues helped you?

Sometimes, writers give the meaning, or **definition,** of a difficult or unfamiliar word. Often, the meaning is signaled by commas or dashes. In the next story, "Breeds of Dogs," for example, notice how the writer gives the definition of the word *zoologists.*

> **Zoologists**—people who study animals—think that humans tamed dogs as long as 12,000 years ago.

Below are two passages from "Breeds of Dogs." Use context clues to find the meaning of the words that are underlined. Be prepared to explain your answers.

> Perhaps the most striking thing about dogs, when compared to other animals, is their tremendous variety. There are more than 150 breeds of dogs.
>
> Today we can easily guess the origin of many breeds just by looking at their names. Spaniels come from Spain. Afghan hounds come from Afghanistan. Irish setters come from Ireland.

As you read the story, use context clues to figure out the meaning of *dense, nobility,* and *hardy.* Find definitions for *retrieved, terriers,* and *mongrels.*

# —BREEDS OF DOGS—

by SIMON J. B. DAVIS

**People often think of dogs merely as pets. However, in the past, dogs were especially bred to perform various tasks. This article tells about many of the breeds of dogs, where they come from, and what jobs the dogs are bred to do.**

**Which animal is the modern dog's ancestor? What is perhaps the most striking thing about dogs?**

The dog is probably people's oldest animal companion.

Zoologists—people who study animals—think that humans tamed dogs as long as 12,000 years ago. They are almost certain that these first dogs were bred from wolves. Even today, wolf cubs raised by people develop greater affection for their human caretakers than for other wolves. But when the cubs grow up, they often return to their wild ways.

Perhaps the most striking thing about dogs, when compared to other animals, is their tremendous variety. Today there are more than 150 recognized breeds of dogs. All of them, from tiny Chihuahuas and Pekingese to the much larger Labradors

and Afghan hounds, have been bred from the same ancestor—the wolf. All these types of dogs have been developed over the years by people who valued different qualities in dogs.

We know from paintings and sculptures found in the tombs and palaces of ancient Mesopotamia and Egypt that different types of dogs were already bred more than 5000 years ago. Today we can easily guess the country of origin of many breeds just by looking at their names. Spaniels come from Spain. Afghan hounds come from Afghanistan. Irish setters come from Ireland. Alsatians come from the Alsace region of France. Chihuahuas come from the Mexican city and state of the same name. Pekingese come from the Chinese city of Peking.

Most of today's popular breeds were developed in England, however, for many different purposes. Dogs had to serve as hunters, retrievers, shepherds, guards, or they were simply used for show.

The spaniel, for example, was the original hunting dog. Water spaniels were excellent swimmers. Their thick, dense hair

protected them from even the coldest water, so they were used for hunting ducks. Other spaniels were useful for their habit of "setting" (lying flat on the ground when they found such game as partridge and quail). This behavior alerted their owners, who could then throw a net over both dog and game. Our modern setters developed from these "setting" spaniels.

Once shotguns were invented, setters were no longer as helpful to hunters. Pointers and retrievers were used instead. Pointers used their excellent sense of smell to locate animals and would then "point" to the game's hiding place. Retrievers did just what their name suggests. They retrieved, or brought back, game their owners had shot.

In medieval Britain, hounds were bred for their endurance and sense of smell. They were used to chase down large game such as deer. But only the nobility could own hounds. Only they were allowed to hunt such "luxury" game. The common people had to make do with hunting badgers, polecats, and rats—animals that live underground and in deep dens. That's how the various breeds of small terriers—dogs specially bred for hunting animals that live in the ground—were developed. The name "terrier," in fact, comes from the

French *la terre*, which means "ground."

Dogs have also been bred for strength and were used to pull carts and sleds. Before Europeans brought the horse to North America, Native Americans used dogs to haul their travois, land sleds they made from wood and leather. Even today, special breeds of dogs such as the strong, hardy Siberian husky, Alaskan malamute, and Samoyed are used by Eskimos and others to pull sleds over snow and ice. They have heavy coats to protect them from the cold. Their woolly, oily undercoats shed water. The thick, furry pads on their feet help them walk in deep snow.

Dalmatians, handsome white dogs with black spots, were originally kept as coach dogs to accompany horse-drawn carriages. They sometimes are kept as fire-station mascots today. And the fragile-looking Saluki is an Arab breed that was valued

for its speed and hardiness in hunting gazelles.

Dogs of mixed breeding are called mongrels. They are often looked down upon. Their sole function in the past was to bark at the approach of strangers. A curious kind of mongrel, the turnspit, was once quite common in England. It was used in kitchens to turn a spit of roasting meat by running around inside a wheel.

People are still developing new breeds of dogs and will continue to do so. Twelve thousand years ago a wolf cub was raised by humans. Now millions of people all over the world own and love dogs, people's oldest—and some say best—animal friend.

## CHECK FOR UNDERSTANDING

1. Where can we find proof that different types of dogs were bred five thousand years ago?
2. Which animal is the modern dog's ancestor?
3. What is perhaps the most striking thing about dogs?
4. Why did the invention of guns make "setting" dogs less useful?
5. Where do you think Great Danes come from?
6. Akitas are bred to be quiet, gentle, and to stay indoors. Why are they a good breed for modern times?

# Cindy

## A HEARING EAR DOG

by PATRICIA CURTIS

Everyone has heard of Seeing Eye dogs—but a hearing ear dog? Just as Seeing Eye dogs are trained to alert their blind owners to what they cannot see, so hearing ear dogs tell their deaf owners about what they cannot hear. This selection tells about the training of one such dog.

Why is the state of Cindy's hearing so important? What might happen to her if she didn't hear well?

A small, fuzzy gray dog sat in the yard at an animal shelter and gazed out through the fence. She did this every day. She seemed to be watching and waiting for someone.

The dog had been found running all by herself along a busy road. A passerby had noticed her and brought her to safety at the shelter. She had no collar, no tags to show whose dog she was. She was very tired, cold, and hungry when she was found.

At first, the people at the shelter hoped that someone would come looking for the little dog. But days passed, and nobody came.

One day, after a few weeks, a man came to the animal shelter looking for a dog to adopt. His name was Mr. MacMunn.

He stopped in front of the fuzzy gray dog's cage and looked carefully at her. She pricked up her ears and studied him hopefully.

"What's this one's name?" Mr. MacMunn asked the woman who was in charge of adoptions.

"We've been calling her Cindy," the woman answered. "She's a very nice dog."

"Here, Cindy," said Mr. MacMunn. Cindy came to the front of her cage, jumped up and down, and wagged her tail hard. She licked the man's hand through the bars of the cage.

"Could I take this one out of the cage, please?" asked Mr. MacMunn, and he let Cindy out. She put her front paws up on him and looked into his face as if to say, "Please take me home!"

"I'll take this one," he said.

Cindy acted as if she were thrilled to be chosen. She jumped up and down some more, wagged her tail, and licked Mr. MacMunn's hands again.

Mr. MacMunn put her in his car and drove off. Cindy was excited at being out of the shelter. Maybe she thought she was going to a home at last. What Cindy didn't know was that before she would have an owner and a home of her own, she was going to school. She was going to be taught to be a hearing ear dog.

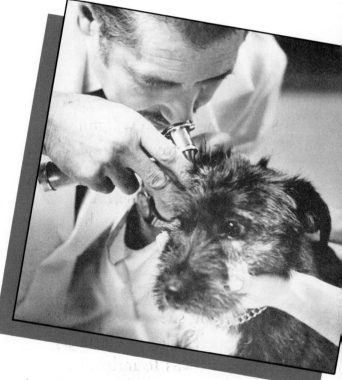

Most people have heard of guide dogs for the blind, such as Seeing Eye dogs. Few people know about hearing ear dogs. These dogs are trained to be helpers and companions to deaf people. The dogs alert their owners to certain sounds their owners can't hear.

Mr. MacMunn was the president of a college where he had started a special program to teach young men and women how to train dogs for the deaf. The dogs that they trained were placed with deaf people who needed them.

All dogs that entered the hearing ear dog training program at the college were first given a thorough checkup by a veterinarian, to be sure they were healthy. The doctor gave special attention to Cindy's ears. This was perhaps the most important part of the examination. Her ears were going to have to hear for two—for herself and for the deaf person who would one day be her owner. Cindy's ears were fine.

"This dog is in perfect health," said the vet to Mr. MacMunn.

But back at the college, Cindy had to pass one more test before she could be enrolled in the hearing ear dog training program. Mrs. Allen, the program director, had to judge if Cindy would make a good pupil. Mrs. Allen gave Cindy a few basic lessons in obedience to see how the dog responded.

Cindy liked being praised and petted when she did the right thing. That was very important. It meant Cindy was eager to learn and wanted to please Mrs. Allen. The

program director knew dogs, and she decided Cindy could be trained. Cindy passed the test.

In the weeks that followed, Mrs. Allen and her students taught Cindy all the basic obedience commands and hand signals. She learned to come, heel, sit, stay, and lie down when she was told to. Two students, Lynn and Bill, also worked with Cindy. She learned to obey commands from them as well as from Mrs. Allen.

However, obeying was not the most important part of her training. The really hard lessons were still to come. To be a hearing ear dog, Cindy

would have to learn to think for herself when she heard certain sounds. A dog on whom a deaf person depends can't wait around for its owner to tell it what to do. When it hears a noise, it must figure out where the noise is and what it means. It must learn to bring its owner to the noise.

One morning, Mrs. Allen said Cindy had learned to obey so well that she was ready to be trained as a hearing ear dog. Lynn and Bill were assigned to teach her at the training cottage. The cottage had many different kinds of bells that could be rung during lessons, so the dogs could learn to respond to them.

The students began Cindy's training with the alarm clock. Lynn played the role of a deaf person. She lay down on a bed and set an alarm clock, while Bill stayed in the next room with Cindy on a leash. The alarm clock rang. Quickly, Bill brought Cindy to Lynn and encouraged the dog to jump up on the bed. Lynn, pretending to wake up, hugged Cindy and praised her.

After they did that exercise a few times, Bill let Cindy off the leash in the next room. *Ding ding ding*! went the alarm clock.

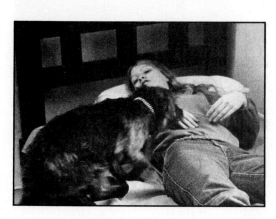

"*Sound*, Cindy!" cried Bill. "*Go tell!*"

Cindy rushed into the bedroom, jumped up on the bed with Lynn, and licked her, wiggling with joy. She seemed to love learning. Again, Lynn hugged her and told her she had done well. In a few days, Cindy learned always to make the right response to the alarm clock. In the future she would be able to tell her deaf owner an important piece of information: The alarm clock is ringing, it's time to get up.

In the hearing ear dog training program, dogs were never punished for making mistakes or not responding, and they were allowed to rest whenever they got tired. But when they caught on and did the right thing, they were rewarded with praise and petting.

The next lesson Cindy learned was to tell Lynn when the doorbell rang. Most dogs will run to the door anyway whenever the bell rings. But a hearing ear dog must bring its owner to the door as well.

Bill went outside the cottage while Lynn put Cindy on a pulley that was attached to the door. Again, Lynn pretended

to be the deaf person. When Bill rang the doorbell, Cindy ran to the door. "*Sound*, Cindy!" said Lynn. Then she used the pulley to lead Cindy back to her, saying "*Tell*, Cindy!"

Bill rang the doorbell again.

"*Sound*, Cindy," said Lynn as Cindy ran to the door. "*Tell*, Cindy," she said, pulling Cindy back to her. Then she got up and went and opened the door.

Cindy soon grasped the idea that when the doorbell rang, she was supposed to run back and forth between the door and Lynn. She seemed pleased with herself when Lynn and Bill praised her.

Over several weeks, Cindy learned to respond to other sounds, too. When the teakettle on the stove began to sing or when the oven timer buzzed, Cindy ran to tell Lynn or Bill and lead them to the sound. She also learned to tell them when the telephone rang. Most deaf people can't hear over a regular telephone, but some people who are only partly deaf can use special telephones.

The training cottage had four different types of doorbells that rang, buzzed, or chimed. Cindy learned them all. Later, she also learned to tell Lynn when there was a knock at the door.

Cindy learned fast. If she'd been given a report card she would have earned all A's.

One day Lynn and Bill were told that an owner had been selected for Cindy—a deaf teenager named Jennifer. As soon as her junior high school classes were over for the summer, Jennifer would come to the college to meet Cindy and spend two weeks working with her. Jennifer would be taught to give commands and hand signals to Cindy. Cindy would learn to tell Jennifer instead of Lynn or Bill about the different sounds she knew. If all went well, Cindy would become Jennifer's hearing ear dog.

The big day arrived. Cindy, of course, knew nothing of the

plans for her. She was taking a nap on the couch in the training cottage when Jennifer walked in. The dog opened her eyes and peeked out at the girl from between the pillows. Jennifer sat down and called Cindy to her. Cindy jumped off the couch and walked away, ignoring her. Jennifer was very disappointed.

Lynn knew American Sign Language, which many deaf people use, so she could communicate with Jennifer. "Don't feel bad," Lynn signed. "It always takes a little time for one of our dogs to get to know its new owner. After you have been taking care of Cindy for a few days, she'll come to you."

Cindy let Jennifer hug her, but she looked as if she were saying, "How long do I have to put up with this pushy girl?"

As the days passed, however, Cindy spent more and more time with Jennifer. She slept on the floor in Jennifer's room in the dormitory. Jennifer fed her and took her for walks. Jennifer had brought her bicycle to the college, and Cindy especially loved to run beside her when she rode it. Jennifer learned to bathe and brush the dog.

Without thinking about it, Cindy began to accept Jennifer as her owner.

The next step was to teach Cindy to tell Jennifer instead of the trainers when the dog heard the sounds she had learned to respond to.

First they tried the doorbell. One trainer went outside the door while the other stood behind Jennifer. When the bell rang, Cindy began to run back and forth between the door and the trainer.

"No, Cindy, *tell Jennifer!*" the trainer said.

They tried again. This time, Cindy ran to Jennifer. They kept up this lesson until Cindy always went to Jennifer when the doorbell rang. It was clear that Cindy was beginning to ally herself with Jennifer.

One very important bell that hearing ear dogs are taught to respond to is a smoke alarm that warns of fire. In the kitchen of the training cottage, there was such a bell. Of course, it could be made to ring without smoke. Lynn

went into the kitchen with Cindy while Jennifer sat in the next room. Lynn made the smoke alarm go off.

"*Sound*, Cindy!" exclaimed Lynn. "*Tell Jennifer*!"

And Cindy dashed into the next room to Jennifer and led her out of the cottage.

Cindy's favorite bell was still the alarm clock. She seemed to think it was so much fun to jump on the bed and wake up Jennifer.

Jennifer, of course, had to learn her part, too. Lynn taught her to give Cindy all the obedience commands and hand signals. Whenever Cindy responded correctly, Jennifer hugged and petted her, just as the trainers had done.

The trainers also told Jennifer to watch Cindy when they were outdoors together. If Cindy pricked up her ears and turned her head, it would mean she heard a noise. It might be a siren, an automobile horn, a person shouting, an object falling onto the sidewalk—something going on that Jennifer should know about.

The two weeks went by swiftly. Lynn and Bill felt they would miss Cindy. But they had more dogs to teach to become hearing ear dogs for people who needed them.

Finally, Jennifer packed up her suitcase, took Cindy by the leash, and walked out the door of the dormitory. Cindy at last had an owner who loved her. She was going to a home of her own, where she was needed and wanted.

## CHECK FOR UNDERSTANDING

1. How did Cindy show that she was eager to learn?
2. Why was the state of Cindy's hearing so important?
3. What might have happened to her if she didn't hear well?
4. Why do you think hearing ear dogs are never punished for doing the wrong thing?
5. Which bell that Cindy learned to respond to was the most important? Why?

## WRITE ABOUT *"Cindy, a Hearing Ear Dog"*

Jennifer wanted to write a thank-you letter to Mr. MacMunn, the president of the college where Cindy was trained. Write Jennifer's letter. Describe the ways in which Cindy helps you each day.

# STUDY SKILLS

## Reading Textbooks

There are different ways of reading. When you are in a bike race, you don't ride in the same way as when you are just riding for fun. It's the same with reading. You should read in different ways, according to *what* you are reading, and *why* you are reading.

When you are reading a story, sometimes you read pretty fast. You are eager to see what happens. So you skim.

But you don't read that way if you are reading a textbook. Because then you're reading with a different purpose. You're reading in order to learn.

The subject may be new to you. There may be things that you don't quite understand. There may be names and details that you have to remember. It's not easy.

But there are certain things you can do that will help you a lot in your school reading. They are not hard to remember. Think of them as **PQRST**.

## Step 1

**P** stands for **Preview**. This means looking at something ahead of time. Do this with your reading. Before beginning to read, just look the material over. Look at the *title* of the chapter. Look at the *headings*. These will give you clues as to what it's going to be about. The title and headings are just a few words, but they are important: they give you clues as to what's to come.

It's a good idea to look at the end of the chapter, to see if there are any questions. The questions, if there are any, will give you an idea of what facts are important. You can then watch out for them.

It's like finding your way to a place you've never been to before. When people give you directions, they mention landmarks, things to watch out for. They may say: "Turn left at the big yellow house." So you know the big yellow house is important, and you watch for it.

In the same way, titles, headings, and questions are like landmarks in your reading. They tell you what to watch for as you read.

## Step 2

**Q** stands for **Question**—not the questions at the end of the chapter, *your own* questions. Look at the title and headings. Then make up questions about them.

Let's try it out. Preview the following passage. Then make up your own questions.

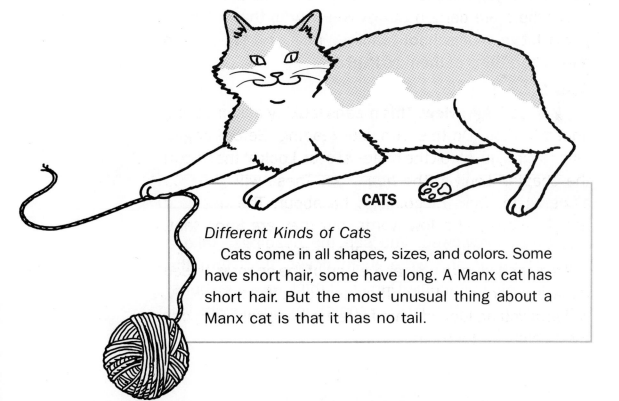

**CATS**

*Different Kinds of Cats*

Cats come in all shapes, sizes, and colors. Some have short hair, some have long. A Manx cat has short hair. But the most unusual thing about a Manx cat is that it has no tail.

Persian cats have long hair. They have long, fluffy fur. They're pretty. But they have to be brushed a lot!

Some cats are just one color. Gray. Black. White. A Persian cat can have as many as forty different colors in its fur.

Some cats have eyes of different colors.

*A New Breed of Cat*

Not long ago, a new kind of cat came into existence. It is called the Rex cat. A Rex is very slim. Its fur is short and curly. And it has very big ears. The Rex was first bred in the 1950s, in Great Britain.

You have previewed. You see the headings. Take a piece of paper and write them down. Then turn the headings into questions. Don't just think your questions. *Write* them down, too. Writing something down helps you to remember it.

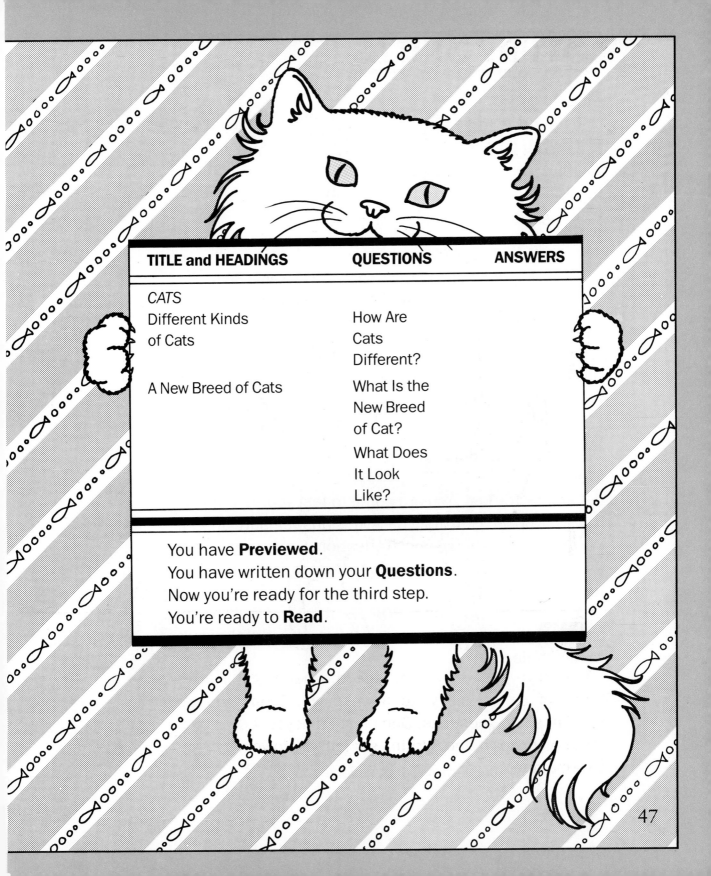

| TITLE and HEADINGS | QUESTIONS | ANSWERS |
|---|---|---|
| *CATS* Different Kinds of Cats | How Are Cats Different? | |
| A New Breed of Cats | What Is the New Breed of Cat? | |
| | What Does It Look Like? | |

You have **Previewed**.
You have written down your **Questions**.
Now you're ready for the third step.
You're ready to **Read**.

# STUDY SKILLS

## Step 3

**R** stands for **Read**. Remember — you should not read as fast as you do when you are reading a story. As you read, you have to watch out for the answers to your questions and you may think of more questions. Add them to your list. You may want to add this:

| |
|---|
| Where was Rex First Bred?        When? |

Now you're ready for your next step, **Study**.

## Step 4

**S** stands for **Study**. You study by answering your own questions. Were your answers right? Is there more you can add to them? If so, do.

You have now done **P, Q, R, S**. Now you're ready for the last step, **Test**.

## Step 5

**T** stands for **Test**. You are going to test yourself. This is how you do it. First fold back the *answer* part of your paper. Then ask yourself each question. Do you remember the answer? Check your written answer to make sure it is right. If it's not, go back to the text.

What's important about **PQRST**? It will make it easier for you to study and to remember things. It will make you a better student.

**P**  Preview the pages.
**Q**  Make up the questions.
**R**  Read for the answers.
**S**  Study by writing the answers.
**T**  Test yourself with your questions.

Now you are ready to try **PQRST** on a longer passage. Read **Horses** and follow the same steps.

**Horses**

### The First Horses

Nowadays, horses are large, strong animals. But they were not always that way. The very earliest ancestors of the horse that we know about looked nothing like horses today. They were very small. Though it is hard to believe, they were only about fifteen inches high. They were about the size of a medium-sized dog.

We call this early animal *Eohippus.* In Greek, this means "dawn horse." *Eohippus* lived more than fifty million years ago. It lived in the forests of North America.

### How Horses Have Helped People

Over time, the horse has developed into a large animal. For tens of thousands of years or more, these large, swift, strong animals have been helpful

to people. They have been tamed, and used as a way of transportation. You could travel faster and further on horseback than you could on foot.

Horses are used to carry things and to pull things —wagons and carriages. They have helped the farmer by pulling the plow. In the time of the Pony Express, they were used to carry the mail.

The first people who delivered milk to houses used to pull their wagons themselves. Then they used horses to pull the milk wagons. Now trucks are used. Many farmers use mechanical equipment, but some farmers still use horses.

### Horses and People Today

Horses are still used for transportation. Cowhands ride them on the range, while herding cattle. For this purpose, a horse is still better than a car, truck, or cycle.

Many people like to ride horses for sport. Even in cities, and in parks, you can see people riding horseback. The link between horses and people is still a strong one.

## Using What You Have Learned

Find a passage in a book. Study it, using **PQRST**. Don't forget to write down your questions and answers.

## Expanding Your Skills

You have now finished studying **Horses** using **PQRST**. Now make up a quiz on the facts. It should contain five True or False statements about horses.

Here are two samples:

| | |
|---|---|
| The first horses were very small. | (T) |
| People only learned to ride horses about 1000 years ago. | (F) |

Exchange quizzes with your neighbor. Answer the questions. Write *T* if the statement is true. Write *F* if the statement is false.

You may need more practice using **PQRST**. Once you get used to it, **PQRST** will help you learn. It will help you remember things. It will help you be a better student.

# The Day After Thanksgiving

by MAUREEN ASH

**Many people choose friends who are steadfast, sure, and dependable. Even animal friends can possess these different qualities, as the narrator of this story discovers when her ride in the woods turns into a nightmare.**

**What lesson does the narrator learn from her two horses? How can she apply this lesson to other areas of her life?**

It wasn't hard at all to lie in bed that morning after Thanksgiving. My two horses were being kept in our far pasture until the snow flew, and the view from my bedroom seemed empty without their dark shapes under the trees or near the little barn.

I planned my day as I lay listening to the breakfast noises my mother was making in the kitchen. Skating first, I decided, before the sun had time to weaken the ice on the pond. And then a good, long ride.

My mother had other plans for me, though. It wasn't until after lunch that I could grab my skates and a bridle and head for the far pasture. My dad came by with a tractor and wagon, on his way to pick corn. He slowed to let me jump on the wagon. I bumped along the highway behind him, watching the woods and swamps and hoping I would see a deer. He stopped at the rutted road to the pasture gate, and I jumped off. "Careful," he yelled over the tractor's sputtering.

"You, too," I hollered back and slipped under the fence.

The pond was smoothly frozen. But when I tested the ice, it bent under my weight. I could see by the bubbles trapped in it that the ice wasn't thick enough for skating. Oh well, I thought, and dropped my skates and whistled the special whistle.

"Hurry up!" I yelled at the two horses as they trotted out of the woods near the end of the pasture. My gray horse, Keko, broke into a canter when she saw me. But I had to wave one of the corncobs I'd brought over my head to coax Thor, my little sorrel pony, into a slow lope.

"Ah, girl." I petted and kissed Keko when she reached me and gave her a corncob. "You poky old thing," I told Thor when he finally arrived, blowing and looking greedily for his corn.

"Poky—old—thing." I kissed him three times in the hollow above his left eye before I gave him his corn. He had just begun to look worried. Keko finished hers, and I put the bridle on her as Thor crunched his treat noisily.

Mounting a tall horse can be tough anytime, but with winter boots it becomes a real challenge. Keko never would stand still for me. By the time I had settled myself on her back, she was beginning to walk. We explored the woods at the far end of the pasture, Keko's hooves swishing through the leaves. We'd been in the woods hundreds of times. Every time it seemed new. And Keko was never

55

bored. She danced along, her neck arched, blowing jets of steam from her flared nostrils.

She was everything I'd ever wanted in a horse. I loved Thor, too, of course. I'd raised him from a colt, trained him to lead, had broken him to ride, and he'd taught me more than I'd taught him. He was a pony, though, short and thick. My legs were getting too long for him. My dad had finally agreed, a year ago, to help me buy a real horse—not a pony. I could hardly believe my luck when we found Keko. "And now that little nag has to go," Dad had said. But he had watched Thor stand on his wobbly legs for the first time, too. I knew he was teasing. As long as we could swing the price of the feed, we'd keep our Thor.

"OK, girl, OK." Keko was edging toward the open meadow. I knew she wanted to run, and I did, too. I clung with my knees and gave her her head, leaning forward like a jockey until her mane whipped my face and the wind filled my eyes with tears. I pulled her up at the far end of the meadow, both of us gasping for air. She danced under me, wanting to run back. We did, racing the wind and the clouds scattering over the treetops. There was only the horse under me and the steely sky above—nothing else in my mind. I didn't see the pheasant start up from a clump of grass. Not at first. There was only Keko's sudden movement to the side, a quick floundering, and the sickening feeling of her falling. Slow motion, slow motion—I hit the ground and watched her roll as if through heavy syrup, over and over and over my leg.

It happened so quickly. Keko was standing over me in seconds, shaking herself, the reins falling to the

ground. She wasn't hurt. Thor ambled toward us, looking bemused. My ankle beat a drum of hot pain, and I lay for a moment, blinking back tears.

My father wouldn't be back for hours. No one would look for me until after dark. I'd often stayed out with my horses past dinner time. I started to cry in earnest, thinking of the long hours, the cold ground, the furious pain in my leg.

"Come here, girl." My voice shook, and Keko looked at me strangely before she came closer. I grabbed her reins and steadied myself on her as I dragged myself up to stand on one foot. I tried to mount her, but she was too tall. The jumping made my useless foot throb all the more. I clung to her mane and thought.

Thor came closer, still a little leery of us. "Come here, fellow," I coaxed. Ah—I had some corn kernels in the pocket of my sweatshirt. Just the thing. Thor's greed got the best of him. I slipped the bridle off Keko and put it on him as he licked up the last of the corn.

He nudged me with his large head, as if to ask for more. I had to clutch his mane to keep my balance. I think he understood then that something was wrong. He stood like a statue while I struggled up on him. He didn't move until I was settled on his broad back and had the reins well in hand.

We headed for the gate, Keko following anxiously. The gate was just a place in the fence that could easily be unwired. I had to dismount to open it. My hands shook as I fumbled with the thick wires. I led Thor through, hopping on one foot, and wired it carefully behind me. I didn't want Keko to follow us onto the highway. She nickered as I mounted again, twisting my hands in Thor's thick, coarse mane, unable to stop shaking. Thor began to quiver, too.

I was afraid of what Thor would do if a car passed us. One did, and he seemed to hold his breath, tensing until it passed. But nothing changed his steady, quiet plod toward home. There were more cars on the road, but he held to his careful walk, though even his thick coat seemed to shake. I could feel the twitch of his muscles under me. I concentrated on holding my legs steady, trying to keep my foot from jiggling. I couldn't see very well.

It was Thor who turned in at our mailbox, who stopped at the house rather than going straight to his pasture gate, and who stood quietly while I sat on him in the yard, shaking and unable to call for help.

My sister saw me, and I didn't have to worry about getting help anymore. I was in the car to the hospital in minutes. During the long wait with my foot swollen till it looked like some horrible stranger's, the trip to a larger hospital where there were doctors who knew more about broken bones, I remembered one thing and kept it like a quiet secret.

As I was being bundled into the car, my brother had come to take Thor back to his pasture. Thor had gone with him obediently, but after a few steps he'd stopped and looked back, his eyes large and dark. I imagined that he knew what had happened and was saying that he was sorry for me. "Take care of him," I called to my brother. "Take good care of him." And I started to cry a little bit. Thor, my gallant pony, looked at me once again and walked on behind my brother.

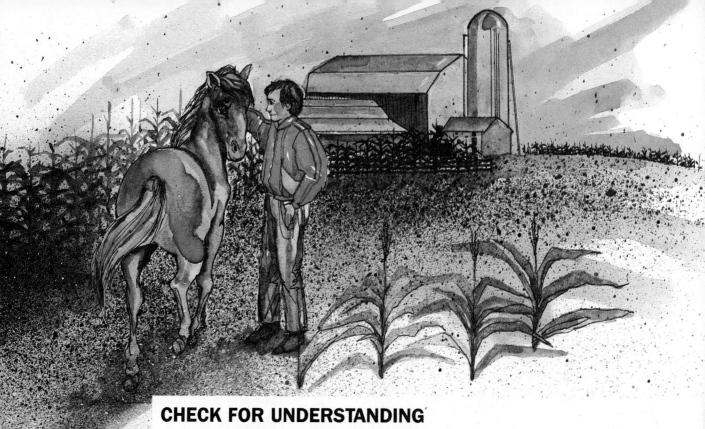

## CHECK FOR UNDERSTANDING

1. Why had the narrator stopped riding Thor?
2. Which horse turned out to be a more valuable friend?
3. Why did the narrator cry at the end of the story?
4. How do you think the narrator's treatment of Thor would change after this incident?
5. What lesson did the narrator learn from her two horses?
6. How could she apply this lesson to other areas of her life?

**WRITE ABOUT** *"The Day After Thanksgiving"*

Imagine that the narrator of the story kept a daily journal. Write her entry for the day of the accident. Tell what happened, as she saw it, and how it made her feel.

# VELVET WHISKERS

by MAXINE KUMIN

I wanted to give
A horse I knew
A sugar lump
That he could chew.

He snuffed my hair.
It made him sneeze.
He didn't say,
Excuse me, please.

He whiffed around
My curled-up fist.
He nuzzled all
Along my wrist.

But when I dared
To spread my hand,
His yellow teeth
Were smooth as sand.

He didn't nip
My thumb, or chew
A single finger
Off. He knew

A way to slurp
The sugar up,
Like too-hot cocoa
From a cup.

And as he crunched,
I felt his nose,
Soft as a
New baby's toes.

Soft as velvet
Gloves would fit.
His whiskers grew
Right out of it.

Velvet whiskers!
But of course—
He was a very
Special horse.

63

# COMPREHENSION

## Sequence

Imagine you are reading a friend's story. All the pages are loose, and none of them are numbered. Suddenly, you drop the story. It scatters all over the floor. When you put the pages back together, they are all out of order.

Can you imagine trying to make sense of the story with the pages out of order? You probably couldn't. But why couldn't you? After all, no part of the story would be missing.

What would be missing is the story's **sequence of events.** By mixing up the pages, you would no longer know what came first, second, and third in the story. Not knowing the order of events would make the story seem like nonsense.

But sometimes it is difficult to keep the order of events in a story straight even when the pages are in order. Many stories you read will not have key words to tell you when events happen. The author will not tell you that one thing happens *first*, another thing happens *next*, and another thing happens *last*. To understand the story, you will have to figure out for yourself what happens first, next, and last.

Also, the author may not write about the events in the order they happened. You may be reading a story about a girl worried about the health of her aging dog. Suddenly the author takes you back to the time when the girl got the dog as a puppy. Then the author comes back to the time when the dog is old again. Remember that authors often use this method of changing the order of events. Be sure you are aware of when each event in the story happened in

relation to the other events.

You had a sample of this in the story you just read, "The Day After Thanksgiving." Pay attention to the changes in time in the following passage from that story. The parts of the story that take place before that Thanksgiving Day are in dark print.

> She danced along, her neck arched, blowing jets of steam from her flared nostrils. She was everything I'd ever wanted in a horse. I loved Thor, too, of course. **I'd raised him from a colt, trained him to lead, had broken him to ride, and he'd taught me more than I'd taught him.** He was a pony, though, short and thick, and my legs were getting too long for him. **My dad had finally agreed, a year ago, to help me buy a real horse—not a pony. I could hardly believe my luck when we found Keko. "And now that little nag has to go," Dad had said.**

You will also find, in stories, that differences in the time between events aren't always equal. For example, a story might begin with an event that takes place on Thursday. The second event in the story might take place the next day, on Friday. But the third event in the story might take place a year later. As you read, make sure you understand not only the order of events, but the time that has passed between one event and another.

# STONE FOX

by JOHN REYNOLDS GARDINER

**Honor is a sense of what is right that goes beyond simple fairness. In this story, a boy and a man compete for a much-needed prize, and it is honor that decides the outcome.**

**Who wins the prize? What role does honor play in the winning?**

————— ❖ ❖ ❖ —————

*Willy's grandfather has been sick for weeks. He lies in bed, not able to sit up or even to speak. Doc Smith can find nothing wrong with him.*

*While looking for money to buy supplies, ten-year-old Willy discovers a notice from the tax collector. Grandfather owes five hundred dollars in back taxes! If the taxes are not paid, Grandfather and Willy will lose the farm.*

*The National Dogsled Races are Willy's only hope. First prize is five hundred dollars, exactly the amount needed to save the farm. But to win, Willy and his dog, Searchlight, must race against Stone Fox and his team of well-trained sled dogs. Stone Fox has never lost a race, and he wants to win this one as badly as Willy does. Stone Fox plans to use the prize money to buy land for his people, the Shoshone.*

————— ❖ ❖ ❖ —————

The day of the race arrived. Little Willy got up early and fed Grandfather his oatmeal. After adding more wood to the fire, little Willy kissed Grandfather, hitched up Searchlight, and started off for town.

At the edge of their property, he stopped the sled for a moment and looked back at the farmhouse. The roof was covered with freshly fallen snow. A trail of smoke escaped from the stone chimney. The jagged peaks of the Teton Mountains shot up in the background toward the clear blue sky overhead. "Yes, sir," he remembered Grandfather saying. "There are some things in this world worth dying for."

Little Willy loved this country. He loved to hike
and to fish and to camp out by a lake. But he did
not like to hunt. He loved animals too much to be a
hunter.

He had killed a bird once with a slingshot. But
that had been when he was only six years old. And
that had been enough. In fact, to this day, he still
remembered the spot where the poor thing was
buried.

Lost in his thoughts, little Willy got to town
before he knew it. As he turned onto Main Street,
he brought the sled to an abrupt halt.

He couldn't believe what he saw.

Main Street was jammed with people, lined up
on both sides of the street. There were people on

rooftops and people hanging out of windows. Little Willy hadn't expected such a big turnout. They must have all come to see Stone Fox.

Searchlight pulled the sled down Main Street past the crowd. Little Willy saw Miss Williams, his teacher, and Hank from the post office. And there was Doc Smith and Mayor Smiley and Lester from the general store. The city slickers were there. And even Clifford Snyder, the tax man. Everybody.

Lester came out of the crowd and walked alongside little Willy for a while. It was one of the few times little Willy had ever seen Lester without his white apron.

"You can do it, Willy. You can beat him," Lester kept saying over and over again.

They had a race for the youngsters first, and the crowd cheered and rooted for their favorites. It was a short race. Just down to the end of Main Street and back. Little Willy didn't see who won. It didn't matter.

And then it was time.

The old church clock showed a few minutes before ten as the contestants positioned themselves directly beneath the long banner that stretched across the street. They stood nine abreast. Stone Fox in the middle. Little Willy right next to him.

Little Willy had read all about the other contestants in the newspaper. They were all well-known mountain men with good racing records and excellent dog teams. But, even so, everyone thought Stone Fox would win.

Stone Fox looked bigger than ever standing next to little Willy. In fact, the top of little Willy's head was dead even with Stone Fox's waist.

"Morning, Mr. Stone Fox," little Willy said, looking practically straight up. "Sure's a nice day for a race."

Stone Fox must have heard little Willy, but he did not look at him. His face was frozen like ice, and his eyes seemed to lack that sparkle little Willy remembered seeing before.

The crowd became silent as Mayor Smiley stepped out into the street.

Miss Williams clenched her hands together until

her knuckles turned white. Lester's mouth hung open, his lips wet. Hank stared without blinking. Doc Smith held her head up proudly. Clifford Snyder removed a gold watch from his vest pocket and checked the time.

Tension filled the air.

Little Willy's throat became dry. His hands started to sweat. He could feel his heart thumping.

Mayor Smiley raised a pistol to the sky and fired.

The race had begun!

Searchlight sprang forward with such force that little Willy couldn't hang on. If it weren't for a lucky grab, he would have fallen off the sled for sure.

In what seemed only seconds, little Willy and Searchlight had traveled down Main Street, turned onto North Road, and were gone. Far, far ahead of the others. They were winning. At least for the moment.

Stone Fox started off dead last. He went so slowly down Main Street that everyone was sure something must be wrong.

Swish! Little Willy's sled flew by the school-house on the outskirts of town, and then by the old deserted barn.

Swish! Swish! Swish! Other racers followed in hot pursuit.

"Go, Searchlight! Go!" little Willy sang out. The cold wind pressed against his face. The snow was well packed. It was going to be a fast race today. The fastest they had ever run.

The road was full of dangerous twists and turns, but little Willy did not have to slow down as the other racers did. With only one dog and a small sled, he was able to take the sharp turns at full speed without risk of sliding off the road or losing control.

Therefore, with each turn, little Willy pulled farther and farther ahead.

Swish! The sled rounded a corner, sending snow flying. Little Willy was smiling. This was fun!

About three miles out of town the road made a half circle around a frozen lake. Instead of following the turn, little Willy took a shortcut right across the lake. This was tricky going, but Searchlight had done it many times before.

Little Willy had asked Mayor Smiley if he was permitted to go across the lake, not wanting to be disqualified. "As long as you leave town heading north and come back on South Road," the mayor had said, "anything goes!"

None of the other racers attempted to cross the lake. Not even Stone Fox. The risk of falling through the ice was just too great.

Little Willy's lead increased.

Stone Fox was still running in last place. But he was picking up speed.

At the end of five miles, little Willy was so far out in front that he couldn't see anybody behind him when he looked back.

He knew, however, that the return five miles, going back into town, would not be this easy. The trail along South Road was practically straight and very smooth, and Stone Fox was sure to close the gap. But by how much? Little Willy didn't know.

Doc Smith's house flew by on the right. The tall trees surrounding her cabin seemed like one solid wall.

Grandfather's farm was coming up next.

When Searchlight saw the farmhouse, she started to pick up speed. "No, girl," little Willy yelled. "Not yet."

As they approached the farmhouse, little Willy thought he saw someone in Grandfather's bedroom window. The someone was a man. With a full beard.

It couldn't be. But it was! It was Grandfather!

Grandfather was sitting up in bed. He was looking out the window.

Little Willy was so excited he couldn't think straight. He started to stop the sled, but Grandfather indicated no, waving him on. "Of course," little Willy said to himself. "I must finish the race. I haven't won yet."

"Go, Searchlight!" little Willy shrieked. "Go, girl!"

Grandfather was better. Tears of joy rolled down little Willy's smiling face. Everything was going to be all right.

And then Stone Fox made his move.

One by one he began to pass the other racers. He went from last place to eighth. Then from eighth place to seventh. Then from seventh to sixth. Sixth to fifth.

He passed the others as if they were standing still.

He went from fifth place to fourth. Then to third. Then to second.

Until only little Willy remained.

But little Willy still had a good lead. In fact, it was not until the last two miles of the race that Stone Fox got his first glimpse of little Willy since the race had begun.

The five Samoyeds looked magnificent as they moved effortlessly across the snow. Stone Fox was gaining, and he was gaining fast. And little Willy wasn't aware of it.

Look back, little Willy! Look back!

But little Willy didn't look back. He was busy thinking about Grandfather. He could hear him laughing . . . and playing his harmonica . . . Finally little Willy glanced back over his shoulder. He couldn't believe what he saw! Stone Fox was nearly on top of him!

This made little Willy mad. Mad at himself.

Why hadn't he looked back more often? What was he doing? He hadn't won yet. Well, no time to think of that now. He had a race to win.

"Go, Searchlight! Go, girl!"

But Stone Fox kept gaining. Silently. Steadily.

"Go, Searchlight! Go!"

The lead Samoyed passed little Willy and pulled up even with Searchlight. Then it was a nose ahead. But that was all. Searchlight moved forward, inching *her* nose ahead. Then the Samoyed regained the lead. Then Searchlight . . .

When you enter the town of Jackson on South Road, the first buildings come into view about a half mile away. Whether Searchlight took those buildings to be Grandfather's farmhouse again, no one can be sure, but it was at this time that she poured on the steam.

Little Willy's sled seemed to lift up off the ground and fly. Stone Fox was left behind.

But not that far behind.

The crowd cheered madly when they saw little Willy come into view at the far end of Main Street, and even more madly when they saw that Stone Fox was right on his tail.

"Go, Searchlight! Go!"

Searchlight forged ahead. But Stone Fox was gaining!

"Go, Searchlight! Go!" little Willy cried out.

Searchlight gave it everything she had.

She was a hundred feet from the finish line when her heart burst. She died instantly. There was no suffering.

The sled and little Willy tumbled over her, slid along the snow for a while, then came to a stop about ten feet from the finish line. It had started to snow—white snowflakes landed on Searchlight's dark fur as she lay motionless on the ground.

The crowd became deathly silent.

Lester's eyes looked to the ground. Miss Williams had her hands over her mouth. Doc Smith started to run out to little Willy, but stopped. Mayor Smiley looked shocked and helpless. And so did Hank, and so did the city slickers, and so did Clifford Snyder, the tax man.

Stone Fox brought his sled to a stop alongside little Willy. He stood tall in the icy wind and looked down at the young challenger, and at the dog that lay limp in his arms.

"Is she dead, Mr. Stone Fox? Is she dead?" little Willy asked.

Stone Fox knelt down and put one massive hand on Searchlight's chest. He felt no heartbeat. He looked at little Willy, and the boy understood.

Little Willy squeezed Searchlight with all his might.

"You did real good, girl. Real good. I'm real proud of you. You rest now. Just rest." Little Willy began to brush the snow off Searchlight's back.

Stone Fox stood up slowly.

No one spoke. No one moved. All eyes were on the Indian, the one called Stone Fox, the one who had never lost a race, and who had another victory within his grasp.

But Stone Fox did nothing.

He just stood there. Like a mountain.

His eyes shifted to his own dogs, then to the

finish line, then back to little Willy, holding Search-light.

With the heel of his moccasin, Stone Fox drew a long line in the snow. Then he walked back over to his sled and pulled out his rifle.

Down at the end of Main Street, the other racers began to appear. As they approached, Stone Fox fired his rifle into the air. They came to a stop.

Stone Fox spoke.

"Anyone crosses this line—I shoot."

And there wasn't anybody who didn't believe him.

Stone Fox nodded to the boy.

The town looked on in silence as little Willy, carrying Searchlight, walked the last ten feet and across the finish line.

## CHECK FOR UNDERSTANDING

1. How did Willy's size and weight help him in the race?
2. Who won the prize?
3. What role did honor play in the winning?
4. Grandfather had said about the farm, "There are some things in this world worth dying for." How did this statement give a clue about what would happen later in the story?
5. Do you think Grandfather would approve of the way Willy won the race? Explain your answer.

**WRITE ABOUT** *"Stone Fox"*

Imagine that Stone Fox had to go back to his tribe and explain why he did not win the money needed to buy them their land. Write the speech that Stone Fox makes to his people. In it describe the race and Stone Fox's feelings about the outcome.

# FOR MUGS

by MYRA COHN LIVINGSTON

He is gone now. He is dead.
There is a hurting in my head.

I listen for his bark, his whine.
The silence answers. He was mine.

I taught him all the greatest tricks.
I had a way of throwing sticks

So he could catch them, and a ball
We bounced against the backyard wall.

I can see him, chasing cats,
Killing all the mountain rats,

Drinking water from his bowl.
There's a place he had a hole

To bury bones, but now it's gone.
His footprints fade upon the lawn.

He used to snuggle on my bed
But now he's gone. He died. He's dead.

# THE CRANE MAIDEN

by MIYOKO MATSUTANI

**To come to the aid of an injured and helpless animal is a noble deed. In this folk tale, an old man helps an injured crane.**

**How does helping the crane bring the man and his wife good luck? What promise does the old couple make?**

Long years ago, at the edge of a small mountain village in the snow country of Japan, there lived an old man and his wife. They had little in this world that they could call their own, but they were happy in their life together.

Now one winter morning the old man set out for the village, with a bundle of firewood fastened to his back. It was bitter cold. He knew he would have little trouble selling the wood. Then with the money, he would buy some food so that he and his wife could have a good supper.

As the old man trudged through the falling snow, he was suddenly aware of a fluttering sound, and a pitiful cry of *Koh, koh*. Turning from the path to investigate, he came upon a great crane frantically trying to free herself from a trap.

The old man's heart was touched with pity for the magnificent bird. While he tried to soothe the crane with tender words, his hands released the cruel spring of the trap. At once the crane flew up, joyfully calling *Koh, koh,* and disappeared into the snowy sky.

With a lighter step the old man went on through the snow. When he had sold his wood he returned once more to his humble house. As his old wife busied herself with preparing supper, he told her about rescuing the crane.

"That was a good deed," she said. "Surely you will one day be rewarded for your kind heart."

As she spoke these words there came a tapping on the door. The old wife hastened to see who was there. Upon opening the door she beheld a beautiful young girl standing in the swirling snow. Her delicate face glowed like a peach beginning to ripen in the summer sun. Her dark eyes sparkled in the dancing firelight from the hearth.

"Forgive my knocking at your door," she said in a soft voice. "I have lost my way in the snow. May I share the warmth of your fire tonight?" Then bowing low before the two old people, she said, "My name is Tsuru-san."

"Oh, you poor child!" cried the old wife. "Come in at once before you freeze in the bitter cold." They sat the girl down close to the hearth, and the old wife piled more wood on the flames so that the girl would soon be warm.

The old couple shared their simple supper of hot porridge with Tsuru-san. Then they gave her their bed with its warm quilts to sleep on, while they spent the night huddled on a pile of straw.

In the morning when they awoke, the old man and his wife were surprised to see a good fire already burning on the hearth. The water urn was filled with fresh clear water. The floors had been swept. All the rooms were clean and tidy.

Tsuru-san, the sleeves of her kimono neatly tied back with a red cord, was busily stirring a pot over the fire. "Good morning," she said, bowing to the old couple. "If you will wash your hands we may eat breakfast. The porridge is cooked and ready."

"In our old age we have a daughter!" said the old man, laughing.

"We are being rewarded for your good deed of yesterday," replied his wife happily.

The snow and bitter cold continued for many days, and so Tsuru-san stayed in the shelter of the old couple's home. As she had neither mother nor father, it was at last decided that she would remain as a daughter to these people.

The children of the neighborhood were soon attracted to the house, because the girl was such a delight to be with. The house rang with happy laughter. The hearts of the old man and his wife were filled with joy at the sound.

And so the days of early winter passed. Soon it would be time for the great New Year celebration. The old man spoke to his wife, saying, "Tsuru-san has been such a delight to us. If only I could give her a gift of a new kimono."

"Or if I could make her a rice cake for the New Year," his wife added.

But the winter had been hard. The old man had not been able to cut wood to sell, so there was no money to buy even rice, much less a kimono.

Now Tsuru-san had overheard them talking. It grieved her that these good people should be so poor. Coming before them she bowed low and said, "Dear parents, I know there has been no wood to sell. Perhaps I can help you and repay your great kindness to me. There is an old loom in the back room. I will weave cloth on it for you to sell in the village. Only you must promise that no one shall look at me while I am weaving." The old man and his wife thought this was an odd request, but they readily agreed.

Tsuru-san locked herself in the room. Soon they heard the sound of *Tin kola, kola, pon, pon, Tin kola, kola, pon, pon*—as the shuttle sped back and forth and the fabric grew in length.

For three days this continued. Tsuru-san paused for neither food nor rest. Then at last the door opened and she stepped out, holding in her hands a bolt of cloth such as the old man and his wife had never seen in all their lives. They gasped at its beauty, and marveled at its incredible softness.

"Dear father," said the girl, "take this cloth into the village and sell it. It will be but small payment for the happy home you have given me. Remember this, however," she continued. "Do not put a price on this cloth, and you will fare better than you can imagine."

Without wasting a moment, the old man hurried into the center of the village. When people saw the beautiful cloth he was carrying, a crowd soon gathered.

"I will pay ten gold pieces for your cloth," said one man. "No, no!" cried another. "Sell it to me for twenty gold pieces!" "You would be a fool to sell it for such a price, old man," said another. "This is a bolt of rare twilled brocade. I will pay you fifty gold pieces for it." And so it went, with each man offering more, until the old man finally sold the cloth for one hundred pieces of gold.

Pausing only long enough to buy rice for rice cakes, a kimono for Tsuru-san and a few delicacies for New Year's Day, the man hurried home with his pockets jingling. "Tomorrow, tomorrow is the New Year's Day," he sang. "The New Year is the happy time, eating rice cakes whiter than snow."

Then such a hustle and bustle there was, as the old man and his wife prepared for the feast. As he pounded the rice, his wife made it into fine white cakes. And on New Year's Day all the children came in for a great party with their friend, Tsuru-san.

Still the cold days of winter followed one after the other. At last one day Tsuru-san said to the old couple,

"It is time for me to weave another bolt of cloth for you so that you will have money to live on until the spring returns. But remember what I told you. No one is to look at me while I am working."

Again they promised that they would not, and the girl once more locked herself in the room and began weaving. *Tin kola, kola, pon, pon, Tin kola, pon, pon*— went the loom. One day passed, and then the second. Still the sound of the loom filled the house. By now, the neighbors had grown curious.

"Is Tsuru-san weaving again?" asked one. "Ah, soon you will have more gold pieces to hide under the floor," said another with a smile and a wink. "The loom makes such an interesting sound," remarked the first one. "I would love to see what Tsuru-san is doing."

"We have promised not to watch her while she works," said the old man.

"What an odd request," cried one of the people. "I would not make such a promise to *my* daughter, you can believe me. What harm could there be in taking one look?"

Now in truth, the old woman had been most curious about Tsuru-san's weaving. Encouraged by her neighbor's remarks, she stepped up to a crack in the door.

"Stop, stop, old woman!" cried her husband when he saw what was happening. "Tsuru-san has forbidden it!" But it was too late. His wife had already peeked through the crack.

What a sight it was that met her eye! There, sitting at the loom, was a great white crane, pulling feathers from her body and miraculously weaving them into cloth.

The old woman stepped back from the door, and before she could relate what she had seen, the door opened. Out stepped Tsuru-san, thin and pale, holding in her hands a half-finished bolt of cloth.

"Dear parents," she said in a weak voice, "I am the crane you rescued from the trap. I wanted to repay your kindness by weaving you another bolt of cloth." Then her eyes filled with tears. "But now that you have seen me in my true form I can no longer stay with you."

With this she kissed the man and his wife tenderly, and walked out of the house. Instantly she became a crane once more. With a great whish of her wings she flew up into the sky. Slowly she circled overhead, then with a single cry of *Koh* as if to say good-by, the crane maiden was gone forever.

## CHECK FOR UNDERSTANDING

1. How did helping the crane bring the man and his wife good luck?
2. Why did Tsuru-san decide to weave cloth for the old couple?
3. What promise did the old couple make?
4. Why did the old woman look at Tsuru-san while she was weaving?
5. How do you think the old couple felt about Tsuru-san's leaving?
6. If they had known the sad outcome of her stay, do you think the old couple would have chosen to have Tsuru-san stay? Explain your answer.

## WRITE ABOUT *"The Crane Maiden"*

Think about how Tsuru-san must have felt when the old woman saw her weaving. Imagine that she left a note for the old man and woman telling how she feels about them and about having to leave. Write Tsuru-san's note. Include a brief description of the life to which she is returning.

# LITERATURE

## Elements of Humor

Humor is the easiest thing in the world to define: it's whatever makes people laugh. Defining humor, however, is a lot easier than actually knowing what *does* make people laugh.

There are some things that almost always seem to make people laugh, or at least grin. The following is a list of some of the elements of humor you are likely to see in your reading.

1. **Exaggeration.** Exaggeration is the art of stretching the truth until it almost breaks. Many jokes are based on exaggeration. For exaggeration to be funny, most of the situation should be fairly normal. When one part of the situation is made "larger than life," it seems funny. Later on in this book, for example, you will read a story about some boys going on an expedition. They pack their knapsacks with everything they would need if they were climbing Mount Everest. As it turns out, they are only going to spend an afternoon walking through a city park.

2. **Surprise.** Surprise is often used to create the humor in a story. Again, for surprise to be funny, the situation it occurs in has to be fairly normal. Surprise may occur because someone says something that doesn't make sense in the situation. It may occur because some object is completely out of place in a situation.

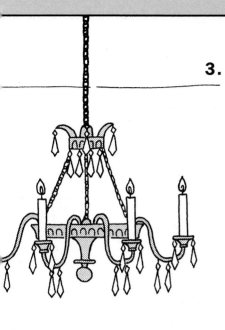

**3. Ridiculousness.** Authors often put some ridiculous behavior in the middle of a believable situation to create humor. For example, imagine a restaurant full of quiet people and friendly waiters. Most of the waiters bustle around with trays, taking away dishes. One waiter, however, comes to the table, smiles at the guests, and begins clearing the table. But instead of stacking the dishes on a tray, he smiles as he stuffs them inside his coat, into his coat pockets, and into his pants pockets, just as if that were the normal thing to do. Isn't that funny?

Of course, it is possible to combine two or all of these methods of getting a laugh. You could say that one part of what is funny about the waiter's behavior is that it comes as a surprise. You could also say that his acting as if this were the normal way to clear a table is an exaggeration of real life.

As you read further selections, note the times you find yourself grinning, smiling, or even laughing out loud. Study the thing you read that caused this reaction. Try to decide how the author got to your funnybone.

# MR. POPPER'S PENGUINS

## By RICHARD and FLORENCE ATWATER

# OUT
## of the
# ANTARCTIC

Getting a pet would be a wonderful thing for someone who dreamed of owning a pet. But how could a pet help Mr. Popper? Mr. Popper is a house-painter who dreams of only one thing: going to the South Pole. There is little chance, however, that Mr. Popper will ever get there. So Mr. Popper must content himself with reading about Antarctica.

What does Mr. Popper think is the nicest thing about Antarctica? What surprise does Mr. Popper get when he tunes in to the Drake Antarctic Expedition broadcast?

That evening, when the little Poppers had been put to bed, Mr. and Mrs. Popper settled down for a long, quiet evening. The neat living room at 432 Proudfoot Avenue was much like all the other living rooms in Stillwater, except that the walls were hung with pictures from *National Geographic* magazine. Mrs. Popper picked up her mending, while Mr. Popper collected his pipe, his book, and his globe.

From time to time Mrs. Popper sighed a little as

she thought about the long winter ahead. Would there really be enough beans to last? she wondered.

Mr. Popper was not worried, however. As he put on his spectacles, he was quite pleased at the prospect of a whole winter of reading travel books, with no work to interrupt him. He set his little globe beside him and began to read.

"What are you reading?" asked Mrs. Popper.

"I am reading a book called *Antarctic Adventures*. It is very interesting. It tells all about the different people who have gone to the South Pole and what they have found there."

"Don't you ever get tired of reading about the South Pole?"

"No, I don't. Of course I would much rather go there than read about it. But reading is the next best thing."

"I think it must be very boring down there," said Mrs. Popper. "It sounds very dull and cold, with all that ice and snow."

"Oh, no," answered Mr. Popper. "You wouldn't think it was dull if you had gone with me to see the movies of the Drake Expedition at the Bijou last year."

"Well, I didn't, and I don't think any of us will have any money for movies now," answered Mrs. Popper, a little sharply. She was not at all a disagreeable woman, but she sometimes got rather cross when she was worried about money.

"If you had gone, my love," went on Mr. Popper, "you would have seen how beautiful the Antarctic is. But I think the nicest part of all is the penguins. No wonder all the men on that expedition had such a good time playing with them. They are the funniest birds in the world. They don't fly like other birds. They walk erect like little men. When they get tired of walking, they just lie down on their stomachs and slide. It would be very nice to have one for a pet."

"Pets!" said Mrs. Popper. "First it's Bill wanting a dog and then Janie begging for a kitten. Now you and penguins! But I won't have any pets around. They make too much dirt in the house and I have enough work now, trying to keep this place tidy. To say nothing of what it costs to feed a pet. Anyway, we have the bowl of goldfish."

"Penguins are very intelligent," continued Mr. Popper. "Listen to this, Mamma. It says here that when they want to catch some shrimps, they all crowd over to the edge of an ice bank. Only they don't just jump in, because a sea leopard might be waiting to eat the penguins. So they crowd and push until they manage to shove one penguin off, to see if it's safe. I mean if he doesn't get eaten up, the rest of them know it's safe for them to all jump in."

"Dear me!" said Mrs. Popper in a shocked tone. "They sound to me like pretty heathen birds."

"It's a queer thing," said Mr. Popper, "that all

the polar bears live at the North Pole and all the penguins at the South Pole. I should think the penguins would like the North Pole, too, if they only knew how to get there."

At ten o'clock, Mrs. Popper yawned and laid down her mending. "Well, you can go on reading about those heathen birds, but I am going to bed. Tomorrow is Thursday, September thirtieth, and I have to go to the first meeting of the Ladies' Aid and Missionary Society."

"September thirtieth!" said Mr. Popper in an excited tone. "You don't mean that tonight is Wednesday, September twenty-ninth?"

"Why, yes, I suppose it is. But what of it?"

Mr. Popper put down his book of *Antarctic Adventures* and moved hastily to the radio.

"What of it!" he repeated, pushing the switch. "Why, this is the night the Drake Antarctic Expedition is going to start broadcasting."

"That's nothing," said Mrs. Popper. "Just a lot of men at the bottom of the world saying 'Hello, Mamma. Hello, Papa.'"

"*Sh!*" commanded Mr. Popper, laying his ear close to the radio.

There was a buzz, and then suddenly, from the South Pole, a faint voice floated out into the Popper living room.

"This is Admiral Drake speaking. Hello, Mamma. Hello, Papa. Hello, Mr. Popper."

"Gracious goodness," exclaimed Mrs. Popper. "Did he say 'Papa' or 'Popper'?"

"Hello, Mr. Popper, up there in Stillwater. Thanks for your nice letter about the pictures of our last expedition. Watch for an answer. But not by letter, Mr. Popper. Watch for a surprise. Signing off. Signing off."

"*You* wrote to Admiral Drake?"

"Yes, I did," Mr. Popper admitted. "I wrote and told him how funny I thought the penguins were."

"Well, I never," said Mrs. Popper, very much impressed.

Mr. Popper picked up his little globe and found the Antarctic. "And to think he spoke to me all the way from there. And he even mentioned my name. Mamma, what do you suppose he means by a surprise?"

"I haven't any idea," answered Mrs. Popper, "but I'm going to bed. I don't want to be late for the Ladies' Aid and Missionary Society meeting tomorrow."

What with the excitement of having the great Admiral Drake speak to him over the radio, and his curiosity about the admiral's message to him, Mr. Popper did not sleep very well that night. He did not see how he could possibly wait to find out what the admiral meant. When morning came, he was almost sorry that he had nowhere to go, no houses to paint, no rooms to paper. It would have helped to pass the time.

"Would you like the living room papered over?" he asked Mrs. Popper. "I have quite a lot of Paper Number 88, left over from the Mayor's house."

"I would not," said Mrs. Popper firmly. "The paper on now is plenty good enough. I am going to the first meeting of the Ladies' Aid and Missionary Society today and I don't want any mess around to clean up when I get home."

"Very well, my love," said Mr. Popper meekly, and he settled down with his pipe, his globe and his book of *Antarctic Adventures*. But somehow, as he read today, he could not keep his mind on the printed words. His thoughts kept straying away to Admiral Drake. What could he have meant by a surprise for Mr. Popper?

Fortunately for his peace of mind, he did not have so very long to wait. That afternoon, while Mrs. Popper was still away at her meeting, and Janie and Bill had not yet come home from school, there was a loud ring at the front door.

"I suppose it is just the postman. I won't bother to answer it," he said to himself.

The bell rang again, a little louder this time. Grumbling to himself, Mr. Popper went to the door.

It was not the postman who stood there. It was an expressman with the largest box Mr. Popper had even seen.

"Party by the name of Popper live here?"

"That's me."

"Well, here's a package that's come Air Express all the way from Antarctica. Some journey, I'll say."

Mr. Popper signed the receipt and examined the box. It was covered all over with markings. "Unpack At Once," said one. "Keep Cool," said another. He noticed that the box was punched here and there with air holes.

You can imagine that once he had the box inside the house, Mr. Popper lost no time in getting the screwdriver, for by this time, of course, he had guessed that it was the surprise from Admiral Drake.

He had succeeded in removing the outer boards and part of the packing, which was a layer of dry ice, when from the depths of the packing case he suddenly heard a faint *"Ork."* His heart stood still. Surely he had heard that sound before at the Drake Expedition movies. His hands were trembling so that he could scarcely lift off the last of the wrappings.

There was not the slightest doubt about it. It was a penguin.

Mr. Popper was speechless with delight.

But the penguin was not speechless. *"Ork,"* it said again, and this time held out its flippers and jumped over the packing debris.

It was a stout little fellow about two and a half feet high. Although it was about the size of a small child, it looked much more like a little gentleman,

with its smooth white waistcoat in front and its long black tail coat dragging a little behind. Its eyes were set in two white circles in its black head. It turned its head from one side to the other, as first with one eye and then with the other, it examined Mr. Popper.

Mr. Popper had read that penguins are extremely curious, and he soon found that this was true, for stepping out, the visitor began to inspect the house. Down the hall it went and into the bedrooms, with its strange, pompous little strut. When it, or he—Mr. Popper had already begun to think of it as he—got to the bathroom, it looked around with a pleased expression on its face.

"Perhaps," thought Mr. Popper, "all that white tiling reminds him of the ice and snow at the South Pole. Poor thing, maybe he's thirsty."

Carefully, Mr. Popper began to fill the bathtub with cold water. This was a little difficult, because the inquisitive bird kept reaching over and trying to bite the faucets with its sharp red beak. Finally, however, he succeeded in getting the tub all filled. Since the penguin kept looking over the rim, Mr. Popper picked it up and dropped it in. The penguin seemed not to mind.

"Anyway, you're not shy," said Mr. Popper. "I guess you've got sort of used to playing around with those explorers at the Pole."

When he thought the penguin had had enough

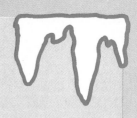

of a bath, he drew out the stopper. He was just wondering what to do next when Janie and Bill burst in from school.

"Papa," they shouted together at the bathroom door. "What is it?"

"It's a South Pole penguin sent to me by Admiral Drake."

"Look!" said Bill. "It's marching."

The delighted penguin was indeed marching. With little pleased nods of his handsome black head, he was parading up and down the inside of the bathtub. Sometimes he seemed to be counting the steps it took—six steps for the length, two steps for the width, six steps for the length again, and two more for the width.

"For such a big bird, he takes awfully small steps," said Bill.

"And look how his little black coat drags behind. It almost looks as if it were too big for him," said Janie.

But the penguin was tired of marching. This time, when it got to the end of the tub, it decided to jump up the slippery curve. Then it turned, and with outstretched flippers, tobogganed down on its white stomach. They could see that those flippers, which were black on the outside, like the sleeves of a tailcoat, were white underneath.

"*Gook! Gook!*" said the penguin, trying its new game again and again.

"What's his name, Papa?" asked Janie.

"*Gook! Gook!*" said the penguin, sliding down once more on his glossy white stomach.

"It sounds something like 'Cook,' " said Mr. Popper. "Why, that's it, of course. We'll call him Cook—Captain Cook."

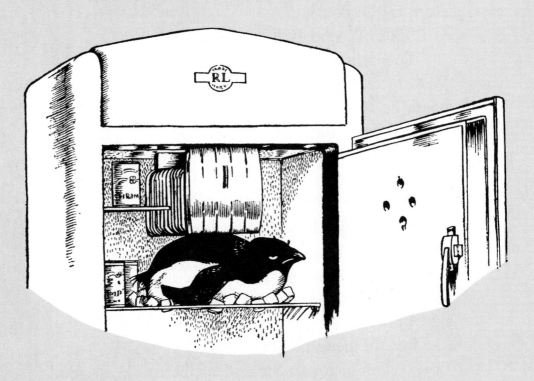

*Trying to keep a penguin happy and content at 432 Proudfoot Avenue puts Mr. Popper in many a funny predicament. To find out what happens to Mr. Popper and his unusual new pet, read the rest of the novel* Mr. Popper's Penguins, *by Richard and Florence Atwater.*

## CHECK FOR UNDERSTANDING

1. What did Mr. Popper think was the nicest thing about Antarctica?
2. In what ways, according to Mr. Popper, are penguins different from other birds?
3. What surprise did Mr. Popper get when he tuned in to the Drake Antarctic Expedition broadcast?
4. Why did Mr. Popper decide to name the penguin Captain Cook?
5. How do you think Mrs. Popper will react when she finds a penguin in the house?
6. Penguins live in Antarctica, where it is very cold. What kinds of problems do you think Mr. Popper will face trying to keep a penguin as a house pet?

**WRITE ABOUT** *"Out of the Antarctic"*

Mr. Popper got the penguin as a result of writing a letter to Admiral Drake. Now that he has received his surprise, Mr. Popper will probably write another letter to Admiral Drake. Imagine that you are Mr. Popper. Write a letter to Admiral Drake telling him how surprised you were to hear his message over the radio and how delighted you are with the penguin. Also mention how Mrs. Popper and the children feel about the surprise.

# THINK ABOUT IT

Think about the special relationship between the character and the animal in each selection. What important role did the animal play in what happened to each character?

- How can you explain the special feeling that Storm Boy had for Mr. Percival?
- What are some of the different tasks that dogs no longer perform today? Do they do other things just as important instead?
- What changes will Cindy, the hearing ear dog, make in her new owner's life?
- Think about the two horses, Keko and Thor. Do you think that animals can really have different personalities?
- What effects do you think Captain Cook will have on Mr. Popper's life?

After reading and thinking about the different ways in which people are helped by animals, what qualities in an animal do you think are especially important? What do you think life would be like without animals?

# WRITE ABOUT IT

Have you ever had a close relationship with an animal? Write two paragraphs in which you describe the animal and why it was special to you.

# READ ABOUT IT

*The Nightingale* by Hans Christian Andersen. Harper & Row, Publishers, 1965. The sensitive story of the nightingale whose beautiful song saved the Emperor from death.

*Demo and the Dolphin* by Nathaniel Benchley. Harper & Row, Publishers, 1981. A dolphin takes Demo back in time to ask the oracle at Delphi how he can help his father become a successful fisherman.

*The Beast of Lor* by Clyde Robert Bulla. Thomas Y. Crowell Co., 1977. An African elephant helps a young boy from an ancient British tribe rescue his village from the invading Romans.

*The Joker and the Swan* by Dorothy Crayder. Harper & Row, Publishers, 1981. With the help of a talking dog an 11-year-old aspiring ballerina learns to see her own talents.

*The Boy Who Spoke Chimp* by Jane Yolen. Alfred A. Knopf, 1981. Kriss joins forces with an old hermit and a chimp that has been trained to communicate when he is caught in the wilderness during a devastating earthquake.

# 2

# A SPECIAL PLACE

*It may be right around the corner, or it may be far away. It may be a town you have lived in. It may be a place where you stop on the way to somewhere else. It may be a city park or an undiscovered island or a beach. It may even be an imaginary place where nobody but you can go. Everyone has a special place they either have been to or want to visit. What does your special place look like?*

*In this unit, you will discover some places that are special to other people. As you read, think about what makes the place special. Ask yourself if everyone would think the place was special. Or is it special mostly because of the experience the person has there?*

# The DAY OUT

by P. L. TRAVERS

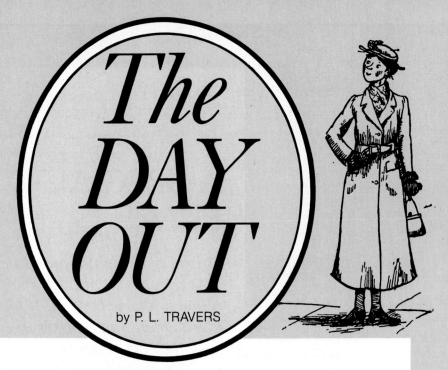

At times it can seem difficult to have fun when you have no money. But fun can't be bought. A little imagination can go a very long way when it comes to having a good time. No one proves this better than Mary Poppins and her friend Bert, who, with imagination—and a little magic—have a day out filled with glorious fun.

Why does Mary Poppins call tea a "stodgy meal"? What happens later to show she doesn't mean it?

Mary Poppins put on her white gloves and tucked her umbrella under her arm—not because it was raining but because it had such a beautiful handle that she couldn't possibly leave it at home. How could you leave your umbrella behind if it had a parrot's head for a handle? Besides, Mary Poppins was very vain and liked to look her best. Indeed, she was quite sure that she never looked anything else.

Mary Poppins walked down the garden path and opened the gate. Once outside in the lane, she set off walking very quickly, as if she were afraid the afternoon would run away from her if she didn't keep up with it. At the corner she turned to the right and then to the left, nodded haughtily to the police officer, who said it was a nice day, and by that time she felt that her Day Out had begun.

She stopped beside an empty motorcar in order to put her hat straight with the help of the windscreen, in which it was reflected, then she smoothed down her frock and tucked her umbrella more securely under her arm so that the handle, or rather the parrot, could be seen by everybody. After these preparations she went forward to meet the Match-Man.

Now, the Match-Man had two professions. He not only sold matches like any ordinary match-man, but he drew pavement pictures as well. He did these things turnabout according to the weather. If it was wet, he sold matches because the rain would have washed away his pictures if he had painted them. If it was fine, he was on his knees all day, making pictures in colored chalks on the sidewalks, and doing them so quickly that often you would find he had painted up one side of a street and down the other almost before you'd had time to come round the corner.

On this particular day, which was fine but cold, he

was painting. He was in the act of adding a picture of two bananas, an apple, and a head of Queen Elizabeth to a long string of others, when Mary Poppins walked up to him, tiptoeing so as to surprise him.

"Hey!" called Mary Poppins softly.

He went on putting brown stripes on a banana and brown curls on Queen Elizabeth's head.

"Ahem!" said Mary Poppins, with a ladylike cough.

He turned with a start and saw her.

"Mary!" he cried, and you could tell by the way he cried it that Mary Poppins was a very important person in his life.

Mary Poppins looked down at her feet and rubbed the toe of one shoe along the pavement two or three times. Then she smiled at the shoe in such a way that the shoe knew quite well that the smile wasn't meant for it.

"It's my Day, Bert," she said. "Didn't you remember?" Bert was the Match-Man's name—Herbert Alfred for Sundays.

"Of course I remembered, Mary," he said, "but—" and he stopped and looked sadly into his cap. It lay on the ground beside his last picture and there was tuppence in it. He picked it up and jingled the pennies.

"That all you got, Bert?" said Mary Poppins, and she said it so brightly you could hardly tell she was disappointed at all.

"That's the lot," he said. "Business is bad today. You'd think anybody'd be glad to pay to see that,

114

wouldn't you?'' And he nodded his head at Queen Elizabeth. ''Well—that's how it is, Mary,'' he sighed. ''Can't take you to tea today, I'm afraid.''

Mary Poppins thought of the raspberry jam-cakes they always had on her Day Out, and she was just going to sigh, when she saw the Match-Man's face. So, very cleverly, she turned the sigh into a smile—a good one with both ends turned up—and said:

''That's all right, Bert. Don't you mind. I'd much rather not go to tea. A stodgy meal, I call it—really.''

And that, when you think how very much she liked raspberry jam-cakes, was rather nice of Mary Poppins.

The Match-Man apparently thought so, too, for he took her white-gloved hand in his and squeezed it hard. Then together they walked down the row of pictures.

''Now *there's* one you've never seen before!'' said the Match-Man proudly, pointing to a painting of a mountain covered with snow and its slopes simply littered with grasshoppers sitting on gigantic roses.

This time Mary Poppins could indulge in a sigh without hurting his feelings.

''Oh, Bert,'' she said, ''that's a fair treat!'' And by the way she said it she made him feel that by rights the picture should have been in the Royal Academy, which is a large room where people hang the pictures they have painted. Everybody comes to see them, and when they have looked at them for a very

long time, everybody says to everybody else: "The idea—my dear!"

The next picture Mary Poppins and the Match-Man came to was even better. It was the country—all trees and grass and a little bit of blue sea in the distance, and something that looked like Margate in the background.

"My word!" said Mary Poppins admiringly, stooping so that she could see it better. "Why, Bert, whatever is the matter?"

For the Match-Man had caught hold of her other hand now, and was looking very excited.

"Mary," he said, "I got an idea! A real *idea*. Why don't we go there—right now—this very day? Both together, into the picture. Eh, Mary?" And still holding her hands he drew her right out of the street, away from the iron railings and the lampposts, into the very middle of the picture. Pff! There they were, right inside it!

How green it was there and how quiet, and what soft, crisp grass under their feet! They could hardly believe it was true, and yet here were green branches huskily rattling on their hats as they bent beneath them, and little colored flowers curling round their shoes. They stared at each other, and each noticed that the other had changed. To Mary Poppins the Match-Man seemed to have bought himself an entirely new suit of clothes, for he was now wearing a bright green-and-red striped coat and white flannel trousers and, best of all, a new straw hat. He looked unusually clean, as though he had been polished.

"Why, Bert, you look fine!" she cried in an admiring voice.

Bert could not say anything for a moment, for his mouth had fallen open and he was staring at her with round eyes. Then he gulped and said: "Wow!"

That was all. But he said it in such a way and stared so steadily and so delightedly at her that she took a little mirror out of her bag and looked at herself in it.

She, too, she discovered, had changed. Round her shoulders hung a cloak of lovely artificial silk with watery patterns all over it, and the tickling feeling at the back of her neck came, the mirror told her, from a long, curly feather that swept down from the brim of her hat. Her best shoes had disappeared, and in their place were others much finer and with large diamond buckles shining upon them. She was still wearing the white gloves and carrying the umbrella.

"My goodness," said Mary Poppins, "I *am* having a Day Out!"

So, still admiring themselves and each other, they moved on together through the little wood, till presently they came upon a little open space filled with sunlight. And there on a green table was Afternoon Tea!

A pile of raspberry jam-cakes as high as Mary Poppins' waist stood in the center, and beside it tea was

boiling in a big brass urn. Best of all, there were two plates of whelks and two pins to pick them out with.

"Strike me pink!" said Mary Poppins. That was what she always said when she was pleased.

"Wow!" said the Match-Man. And that was *his* particular phrase.

"Won't you sit down, Moddom?" inquired a voice, and they turned to find a tall man in a black coat coming out of the wood with a table-napkin over his arm.

Mary Poppins, thoroughly surprised, sat down with a plop upon one of the little green chairs that stood round the table. The Match-Man, staring, collapsed onto another.

"I'm the Waiter, you know!" explained the man in the black coat.

"Oh! But I didn't see you in the picture," said Mary Poppins.

"Ah, I was behind the tree," explained the Waiter.

"Won't you sit down?" said Mary Poppins, politely.

"Waiters never sit down, Moddom," said the man, but he seemed pleased at being asked.

"Your whelks, Mister!" he said, pushing a plate of them over to the Match-Man. "*And* your pin!" He dusted the pin on his napkin and handed it to the Match-Man.

They began upon the Afternoon Tea, and the Waiter stood beside them to see they had everything they needed.

"We're having them after all," said Mary Poppins

in a loud whisper, as she began on the heap of rasp-berry jam-cakes.

"Wow!" agreed the Match-Man, helping himself to two of the largest.

"Tea?" said the Waiter, filling a large cup for each of them from the urn.

They drank it and had two cups more each and then, for luck, they finished the pile of raspberry jam-cakes. After that they got up and brushed the crumbs off.

"There is nothing to pay," said the Waiter, before they had time to ask for the bill. "It is a pleasure. You will find the Merry-go-Round just over there!" And he waved his hand to a little gap in the trees, where Mary Poppins and the Match-Man could see several wooden horses whirling round on a stand.

"That's funny," said she. "I don't remember seeing that in the picture either."

"Ah," said the Match-Man, who hadn't remem-bered it himself, "it was in the background, you see!"

The Merry-go-Round was just slowing down as they approached it. They leapt upon it, Mary Pop-pins on a black horse and the Match-Man on a gray. And when the music started again and they began to move, they rode all the way to Yarmouth and back, because that was the place they both wanted most to see.

When they returned it was nearly dark and the Waiter was watching for them.

"I'm very sorry, Moddom and Mister," he said politely, "but we close at seven. Rules, you know. May I show you the Way Out?"

They nodded as he flourished his table-napkin and walked on in front of them through the wood.

"It's a wonderful picture you've drawn this time, Bert," said Mary Poppins, putting her hand through the Match-Man's arm and drawing her cloak about her.

"Well, I did my best, Mary," said the Match-Man modestly. But you could see he was really very pleased with himself indeed.

Just then the Waiter stopped in front of them, beside a large white doorway that looked as though it were made of thick chalk lines.

"Here you are!" he said. "This is the Way Out."

"Good-by, and thank you," said Mary Poppins, shaking his hand.

"Moddom, good-by!" said the Waiter, bowing so low that his head knocked against his knees.

He nodded to the Match-Man, who cocked his head on one side and closed one eye at the Waiter, which was his way of bidding him farewell. Then Mary Poppins stepped through the white doorway and the Match-Man followed her.

And as they went, the feather dropped from her hat and the silk cloak from her shoulders and the diamonds from her shoes. The bright clothes of the Match-Man faded, and his straw hat turned into his old ragged cap again. Mary Poppins turned and looked at him, and she knew at once what had happened. Standing on the pavement, she gazed at him for a long minute, and then her glance explored the wood behind him for the Waiter. But the Waiter was nowhere to be seen. There was nobody in the picture. Nothing moved there. Even the Merry-go-Round had disappeared. Only the still trees and the grass and the unmoving little patch of sea remained.

But Mary Poppins and the Match-Man smiled at one another. They knew, you see, what lay behind the trees. . . .

## CHECK FOR UNDERSTANDING

1. Why couldn't Bert take Mary Poppins to tea?
2. Why did Mary Poppins call tea a "stodgy meal"?
3. What happened later to show she didn't mean it?
4. Why couldn't Mary Poppins and Bert see the waiter in Bert's picture?
5. Why do you think Mary Poppins and Bert had on new clothes when they entered the picture?
6. What happened when Mary Poppins and Bert went back through the white doorway?

## WRITE ABOUT *"The Day Out"*

Mary Poppins was someone who believed in good manners. She would probably have written to Bert to thank him for the day out. Write Mary Poppins's thank-you note to Bert, as she would have written it. Tell what you think Mary Poppins would have liked best about the day out.

# VOCABULARY • LANGUAGE

## Base Words and Suffixes

In "The Day Out," Mary Poppins walked down the lane *quickly*. When she saw Bert, she called to him *softly*. Then she spoke to him *brightly*.

The words *quickly*, *softly*, and *brightly* are all adverbs. They describe, or tell about, Mary Poppins' actions. What else do these words have in common?

Each word contains a **base word** and the letters *-ly*. A base word is a word on which other words are **based,** or built. The base word in *quickly* is *quick*. The base word in *softly* is *soft*. What is the base word in *brightly*?

The letters *-ly* are known as a **suffix.** A suffix is a group of letters added to the end of a word. When the suffix *-ly* is added to the base word *quick*, a new word, *quickly*, is created. Since the suffix *-ly* means "in the manner of," *quickly* means "in a quick manner." Add the suffix *-ly* to the base word *soft*. The new word, *softly*, means "in a soft manner." What is the meaning of *brightly*? Explain how you figured out the answer.

Here are some other suffixes and their meanings.

| | |
|---|---|
| **-ful** = "full of" | **-able** = "able to" |
| **-less** = "without" | **-ness** = "the state of being" |
| **-ous** = "full of" | **-y** = "like" |

Mary Poppins and Bert had a <u>delightful</u> time when they entered the picture. Bert was <u>suddenly</u> dressed in a <u>spot-</u>

less new suit. Mary found herself wearing a silk dress with underline_watery patterns.

Look at the words that are underlined above. Each contains a base word and a suffix. For example, the base word in *delightful* is *delight*. The suffix *-ful* means "full of." Therefore, the meaning of *delightful* is "full of delight."

The base word in *suddenly* is *sudden*. You know that the suffix *-ly* means "in the manner of." Therefore, *suddenly* means "in a sudden manner." Find the base word and suffix in *spotless* and *watery*. Show how the suffixes help you to figure out the meaning of the words.

As you read "A Hike in New York City," you will notice several words which contain a base and a suffix. For example, you will learn that

> The children in this story approach their "hike" with all the *careful preparation* of mountain climbers getting ready to scale Mount Everest.

The base word in *careful* is *care*. The suffix *-ful* means "full of." Therefore, *careful* means "full of care."

Look closely at the word *preparation* in the passage. The suffix *-ation* means "the act of doing something." The base word *prepare* means "to get ready." What do you think is the meaning of the word *preparation*?

See what other base words and suffixes you can find in the story.

# A HIKE IN NEW YORK CITY

by SAM LEVENSON

For city kids, raised in a maze of concrete and blacktop, the country has a special, wild appeal. Even the little bit of country found in a city park can seem like wilderness. The children in this story approach their "hike" with all the careful preparation of mountain climbers getting ready to scale Mount Everest.

Is the hike a success? Do you think the children will want to go again?

At least once each summer we kids went off on a hike, but never without strong opposition from Mama. When it came to the open road, Mama had a closed mind.

Her method of discouraging us from venturing into the unknown was to make the entire project appear ridiculous:

"You're going on a what?"

"We're going on a hike."

"What's a hike?" Mama would ask.

When we started to explain it, the whole idea did in fact become ridiculous.

"We go walking, Ma."

"Walking? For that you have to leave home?

What's the matter with walking right here? You walk; I'll watch."

"You don't understand, Ma. We take lunch along."

"I'll give you lunch here, and you can march right around the table," and she would start singing a march, clapping her hands rhythmically.

"Ma, we climb mountains in the woods."

She couldn't understand why it was so much more enjoyable to fall off a mountain than off a fire escape.

"And how about the wild animals in the woods?"

"Wild animals? What kinds of wild animals?"

"A bear for instance. A bear could eat you up."

"Ma. Bears don't eat little children."

"Okay. So he won't eat you, but he could take a bite and spit out! I'm telling you now, if a wild animal eats you up don't come running to me. And who's going with you?"

"Well, there's Georgie—"

"Georgie! Not him! He's a real wild animal!" She then went on to list all the conditions for the trip. "And remember one thing, don't tear your pants, and remember one thing, don't eat wild berries and bring me home the cramps, and remember one thing, don't tell me tomorrow morning that you're too tired to go to school, and remember one thing, wear boots, a sweater, and an umbrella, and a hat, and remember one thing, if you should get lost in the jungle, call up so I'll know you're all right. And don't dare come home without color in your cheeks. I wish I were young and free like you. Take soap."

Since the consent was specifically granted for the next day only, that night none of us slept. There was always a chance that it might rain. Brother Albert stayed at the crystal set all night like a ship's radio operator with his earphones on, listening to weather bulletins and repeating them aloud for the rest of us. "It's clearing in Nebraska. Hot air masses coming up from the Gulf. They say it's good for planting alfalfa. Storm warning off the coast of Newfoundland. It's drizzling in Montreal."

At six A.M. we were ready for Operation Hike,
rain or shine, but we had to wait for Papa to get
up. We didn't need his permission, but we did need
his blanket.

Into the valley of Central Park marched the six
hundred, bowed down with knapsacks, flashlights, a
cereal box compass-mirror (so you could tell not
only where you were lost but who was lost), a thermos bottle (semiautomatic—you had to fill it but it
emptied by itself), and an ax. Onward! Forward!
Upward! Philip was always the leader. He was the
one to get lost first. Jerry was the lookout. He
would yell, "Look out!" and fall off the cliff. None
of us knew how long we were supposed to march.

We went on because we didn't know what to do if we stopped. One brave coward finally spoke up. "I can't go on anymore. The heat is killing me. Let's start the fire here."

No hike was complete without Georgie and his Uncle Bernie's World War I bugle. This kid had lungs like a vacuum cleaner. With him outside the walls of Jericho, they could have sent the rest of the army home. He used to stand on a hill and let go a blast that had the Staten Island ferries running into each other.

Lunch, naturally, had been packed in a shoe box—sandwiches, fruit, cheese, and napkins all squashed together neatly. The lid would open by itself every twenty minutes for air.

It happened every time—the Miracle of the Sandwiches. One kid always got a "brilliant idea." "Hey. I got a brilliant idea. I'm tired of my mother's sandwiches. Let's everybody trade sandwiches." All the kids exchanged sandwiches, and miraculously we all ended up with salami.

Albert was the true nature lover. "You know, you can learn a lot about human nature from the ants," he always said as he lifted up rock after rock to study his favorite insects. And he was right. While he was studying the ants, someone swiped his apple.

We came home with color in our cheeks—green. To make sure we could go again, we didn't forget Mama. We brought her a bouquet. She took one whiff and broke out in red blotches. Papa yelled but wouldn't come near us. He was afraid it was catching.

## CHECK FOR UNDERSTANDING

1. How did Mama try to discourage the children?
2. Why did the children stay awake all night before their hike?
3. Why do you think their mother was so worried about them?
4. Was the hike a success?
5. Do you think the children will want to go again?

## WRITE ABOUT *"A Hike in New York City"*

Imagine that the narrator of the story decided to write a letter to a friend. His friend lived in the country, and he wanted to impress the friend with a description of the hike. Write the letter.

# CITY

by LANGSTON HUGHES

In the morning the city
Spreads its wings
Making a song
In stone that sings.

In the evening the city
Goes to bed
Hanging lights
About its head.

133

# COMPREHENSION

## Main Idea

When you read an informational article, you can see clearly that there is a **main idea.** Any article—whether in an encyclopedia or a popular magazine—is organized around this idea.

But what about a story? Does a story have a main idea? The answer is yes, it does. But the main idea of a story is almost never stated directly in the story. Nor does the main idea always jump out at you in the course of reading the story.

Even though the main idea of a story isn't as easy to see as the main idea of an article, it is just as important that you know what it is. This is because the main idea is often the key to understanding the actions, details, and the behavior of the characters in the story.

The way you find the main idea in a story is also different from the way you find it in an article. The main idea of a story is revealed indirectly. It might come from one thing a character says or from a theme you discover in all the things a character says. It might come from one important action in the story or from the special meaning of many actions in the story.

Think about the story you just read, "A Hike in New York City." What does the following passage tell you about the main idea of the story?

At six A.M. we were ready for Operation Hike, rain or shine, but we had to wait for Papa to get up. We didn't need his permission, but we did need his blanket.

Into the valley of Central Park marched the six hundred, bowed down with knapsacks, flashlights, a cereal box compass-mirror (so you could tell not only where you were lost but who was lost), a thermos bottle (semiautomatic—you had to fill it but it emptied by itself), and an ax.

---

If you think about what makes this passage funny, you will be close to the main idea of the story itself. Would you say, from this passage, that the main idea is:

**a.** It is important to have the right equipment for a hike.

**b.** The father doesn't have much to say about family decisions.

**c.** The boys are prepared for a jungle hike even though they're only walking in the city.

The final answer probably comes closest to stating the main idea of the story. And it is only by understanding the main idea that the story succeeds in doing what it is supposed to do: *make you laugh.*

The next story you are going to read, "The Beach," also has a main idea that is important to understand in order to get the most out of the story. As you read, pay close attention to the *words* and *actions* of the mother and of the child telling the story. While you are reading "The Beach," pause every once in a while to try to state the main idea of the story to yourself.

# ·T·H·E·
# ·B·E·A·C·H·

by MIRIAM COHEN

Grown-ups are not always predictable or easy to understand. In fact, sometimes they do things that are completely unexpected. In this story, Maria Antonia learns something about her mother when she agrees to take Maria Antonia and her friend to the beach—a decision that surprises Mama almost as much as it does Maria Antonia.

What sort of person does Maria Antonia's mother seem to be at the start of the story? What happens to show she is not quite the person she seems to be?

"Hey, Maria Antonia!" Nilton came up pulling his wagon behind him. It was made out of a crashed baby buggy and wheels from three different bicycles, with a Brazilian flag stuck in front. "Let's go to the beach."

"Just us?"

"Yes, come on. I want to test my underwater goggles."

Nilton had some old sunglasses without the glass. He put the bottoms from plastic soda bottles in the frames with chewed chewing gum to hold them against his face and keep out the water. Nilton's very good at thinking of these things.

"I couldn't go without a grown-up. Mama thinks I'll drown. She'd never let me go."

"Ask her to come. Tell her to bring the baby. We'll hold his hands, and he can put his toes in the water."

"She'll never do it. She'll say she has too much work. And she'll send me to the store."

"Ask her."

We went inside. Mama's face was sweating, and her hair was coming down in straggles from her bobby pins. This morning I washed all the baby's diapers for her. Gramma usually did that, but our neighbor Carolina had swollen legs, and Gramma was helping her. So I prayed Mama would say "Yes."

"Please, can we all go to the beach? We'll pull the baby in Nilton's wagon, and we'll take care of him, and you won't have to do a thing."

She pushed back her hair. "I have too much work to do." I poked Nilton. Then her eyes seemed to see the cold, shiny water. And she said, "Well, if we came back quickly, before it's time for Poppa to come home . . ."

Before she could change her mind, we put a towel in a shopping bag, a fan, and Pop's straw hat to shade Mama's face. "Hurry, hurry, Mama, please," I begged. "So we won't have to come back right away!"

Down the Hill we started. Mama carried the baby because she didn't trust Nilton's wagon. He left it by

his uncle's place. Halfway to the bottom, she was worrying that she shouldn't have gone away from her house. But we helped her up the steps of the bus before she could change her mind.

We got off when we got to the City so Mama could look in the shop windows. Nilton and I slipped around the gray suits of the businesspeople and flew by the shoppers carrying their heavy shopping bags. We were at the end of a block before Mama had even started. We couldn't wait!

Past the high buildings, the different, lighter air was telling us, "Here! The beach is here. And the ocean is waiting!"

Again and again we ran back, circling Mama, trying to help her walk faster. We were so afraid she'd say, "I never should have come."

Our family goes to the beach only a few times every year. It's far. And think how much bus fare it would take for all of us! Besides, Poppa is always working, and the brothers and sisters, too. Some kids, like Nilton, go by themselves anytime. I would try it, but you couldn't hide where you'd been from Mama. You'd be too clean.

"Nilton! Where is she? I don't see Mama and Little Sergio!" The people in the streets filled up so quickly the place where my mother had been. Back we ran till we saw the soft, old pink of Mama's dress and Little Sergio's round, black eyes peeping over her shoulder. She was looking in a store window.

It was a souvenir store where tourists buy things to take home. Not pots and pans or rubber sandals or TVs, but things you couldn't use: Indian spears, glass pictures with huge, shiny blue butterflies inside. "Are they real?" Nilton said they were, but I never saw such butterflies.

"What is it? What are you looking at, Mama?" She showed us little brown people pinched out of clay and dried. A lady and her boyfriend danced, holding each other far apart. A teacher was teaching some grown-ups how to spell, and they were scratching their heads. A family walked somewhere in a line with pots and pans and bundles on their heads. Even their parrot was riding on top.

"Why are you looking at these funny little country people, Mama?"

She shook her head and turned away. "I'm finished."

Finally we crossed the last avenue and ran out onto the black-and-white, curvy sidewalk by the beach. They put the black-and-white bits of stone in the sidewalk to look just like the waves in the ocean. Nilton and I held our arms out. We were going to hug the ocean! "The ocean! The ocean!" we shouted.

The ocean was playing with the beach. It shook its head and roared and jumped on the sand, then slid back with a pebbly laugh. "Were you scared? I was just playing!"

A thousand people, brown like cinnamon, walked on the white sand. Their bathing suits painted red, purple, green, and orange on the white.

I held the baby for Mama, and she took off her shoes to walk more easily in the sand. "Let's go there, by the rocks, where the water is quiet." Nilton pointed.

"Don't those rocks look like big fish pulled out of the water?" I asked. "Doesn't the water look like green jelly?"

"Everything doesn't look like something else. It looks like itself," Nilton said.

"Anyway, Mama, here's a nice place. Put your things down and sit on the towel with Little Sergio. Here's your hat so the sun doesn't give you a headache. Nilton and I will be right back."

You can swim just as well in your regular clothes. Then you don't have to bother about changing into bathing suits. Sometimes I wish I had a purple elastic one that ties around your neck, with a ruffle on the back.

Kicking our feet high, we ran and threw ourselves into the ocean. Nilton kept on going. He ducked under and only the bottoms of his feet showed where he was. I stayed where the little waves catch you and make you scream, you like it so much.

I could see Mama, sitting up straight with her legs in front of her and her skirt pulled tight over her knees. Little Sergio patted the sand. "Mama! Watch this!" Pinching my nose I sat all the way under, to the bottom. Then I jumped up and splashed toward the beach. "Mama, I'm coming to play with Little Sergio."

Nilton was coming out of the water, too. "Did the goggles work? What did you see with them?"

"I have to think of something else. The chewing gum didn't stay, and the water came in."

We flopped down next to Mama and began to build a tunnel for the baby. He laughed when Nilton's foot wiggled through it.

"Mama, why don't you lie down and rest?"

She wouldn't, we knew she wouldn't, but Nilton and I wiggled ourselves into the hot sand. "Mama, did you come to the beach when you were a kid?"

"No, no. In the Northeast there was no beach. There was no water. In the backlands, where we lived, it was dry. So dry the people had to move all the time, looking for water. We had to leave our house, with the little fig tree—we couldn't take it, of course—and go on the road, trying to find some food and water. It was very bad. We came in a truck to the City, to Rio, and it was better then.

"I got married to your Poppa. And I remember he took me to the movies for the first time in my life. I couldn't believe what a beautiful place the theater was! I didn't want to go out when the picture was over. And all the fruits and meats and vegetables! You could walk right up and buy them! Sometimes I'm afraid about moving again, with everything on our heads, like the little dry people in the store window. . . ."

Nilton and I looked at each other. My mother never told these things before. "Well," I said, "it can't happen again because this is Rio. And you have Pop and all your sons and daughters to work for you. And some of us might be famous TV stars or Queen of the Samba, and we'd always take care of you and Poppa."

Mama smiled and began gathering up the towel and our sleeping baby. "It's late. If the beans are burned, I don't know what I'll do! Gramma forgets a lot, you know." She frowned. "What got into me today!" Nilton carried the baby, and we went slowly toward the sidewalk.

The tall apartments took the rich people back up into them. The hot-gold sun cooled itself in the ocean. Over the sand hurried the ice cream vendor. His customers were leaving with the sun. Nilton and I couldn't help looking after him, even though we didn't want Mama to think she should buy us a sweet, red ice, or a little vanilla cup.

"Run after him! Get three cups!" Mama was unpinching her little plastic purse and counting out the money. "Ice cream man! Wait! Wait!" I held out my arms for the baby, and Nilton ran after him.

"Here." Nilton gave Mama one cup, me another, and the baby the last one.

"No, no." Mama put hers into his hand. "The baby and I will eat this one. It's much too much for Little Sergio. And I hardly like ice cream at all."

Nilton and I took little wooden spoonfuls so it would last. Mama spooned big ones into Little Sergio, so vanilla was all around his mouth and on his nose.

In between, Mama licked the spoon. We scratched and scraped on the bottom of the cups till there wasn't a bit more.

Then we crossed between the cars on the avenue and started back to our Hill.

## CHECK FOR UNDERSTANDING

1. What sort of person did Maria Antonia's mother seem to be at the start of the story?
2. What did she explain about herself when she described her childhood?
3. How do you think she became so cautious and full of worry?
4. What happened to show that she was not quite the person she seemed to be?
5. What did Maria Antonia's mother buy for Maria Antonia and Nilton?
6. Why do you think she got the children this treat?
7. Do you think Maria Antonia's mother will take them to the beach whenever they wish from now on? Explain your answer.

## WRITE ABOUT *"The Beach"*

The day at the beach was an important day for Maria Antonia. Imagine you are Maria Antonia. Write a letter to one of your older brothers or sisters who works in another town. Describe your beach day in the letter. Tell what you learned about your mother at the beach.

# maggie and milly
# and molly and may

by *e.e. cummings*

maggie and milly and molly and may
went down to the beach (to play one day)

and maggie discovered a shell that sang
so sweetly she couldn't remember her troubles, and

milly befriended a stranded star
whose rays five languid fingers were;

and molly was chased by a horrible thing
which raced sideways while blowing bubbles: and

may came home with a smooth round stone
as small as a world and as large as alone.

For whatever we lose (like a you or a me)
it's always ourselves we find in the sea

# PARMELE

### by ELOISE GREENFIELD and LESSIE JONES LITTLE

Nearly a hundred years ago, life—even small town life—was very different from what it is now. Back then, trains linked the towns of America together. This selection tells what it was like more than eighty years ago in Parmele, a place where the daily train runs were the high point of town life.

Why did the narrator like trains so much? Why do you think the trains were so important to Parmele?

✦

The twentieth century was new, only six years old. Just three years had passed since the Wright brothers flew their famous airplane. Radio broadcasting had not yet begun. The automobile—that strange-looking machine that moved without having to be pulled—was seen so seldom that it was still scaring horses off the road.

I used to hear Papa and Mama and their friends talking about the lumber mill that had been the center of life in Parmele before I was born. But there wasn't any mill when I was growing up. The only thing left of it was the sawdust from all the wood they had sawed there. The sawdust was about a foot thick on the land where the mill had been. I used to love to walk on it. It was spongy, and it made me feel like I was made of rubber. I'd take my shoes off and kind of bounce along on top of it. But that was all that was left of the mill.

My Parmele was a train town. The life of my town moved around the trains that came in and out all day long. About 300 people lived in Parmele. Most of them were black. There were four churches

149

and two schools. There wasn't even one doctor, and not many people would have had the money to pay one, if there had been. If somebody got real sick, a member of the family would go by horse and buggy to a nearby town and bring the doctor back, or sometimes the doctor would ride on his own horse.

Most of the men and women in Parmele earned their living by farming. Some did other things like working at the tobacco factory in Robersonville. But most worked on the farms that were all around in the area. When I was a little girl, they earned fifty cents a day—a farm day, sunup to sundown—plus meals. After they got home, they had all their own work to do, cooking and cleaning, laundry, chopping wood for the woodstove, and shopping.

I used to love to go shopping with Mama. There was so much to see downtown. When people started getting cars, the only gasoline pump in town was down there. There were stores, four or five stores, where you could buy clothes, or yard goods, or groceries, or hardware, and the post office was in the corner of one store. Stokes' Cafe was on one side of the tracks. Powell's Restaurant was on the other side.

There was a little park, too, where we had picnics sometimes. And we had one police officer, and one dance hall. The water tank and the coal chute where the trains got refills were downtown, and so was the train station.

Twice I lived in houses that the trains had to

151

pass right by on their way to the station. I'd hear that whistle blow, and I'd run out on the porch just in time to see the train come twisting around the curve like a long black worm. I'd wave at the people sitting at the windows. And they'd wave back at me.

Trains weren't air-conditioned in those days. When the weather was warm, the windows were always open. I remember a train trip I took when I was small. I had on my pink organdy dress that Mama had made me. I was so proud of the way I looked. But the whole time, I had to keep rubbing the cinders out of my eyes. Soot kept getting on my dress, and every time I tried to brush it off, it made a long, dirty streak. I was a mess by the time I got off the train. I was really dirty, my face and hands and my clothes, and my eyes were red and sore.

Parmele had trains coming in and going out all day long. Passenger trains and freight trains. There was always so much going on at the station that I wouldn't know what to watch. People were changing trains and going in and out of the cafe and the restaurant. They came from big cities like New York and Chicago and Boston, and they were all wearing the latest styles. Things were being unloaded, like furniture and trunks and plows and cases of fruit and crates of clucking chickens, or a puppy, or the body of somebody who had died and was being brought back home. And every year the last two

weeks in May, a special train would come through. It had two white flags flying on the locomotive, and it was carrying one hundred carloads of white potatoes that had been grown down near Pamlico Sound. Everybody said the soil there was so rich they didn't even have to fertilize it.

The train station was a gathering place, too. A lot of people went there to relax after they had finished their work for the day. They'd come downtown to pick up their mail, or buy a newspaper, and then they'd just stand around laughing and talking to their friends. And on Sundays fellows and their girls would come all the way from other towns, just to spend the afternoon at the Parmele train station.

## CHECK FOR UNDERSTANDING

1. How can you tell that Parmele was not a wealthy town?
2. Why did the narrator get so dirty on her train ride?
3. Why did the narrator like trains so much?
4. Why do you think the trains were so important to Parmele?
5. Do you think Parmele has changed since the time the story describes? Explain your answer.

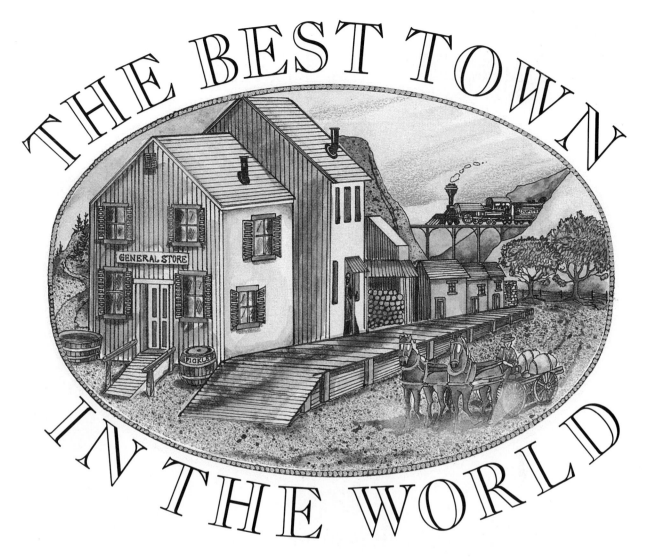

## THE BEST TOWN IN THE WORLD

by BYRD BAYLOR

In "Parmele," the narrator described the town of her childhood. The narrator's father, in "The Best Town in the World," tells his childhood memories to his own children.

Do you think the town he describes really was "the best town in the world"? Why does he see the town that way?

155

All my life I've heard about
a little, dirt-road,
one-store,
country town
not far from a rocky canyon
way back

in the Texas hills.
This town had lots of space
around it
with caves to find
and honey trees
and giant rocks to climb.

the best town in the world
and he just happened
to be born there.
How's that for being
lucky?

We always liked
to hear about
that town
where everything was
perfect.

Of course it had a name
but people called the town
and all the ranches
and the farms around it
just *The Canyon,*
and they called each other
*Canyon People.*
The way my father said it,
you could tell
it was a special thing
to be
one of those people.

It had a creek
and there were panther tracks
to follow
and you could swing
on the wild grapevines.
My father said it was

The best blackberries
in the world
grew wild.

157

My father says
the ones in stores
don't taste a thing
like those
he used to pick.
*Those* tasted just like
a blackberry should.

He'd crawl into
a tangle
of blackberry thicket
and eat all he wanted
and finally
walk home

swinging his bucket
(with enough for four pies)
and his hands
and his face
and his hard bare feet
would be stained
that beautiful color.

All plants
liked
to grow there.
The town was famous for
red chiles
and for melons
and for sweet corn, too.

And it's a well-known fact
that chickens in that canyon
laid prettier brown eggs
than chickens
twenty miles on down the road.

My father says
no scientist
has figured out
why.

The dogs were smarter there.
They helped you herd the goats
and growled at rattlesnakes
before you even saw them.
And if you stopped
to climb a tree
your dogs stopped, too.
They curled up and waited
for you to come down.
They didn't run off
by themselves.

Summer days
were longer there
than they are
in other places,
and wildflowers grew taller
and thicker on the hills—
not just the yellow ones.
There were all shades of
lavender and purple
and orange and red
and blue

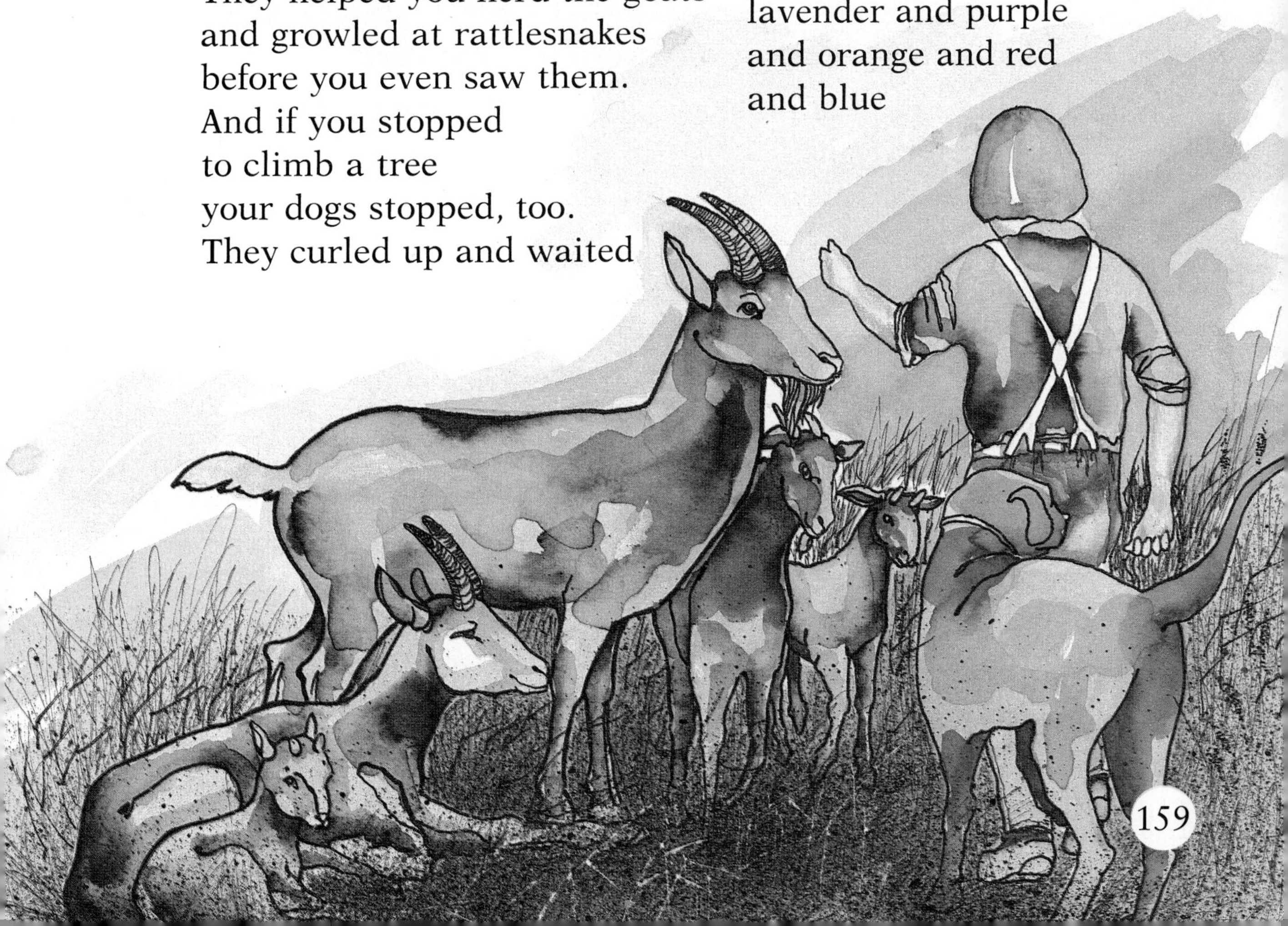

and the palest kind of pink.
They all had butterflies
to match.

Fireflies lit up
the whole place
at night,
and in the distance
you could hear
somebody's fiddle
or banjo
or harp.

My father says
no city water
ever tasted half as good

as water that he carried
in a bucket from the well
by their back door.

And there isn't
any water
anywhere
as clear
as the water
in that ice-cold creek
where all the children swam.
You could look down
and see the white sand
and watch the minnows
flashing by.

But
when my father came to the part
about that ice-cold water
we would always say,
"It doesn't sound
so perfect
if the water was
ice-cold."
He'd look surprised
and say,
"But that's the way
creek water
is supposed to be—
ice-cold."


So we learned that
however
things were
in that town
is just exactly how
things ought to be.


My father said
the smartest people
in the world
were
all
right there.

We asked him
what they did
that was so smart.
He said,
"They all had sense enough
to know the best town
in the world
when they saw it.
That's smart."


And they were smart
in other ways.


For instance,
they could tell time
without wearing a watch.
They just glanced
at the sun
and they knew.
They wouldn't be more
than ten minutes off . . .
and ten minutes off
doesn't matter.


They could tell
by the stars

what the weather would be.
They could tell
by the moon
when to plant.
If they needed
a house
or corral
or a barn,
they didn't pay someone
to come build it for them.
They cut their own trees
and found their own rocks
and dug their own earth.

Then,
whatever it was,
they built it to last
for a hundred years—
and it did.

Suppose
their children
wanted
kites
or jump ropes
or whistles
or stilts . . .

They didn't have to
go to stores
and buy just what
was there.

They knew how to make
the best toys
in the world.

On winter nights
when they were
sitting by the fire,
by lamplight,
talking,
you'd see them
making
bows and arrows
or soft rag dolls
or blocks
or tops
or bamboo flutes
or even a checkerboard
carved out of oak.

My father said
sometimes
they'd let you
paint the checkers

red
or black
and you'd be
proud.

We liked everything
we ever heard
about those people
and that town,
but we always
had to ask:
"If it really was
the best town
in the world,
why weren't
more people
there?"

And he would say,
"Because
if a lot
of people
lived there,
it wouldn't be
the best town
any more.
The best town
can't
be crowded."

We always wished
that we could live there
and be
Canyon People, too.

Still,
we used to wonder
if possibly,
just *possibly*,
there might be
another
perfect town
somewhere.

To find out,
I guess
you'd have to follow
a lot of
dirt roads
past
a whole lot of
wildflower hills.

I guess
you'd have to
try
a lot of
ice-cold

swimming holes
and pat
a lot of dogs.

It seems
like a good thing
to do.

## CHECK FOR UNDERSTANDING

1. Why was the narrator's father lucky?
2. Do you think the town he described really was "the best town in the world"?
3. Why did he see the town that way?
4. Do you think summer days really were longer there than in other places?
5. What was special about the people in the best town in the world?
6. If the father went back to visit the best town in the world, do you think it would look the same to him? Explain your answer.

## WRITE ABOUT *"The Best Town in the World"*

The people who lived in the best town in the world no doubt celebrated holidays in the best possible way. Imagine that you live in that town back when the father did. Describe a holiday of your choice—Thanksgiving, the Fourth of July, or another holiday—as it was celebrated then.

## Reading Diagrams and Graphs

### Diagrams

In "The Best Town in the World," there were lots of things for the children to do. There were caves to explore, trees and rocks to climb, big vines to swing on. On a windy day, they could go out to a nice flat spot and fly a kite. They didn't have to buy a kite. They could make it themselves.

You've seen kites and flown them dozens of times, but have you ever *made* one? How are they constructed? Where is the string attached?

Something that would be a big help to you would be a **diagram** of a kite.

A diagram is a special kind of drawing. It shows all the parts of something. Where they meet. How they are attached to one another.

Each part of a diagram is **labeled**. Arrows or lines are drawn to show exactly what the label is referring to.

Diagrams are important because they help us to understand things.

Here is a simple diagram of a kite.

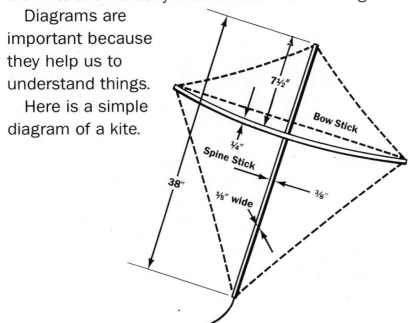

Suppose you have a friend who knew how to make a kite. If he gave you directions you *might* be able to make one.

But how much easier it would be for you to understand all the directions if he had drawn a simple diagram like the one above.

There are different types of diagrams. One type is called a **cross section**. It shows you what you would see if a cut were made through an object. It shows you what is inside.

In "The Best Town in the World," there were lots of trees to climb. But the inside of the tree is a part you would never see, no matter how many times you climbed it. This is a cross section of a large tree. A ring grows every year showing the tree's age.

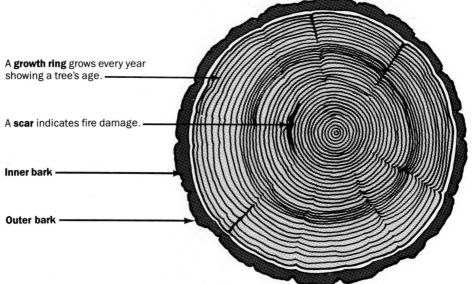

A **growth ring** grows every year showing a tree's age.

A **scar** indicates fire damage.

**Inner bark**

**Outer bark**

## Using What You Have Learned

It's important to know how to *read* a diagram. Look again at the diagram of the kite frame.

What does it tell you about how far from the top of the spine the bow stick is placed?

How thick are the pieces of wood used?

How long is the spine?

You will see that the diagram has given you even more information than your friend did in his explanation. If there is a diagram along with text in a book, often the diagram will give you information you don't find in the text.

## Expanding Your Skills

Draw your own diagram of one of the following:

**(a)** a baseball field

**(b)** a bicycle

**(c)** a flower

Make sure you use labels and lines to identify the various parts.

## Graphs

Years ago, most people in the United States lived in small towns. But in recent years, more than half of the population lives in cities.

Here is a list of the recent populations of some of the large cities around the world:

| | |
|---|---|
| Chicago | 3,005,072 |
| Mexico City | 9,233,770 |
| New York City | 7,481,613 |
| Tokyo | 8,219,888 |
| Beijing (Peking) | 7,570,000 |
| Delhi | 3,287,883 |

| |
|---|
| 9 million |
| 8 million |
| 7 million |
| 6 million |
| 5 million |
| 4 million |
| 3 million |
| 2 million |
| 1 million |
| 0 |

| | |
|---|---|
| Paris | 2,299,830 |
| Houston | 1,594,086 |
| Montreal | 1,080,546 |

Using this list, answer the following question:

Which city is larger, Tokyo or Beijing?
List the following three cities in order of population size: Chicago, Mexico City, and Montreal.

Another way of getting this kind of information is from a **graph**. There are different kinds of graphs. One type is called a **bar graph**.

Here is a bar graph that also gives you information about population.

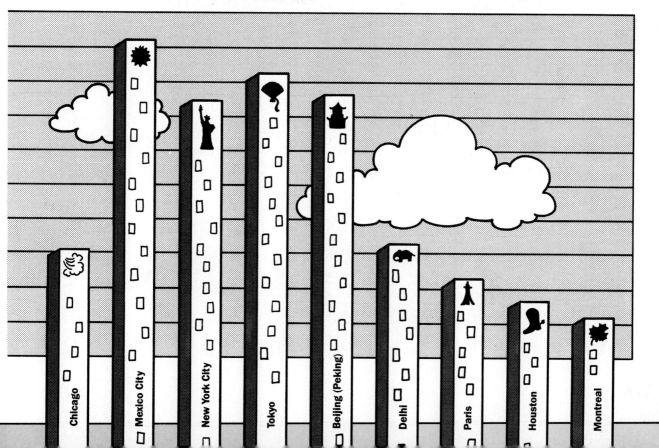

When using a graph to get information, it is important to look at it carefully. What does it tell you? In this graph the cities are listed across the bottom. Populations (in the millions) are given in the column to the left. The height of each bar shows you the population of each city.

Now, using the bar graph to get information, answer the following question:

> Which city is larger, Montreal or Chicago?
> List the following three cities in order of population size: Delhi, New York City, and Paris.

Was it easier — and faster — to answer the questions by using the list? Or by looking at the bar graph? Often it is easier and faster to get certain kinds of information from a graph.

The graph does have a limitation. It does not give you the information as *precisely* as the list does. But to compare information, as we did, a graph is very useful. The information on a graph stands out. You see it quickly. Graphs, like diagrams, are good ways of getting certain kinds of information in a clear form, in a form that is easy to read.

## Using What You Have Learned

Using the bar graph, list all the cities in order of population, listing the largest first.

## Expanding Your Skills

Create a bar graph showing the following information.

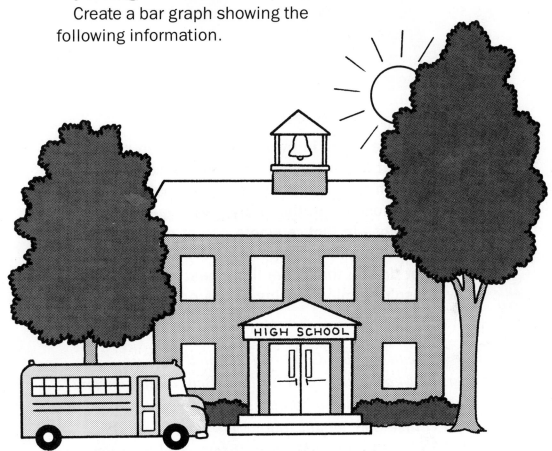

Lincoln High School has **2023** students.
Washington High School has **6325** students.
Seely High School has **3650** students.
Marshall High School has **8500** students.
Jason Foley High School has **4000** students.

# NO NAME ISLAND

by KATHRYN LASKY

There are times in everyone's life when something happens that is so special, so perfectly wonderful, that you wish time would stop so you could go on enjoying the moment. In this story, Jem experiences one such moment—in fact, a whole day of moments!—when he and his dad camp out on No Name Island.

What do you think Jem likes best about his trip? Why doesn't he mind leaving at the end of the story?

*Eleven-year-old Jem Gray had planned his first overnight kayak trip with his dad, Ben, all winter and spring. He had used a compass and some maps to chart what course they would follow. He even chose the island where they would set up camp. The time for the trip has arrived and Jem and his father set off in the Wasso. Unexpectedly, they spot another island, one that had not appeared on the map. A cove extends far into the island and it is full of blind corners and secret turns. Jem and his dad agree that this is where they will camp.*

They coasted to the tip of the water finger. There was a sand beach. There was a rock just right for cast fishing and a cliff just right for climbing. It was a place you got to and you knew exactly what you wanted to do. First Jem swam in the pools and then in the larger part of the cove. His dad watched from the shore.

"How can you stand that cold water, Jem?"

"I just keep my feet on the bottom!" Jem whooped and ducked.

After swimming Jem explored the shoreline. Besides the big rock pools, there were several small tidal pools. Glittering in the late afternoon sun, they looked like oddly cut jewels. Each pool was alive with small plants and seaweeds and some with tiny minnows.

Jem and his father climbed the short cliff. On top of the

island was a thick grove of spruce. From the water this grove of trees had looked like a crown on the round flat top of the island. Through the trees and out the other side of the grove, the land turned brambly with berry bushes. They picked blueberries, raspberries, and blackberries, dropping them into Ben's hat because they had forgotten the pail.

Some islands were "picked out" by hikers and boaters, but "No Name," as Jem had begun to call his island, was not lived on or visited or picked from, except by cormorants and sea gulls and whatever four-footed animals lived there.

"Lucky we dug those clams on Porcupine," Jem said, as he watched his father pan-fry a ridiculously small mackerel that ordinarily they would have thrown back.

"This is just an *hors d'oeuvre**. Those clams will be great!" Ben slid the fish onto a tin plate. It looked even smaller. "Hand me the rest of the butter. We'll melt it for the clams."

Jem wondered what Jessica, Michael, and his mother were doing now, that very moment. Eating dinner, he guessed. Maybe chowder, maybe hamburgers. He wondered if they wondered what he was doing. They must. Two places were empty at the table. They didn't have a table here. There was a slab of rock that did fine. They had pulled *Wasso* above the high tide line and turned her upside down, and now they sat leaning against her hull.

Jem and his dad shared the mackerel—all four bites of it— and a heap of clams, and watched the sun slide down behind the horizon like a thin gold coin. It was good, thinking

*(ôr durv′): A hot or cold appetizer eaten before a meal.

that he and his dad, and his mom and Jess and Michael were miles apart but watching the same sun slide on down—Jem and Ben from a beach on an island with no name and a rock for a table, the other Grays from a beach on an island called Deer with a pine table.

They had finished their berries. "Tell me a story, Dad."

"This is Maine. I'll tell you a Maine story."

"Is it true?"

"You bet."

"Good, let's hear it."

"Once upon a time, a long time ago, on Deer Isle . . ."

"Before the bridge to the mainland?"

"Yes, long before the bridge. If there had been a bridge, this wouldn't have happened. No,

it was before I was born, and your grandfather was just a few years older than yourself, maybe seventeen or eighteen at the most. The winters were long on an island without a bridge, especially when it was the kind of winter cold enough to ice the channel but not cold enough to make the ice safe for walking across to the mainland. Too thin for feet, too thick for canoes. Well, March came, and the ice started to break right up, and your grandfather was sure that his charts from the Survey Department had come. He wanted to pick them up."

"The ones for his trip out the St. Lawrence and around the Gaspé Peninsula?"

"Yes. He'd dreamed of it all winter. He ordered the charts just after Christmas, so he was sure they had arrived. That first morning when the ice had just cleared off, no sooner, a herd of low, dark clouds came in, and the water became choppy. My grandfather—your great-grandfather—said, 'Looks like a Northeaster, Pete. You going?' And your grandfather—his son—said he thought he could make it across and back before anything got nasty."

"He let him go?"

"Yes."

"Did he warn him or anything?"

"He asked him if he was going."

"So he just let him go like that?"

"Yes."

"What happened?"

"He made it across fine, but on the way back the wind started to build really fast, and by the time he was halfway across, the channel was boiling white-tops of waves blowing right off. My dad was paddling along. If he'd turned around to go back, he would have been caught on the side

and swamped. He would have lived about two minutes in that water. He had no choice but to paddle right into the teeth of this thing. Somehow he made it. When he walked up from the beach to the old farmhouse where our family lived, his dad was standing there on the front porch. He'd watched him come back. His dad's cheeks were all wet, his eyes red. He'd been crying. He never thought his son would make it back."

"Did he kiss him?"

"No. He wasn't the kissy kind. I think Dad told me that he said something like 'Charts still dry, Pete?' "

"Huh." Jem thought a minute. "Do you think he was right to let him go?"

"You have to let go some-time."

"Would you have let me go?"

Ben paused. "I guess if I thought you were a good enough paddler, I really couldn't stop you."

"Did your parents try to stop you when you and Uncle Pete went to Alaska?"

"No, but all their friends in Cleveland thought they should have, thought they were crazy to let us go." Ben laughed softly. "Come on, let's you and me go for a night glide!"

"A 'night glide'? What's a 'night glide'?"

"You can only do it on a night like this. No wind, and the water is as still as a dark mirror."

They paddled out of the long cove and turned south-west, skimming close to the steep shore. Overhead a million stars chinked the night sky, and as they paddled Jem picked out Orion's Belt: the three bright studs all in a row and the silver point of the sword that dropped below the belt. There were stars, there was the slender mahogany needle, and there was the dip of the paddle. Jem felt part of it all. It was hard to tell where he left off and the boat began. Wood, water, paddler, and stars, they combined for night gliding around the island. Soon Jem noticed a stream of stars streaking back from the bow. Each paddle dip produced a galaxy of small, luminous specks.

"Phosphorescence!" Ben said. "Stars in the sky! Stars in the water!"

Star paddler, Jem thought, as he dipped his paddle in the water.

They had just rounded the southeast tip of No Name Is-land when Jem felt the pres-ence of something else in the water. Catching his breath, he

saw, amid the galaxies of phosphorescence, a streaking in the night sea like licks of pale fire.

"Dolphins, Dad!" A pair of dolphins swam just off *Wasso's* starboard, or right, side. Amid the showering sparks of phosphorescence, Jem couldn't really see their shapes. Only the trail of watery fire that streamed around the dolphins was visible.

"They probably think we're a new fish in the neighborhood," said Ben. "Watch them play around us."

The dolphins dived and arced over one another, braiding the bright water, swimming alongside, just out of the dip of the paddles. A magical energy seemed to surround the kayak.

Jem and his dad did not put up their tent that night. The moon was riding high when they passed the last knuckle of the long-fingered cove. The night air was warm and they

decided to sleep out instead of covering up the stars. Jem crawled into his sleeping bag feeling a little bit hungry. He realized suddenly that he had never gone to bed feeling a little bit hungry in his life. Tomorrow he would get up early and try to catch a bigger mackerel for breakfast. He didn't need food now, really. He fell asleep paddling the stars.

Mist rose from the still water of the cove. It was the in-between time, just at the tail end of the last gray of a fading night, but before the first pink of dawn. His father still slept, while Jem stood on a rock with his fishing line. There was a reasonable-sized mackerel in the pail, but Jem was hungry enough that it seemed like a good idea to try for another one. There was a tug on the line. He reeled it in. A plump mackerel thrashed on the end, gilded by the sun that was just slipping up in the east.

Ben was up now, bending over the fire, poking in some kindling to bring it back to life. Jem cleaned the fish on the rock and brought them over to the fire.

"Roe!" That was the first word spoken that morning. "One of them has roe, Dad." Fish eggs were a favorite of Jem's. He usually liked them with bacon. But this wasn't usual, so he guessed he would like them without.

It would be time to go soon, to leave No Name Island, to paddle out of the long-fingered surprise of a cove. There was part of Jem that wanted to go—to tell Michael and Jessica and his mother about the galaxies in the water. But there was a bigger part that wanted to stay, that wanted the trip never to end.

They washed their dishes with sea water and sand. They

packed up their sleeping bags, the fishing gear, their plates and pots and pans. The clam shells and fishbones they returned to the sea. The orange peel and empty instant grape juice can they put in a bag to carry with them. They doused the fire with water and a paddleful of sand. Before they left, Ben set up the camera on self-timing and took a picture of the two of them standing with their paddles at the tip of the finger cove called Surprise on No Name Island.

Summer, which always seemed to gallop from August to Labor Day, had briefly stopped for Jem and his dad. Now they put on their spray skirts and slipped *Wasso* into the water. Jem didn't want to leave. It wasn't just the island he didn't want to leave, it was everything since yesterday morning.

Jem lowered himself into the stern seat. There was that first motion of water under the keel. The thrill was stronger. The boat came alive in a new way for Jem. Everything did seem possible. In that moment he knew that he was not leaving anything behind. None of it—not the peace of the island, not the magic of the dolphins, or the small water galaxies of the night glide, or the skill to chart a course. It was all part of him now, forever, and would be a part of his winter dreams.

As they paddled out of the long-fingered cove, past the first knuckle and the second, Jem began to dream a new dream—the dream for summers to come, when his parents would let go, when he and Michael would be old enough to paddle alone to another island for a day, a week, or maybe a summer of a thousand miles.

## CHECK FOR UNDERSTANDING

1. How did Jem comfort himself when he felt homesick during dinner?
2. What was the point of Jem's father's story?
3. What do you think Jem liked best about his trip?
4. Why didn't he mind leaving at the end of the story?
5. Do you think that Jem will return to No Name Island with his father? Explain your answer.

## WRITE ABOUT "No Name Island"

Jem was a thoughtful boy, the kind who might have kept a journal as a record of his thoughts and feelings. Imagine you are Jem. Write the journal entry describing the trip to No Name Island as he might have written it. Explain how the trip changed you and helped you begin to grow up.

# If once you have

by RACHEL FIELD

If once you have slept on an island
    You'll never be quite the same;
You may look as you looked the day before
    And go by the same old name,

You may bustle about in street and shop,
    You may sit at home and sew,
But you'll see blue water and wheeling gulls
    Wherever your feet may go.

# slept on an island

You may chat with the neighbors of this and that
    And close to your fire keep,
But you'll hear ship whistle and lighthouse bell
    And tides beat through your sleep.

Oh, you won't know why, and you can't say how
    Such change upon you came,
But—once you have slept on an island
    You'll never be quite the same!

185

# LITERATURE

## Sense Words

When was the last time you tasted a word? Of course, you can't *really* taste words, but some words do have a special way of appealing to your senses.

Your senses are the physical ways you come in contact with the world. There are five senses: **touch, sight, smell, hearing,** and **taste.** And for each of these senses, there are some words that give you an especially vivid idea of what something feels, tastes, looks, sounds, or smells like.

These special words do not rely on meaning alone to appeal to your senses. What makes these words special is the way they sound or the way your mouth moves when you say them. The sound itself may suggest a particular sense even better than the meaning of the word. Or the way you use your tongue, teeth, and lips to say a word may give a strong suggestion of a physical sense.

For example, there are many things you can say about a steak. You might say it is "tender," or "rare," or "broiled." Those are words that rely on meaning alone to describe the steak. But if you were an author who really wants the reader to *taste* the steak, you would use a word like "juicy." Say the word *juicy* to yourself and pay attention to what your mouth does as you say it. Doesn't the first part of the word almost make your mouth make a chewing motion? Doesn't the second part suggest the wetness of food, just like the meaning of *juicy*? You can see that a word like this makes the steak more real by appealing to your sense of taste.

Other words almost seem to make the sounds represented by their meanings. Listen to the sounds of the underlined words in the following sentences.

> The crunching of our boots in the snow was the only sound in the woods.
>
> We jumped at the sound of screeching brakes.

And what about words that seem to suggest a sense of touch? There are words like that, too. Read and say to yourself the following list of words. Find the two words with sounds that suggest their meaning. As you say each word, exaggerate it slightly to get a better idea of its sound.

> grainy    smooth    cold    spiky    dusty

There are words like these throughout the story you just read, "No Name Island." Read the sentences below from the story. Pay close attention to words that make something seem more real by appealing to your senses.

- Glittering in the sun, they looked like oddly-cut jewels.
- That first morning when the ice had just cleared off, no sooner, a herd of low, dark clouds came in, and the water became choppy.
- Overhead a million stars chinked the night sky.
- Summer, which always seemed to gallop from August to Labor Day, had briefly stopped for Jem and his dad.

# On the Banks of Plum Creek

BY LAURA INGALLS WILDER

**★ Just·A·Taste ★**

On the American prairie in the 1880s, homes did not have many of the things that we now take for granted. Yet moving to a new house was an exciting experience.

How was the new house different from the one in which the Ingalls family had been living?

Which feature of the new house was especially exciting to Laura?

# The Wonderful House

*Laura and her family had traveled many days in the covered wagon. They had crossed Kansas, Missouri, and Iowa. In Minnesota, her father traded horses and the top of the covered wagon for a farm. Near the farm was a sod-covered house dug into the creek bank. The family had spent the winter in the one-room dugout house which had survived heavy rains and a swollen creek. By Christmas Pa had earned enough money to replace the horses he had traded. With spring came a new surprise.*

🌸

The creek went down. All at once the days were warm, and early every morning Pa went to work the wheatfield with Sam and David, the Christmas horses.

"I declare," Ma said, "you're working that ground to death and killing yourself."

But Pa said the ground was dry because there had not been enough snow. He must plow deep and harrow well, and get the wheat sowed quickly. Every day he was working before the sun came up and he worked till dark. Laura waited in the dark till she heard Sam and David splashing in the ford. Then she ran into the dugout for the lantern and she hurried to the stable to hold it so that Pa could see to do the chores.

He was too tired to laugh or talk. He ate supper and went to bed.

At last the wheat was sowed. Then he sowed oats, and he made the potato patch and the garden. Ma and Mary and Laura helped plant the potatoes and sprinkle little seeds in the garden-rows, and they let Carrie think she was helping.

The whole world was green with grass now; the yellow-green willow leaves were uncurling. Violets and buttercups were thick in the prairie hollows, and the sorrel's clover-like leaves and lavender blossoms were sour and good to eat. Only the wheat-field was bare and brown.

One evening Pa showed Laura a faint green mist on that brown field. The wheat was up! Each tiny sprout was so thin you could hardly see it, but so many of them all together made that misty green.

Everyone was so happy that night because the wheat was a good stand.

The next day Pa drove to town. Sam and David could go to town and come back in one afternoon. There was hardly time to miss Pa, and they were not even watching for him when he came home. Laura heard the wagon first, and she was the first one up the path.

Pa was sitting on the wagon seat. His face was one big shining of joy, and lumber was piled high in the wagon box behind him. He sang out, "Here's your new house, Caroline!"

"But, Charles!" Ma gasped. Laura ran and climbed up over the wheel, up onto that pile of boards. She had never seen such smooth,

straight, beautiful boards. They had been sawed by machinery.

"But the wheat's hardly up yet!" Ma said.

"That's all right," Pa told her. "They let me have the lumber, and we'll pay for it when we sell the wheat."

Laura asked him, "Are we going to have a house made of boards?"

"Yes, flutterbudget," said Pa. "We're going to have a whole house built out of sawed lumber. And it's going to have glass windows!"

It was really true. Next morning Mr. Nelson came to help Pa, and they began digging the cellar for that house. They were going to have that wonderful house, just because the wheat was growing.

Laura and Mary could hardly stay in the dugout long enough to do their work. But Ma made them do it.

"And I won't have you giving your work a lick and a promise," said Ma. So they washed every breakfast dish and put them all away. They made their bed neatly. They brushed the floor with the willow-twig broom and set the broom in its place. Then they could go.

They ran down the steps and over the footbridge, and under the willows, up to the prairie. They went through the prairie grasses and up to the top of a green knoll, where Pa and Mr. Nelson were building the new house.

It was fun to watch them set up the skeleton house. The timbers stood up slender and golden-new, and the sky was very blue between them. The hammers made a gay sound. The planes cut long curly shavings from the sweet-smelling boards.

Laura and Mary hung little shavings over their ears for earrings. They put them around their necks for necklaces. Laura tucked long ones in her hair and they hung down in golden curls, just the color she had always wanted her hair to be.

Up on the skeleton roof Pa and Mr. Nelson hammered and sawed. Little blocks of wood fell down, and Laura and Mary gathered them in piles and built houses of their own. They had never had such a good time.

Pa and Mr. Nelson covered the skeleton walls with slanting boards nailed on. They shingled the roof with boughten shingles. Boughten shingles were thin and all the same size; they were far finer shingles than even Pa could hew with an ax. They made an even, tight roof, with not one crack in it.

Then Pa laid the floor of silky-smooth boards that were grooved along the edges and fitted together perfectly. Overhead he laid another floor for the upstairs, and that made the ceiling of the downstairs.

Across the downstairs, Pa put up a partition. That house was going to have two rooms! One was the bedroom, and the other was only to live in. He

put two shining-clear glass windows in that room;
one looking toward the sunrise and the other beside
the doorway to the south. In the bedroom walls he
set two more windows, and they were glass windows, too.

Laura had never seen such wonderful windows.
They were halves. There were six panes of glass in
each half, and the bottom half would push up, and
stay up when a stick was set under it.

Opposite the front door Pa put a back door, and outside he built a tiny room. That was a lean-to, because it leaned against the house. It would keep out the north winds in the wintertime, and it was a place where Ma could keep her broom and mop and washtub.

Now Mr. Nelson was not there and Laura asked questions all the time. Pa said the bedroom was for Ma and Carrie and him. He said the attic was for Mary and Laura, to sleep in and to play in. Laura wanted so much to see it that he stopped work on the lean-to and nailed strips of board up the wall, to make the attic ladder.

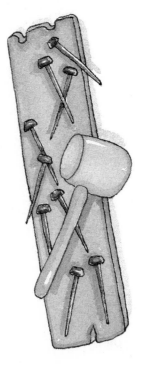

Laura skipped quickly up that ladder till her head came up through the hole in the attic floor. The attic was as big as both rooms downstairs. Its floor was smooth boards. Its slanting roof was the underside of the fresh, yellow shingles. There was a little window at each end of that attic, and those windows were glass windows!

At first Mary was scared to swing off the ladder to the attic floor. Then she was scared to step down through the floor-hole onto the ladder. Laura felt scared, too, but she pretended she didn't. And they soon got used to getting on and off the ladder.

Now they thought the house was done. But Pa nailed black tar-paper all over the outside of the house walls. Then he nailed more boards over that paper. They were long, smooth boards, one lapping over the other all the way up the sides of the house. Then around the windows and the doorways Pa nailed flat frames.

"This house is as tight as a drum!" he said. There was not one single crack in the roof or the walls or the floor of that house, to let in rain or cold winds.

Then Pa put in the doors, and they were boughten doors. They were smooth, and far thinner than slab doors hewed with an ax, and even thinner panels were set into them above and below their middles. Their hinges were boughten hinges, and it was marvelous to see them open and shut. They did not rattle like wooden hinges or let the door drag like leather hinges.

Into those doors Pa set boughten locks, with keys that went into small, shaped holes, and turned and clicked. These locks had white-china doorknobs.

Then one day Pa said, "Laura and Mary, can you keep a secret?"

"Oh yes, Pa!" they said.

"Promise you won't tell Ma?" he asked, and they promised.

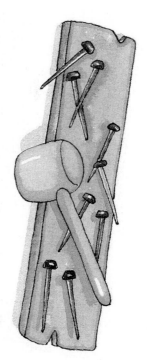

He opened the lean-to door. And there stood a shiny-black cookstove. Pa had bought it from town and hidden it there, to surprise Ma.

On top, that cookstove had four round holes and four round lids fitted them. Each lid had a grooved hole in it, and there was an iron handle that fitted into the holes, to lift the lid by. In front, there was a long, low door. There were slits in this door, and a piece of iron would slide back and forth, to close these slits or open them. That was the draught. Under it, a shelf like an oblong pan stuck out. That was to catch the ashes and keep them from dropping on the floor. A lid swung flat over this hollowed-out shelf. And on the lid were raised iron letters in rows.

Mary put her finger on the bottom row and

spelled out, "P A T. One seven seven ought." She asked Pa, "What's that spell, Pa?"

"It spells *Pat*," Pa said.

Laura opened a big door on the side of the stove, and looked into a big square place with a shelf across it. "Oh, Pa, what's this for?" she asked.

"It's the oven," Pa told her.

He lifted that marvelous stove and set it in the living room, and put up the stovepipe. Piece by piece, the stovepipe went up through the ceiling and the attic and through a hole he sawed in the roof. Then Pa climbed onto the roof and he set a larger tin pipe over the stovepipe. The tin pipe had a spread-out, flat bottom that covered the hole in the roof. Not a drop of rain could run down the stovepipe into the new house.

That was a prairie chimney.

"Well, it's done," Pa said. "Even to a prairie chimney."

There was nothing more that house could possibly have. The glass windows made the inside of that house so light that you would hardly know you were in a house. It smelled clean and piny, from the yellow-new board walls and floor. The cookstove stood lordly in the corner by the lean-to door. A touch on the white-china doorknob swung the boughten door on its boughten hinges, and the doorknob's little iron tongue clicked and held the door shut.

"We'll move in tomorrow morning," Pa said. "This is the last night we'll sleep in a dugout."

Laura and Mary took his hands and they went down the knoll. The wheatfield was a silky, shimmery green rippling over a curve of the prairie. Its sides were straight and its corners square, and all around it the wild prairie grasses looked coarser and darker green. Laura looked back at the wonderful house. In the sunshine on the knoll, its sawed-lumber walls and roof were as golden as a strawstack.

*Although the Ingalls are troubled by a serious blizzard and a problem with grasshoppers, the new house brings the family much happiness. Read about their experiences in the rest of the novel* On the Banks of Plum Creek *by Laura Ingalls Wilder.*

200

# CHECK FOR UNDERSTANDING

1. Why did Pa have to sow the wheat quickly?
2. What was the faint green mist that Pa and Laura saw on the field?
3. Why was Pa so happy when he came back from town?
4. Why were "boughten" shingles better than the ones Pa could make?
5. How would Laura and Mary get up to their attic room?
6. How was the new house different from the one in which the Ingalls family had been living?
7. Which feature of the new house was especially exciting to Laura?

## WRITE ABOUT *"The Wonderful House"*

Pretend that Laura Ingalls kept a journal. Write a journal entry for Laura for the first day she lived in the new house. Explain your thoughts and feelings when you awoke that morning. Write a few sentences about what you did during the day.

## THINK ABOUT IT

Think about what made each place special to the characters in the story. Was it the place itself, or the experiences the characters had there?

- What made Mary and Bert's place special before they even got there?
- What quality did the boys add to their hike that made it special?
- Was the beach as special to the other people there as to the characters in "The Beach"?
- What was ordinary and special at the same time about Parmele?
- What makes almost any island a special place?

After reading and thinking about these different kinds of places, how would you describe a special place? Which is more important, the way the place really is, or how the person feels about it?

## WRITE ABOUT IT

Write one paragraph describing a special place you already have. It may be a corner in your home, or a secret place. Explain the qualities that make the place special to you. Then write another paragraph about a special place you would like to visit. Tell about the qualities that make the place special.

# READ ABOUT IT

*The Shoeshine Girl* by Clyde Robert Bulla. Thomas Y. Crowell Co., 1975. A tough, ten-year-old girl finds friends and develops a sense of responsibility when she becomes a shoeshine girl.

*The Place* by Elizabeth Coatsworth. Holt, Rinehart & Winston, 1965. While vacationing in Mexico, Ellen is shown the secrets of a revered cave or "the place." She must make the difficult choice between betraying a sacred trust or keeping to herself an exciting secret that could change her entire life.

*Not Just Any Ring* by Danita Ross Haller. Alfred A. Knopf, 1982. The silver ring her grandfather buys her does not bring Jesse magic or luck. On the way home their truck stalls, and Grandfather sprains his ankle. Frightened as she scales a dangerously steep canyon wall in search of help, the young Indian girl gains courage from her grandfather's words, "Real magic comes from the heart."

*The Real Me* by Betty Miles. Alfred A. Knopf, 1974. Barbara would like to take over her brother's paper route even though it is not allowed under company rules. Thanks to parental backing, Barbara achieves her goal.

*The Feast of Lanterns* by Allen Say. Harper & Row, Publishers, 1976. The adventures and surprises of a new place are revealed when two brothers from a fishing village on a small Japanese island get away to visit the mainland.

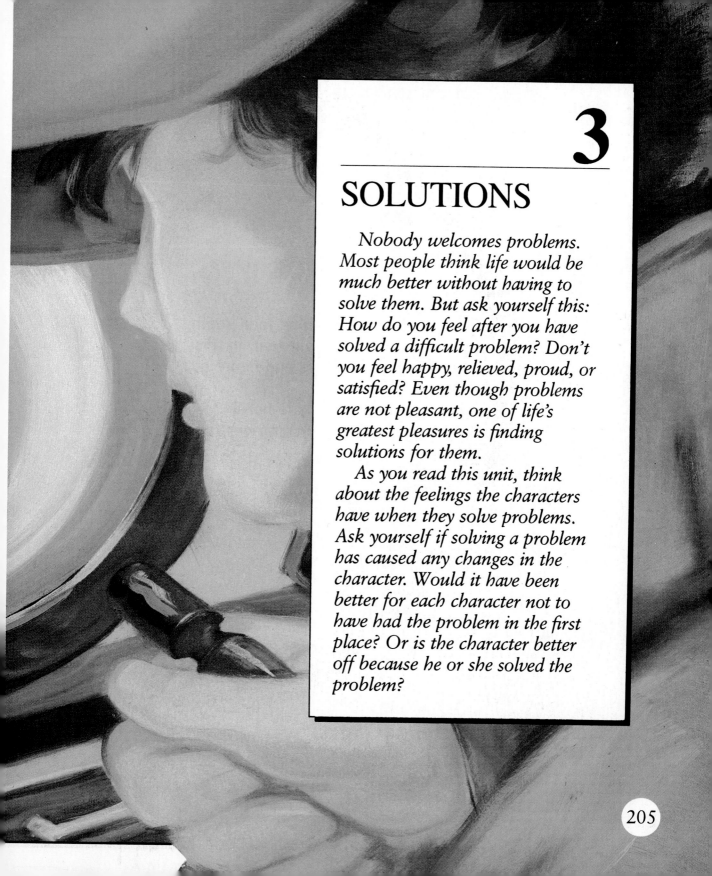

# 3

# SOLUTIONS

Nobody welcomes problems.
Most people think life would be
much better without having to
solve them. But ask yourself this:
How do you feel after you have
solved a difficult problem? Don't
you feel happy, relieved, proud, or
satisfied? Even though problems
are not pleasant, one of life's
greatest pleasures is finding
solutions for them.

As you read this unit, think
about the feelings the characters
have when they solve problems.
Ask yourself if solving a problem
has caused any changes in the
character. Would it have been
better for each character not to
have had the problem in the first
place? Or is the character better
off because he or she solved the
problem?

# DIVING CLASS

by JANE O'CONNOR

**Bravery can be defined as overcoming fear—doing something you are afraid of despite your fear. In this story, Abby must face her fear of diving and figure out how to overcome it.**

**What does Abby's fear of diving make her do? What happens that makes Abby want to overcome her fear?**

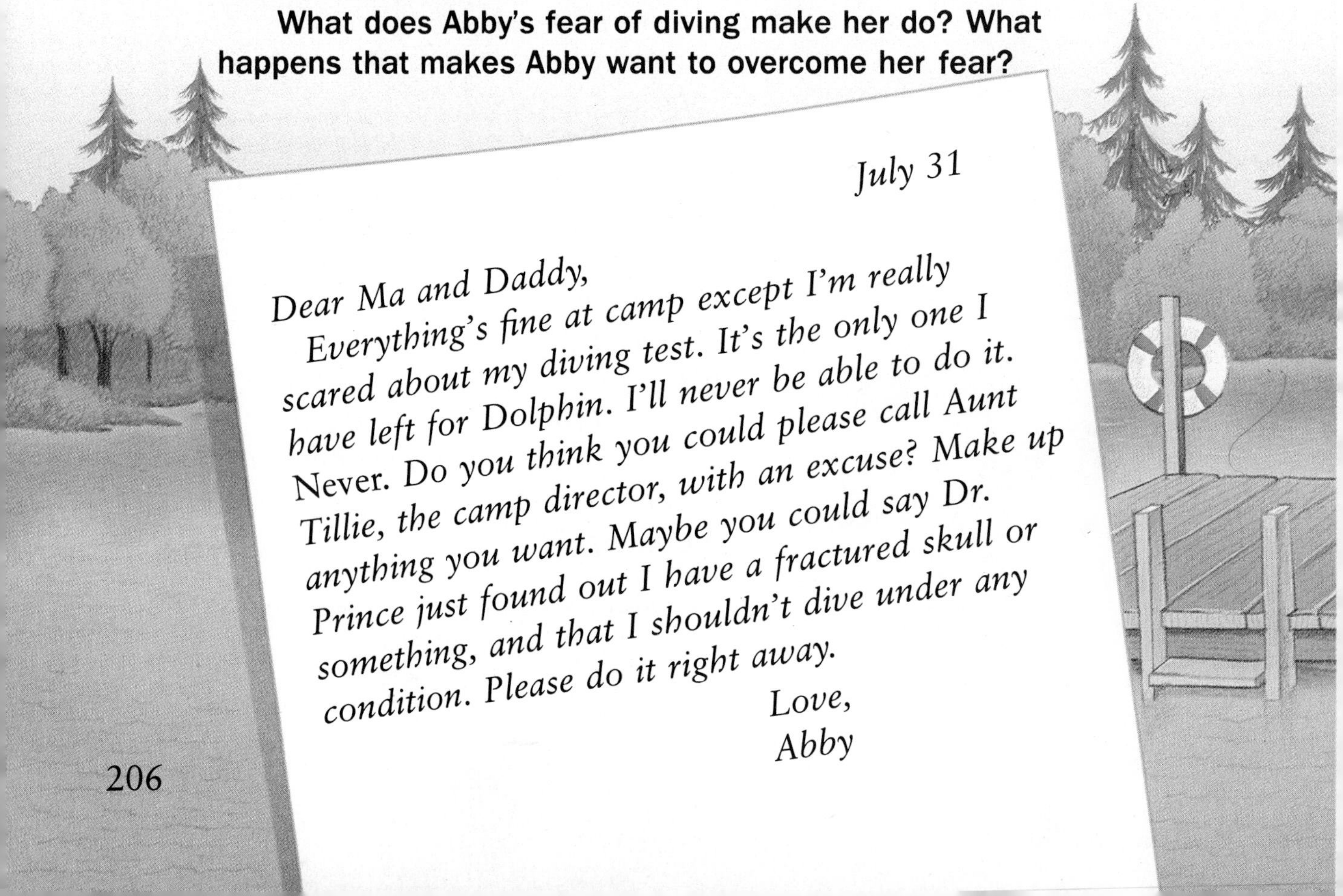

July 31

Dear Ma and Daddy,

Everything's fine at camp except I'm really scared about my diving test. It's the only one I have left for Dolphin. I'll never be able to do it. Never. Do you think you could please call Aunt Tillie, the camp director, with an excuse? Make up anything you want. Maybe you could say Dr. Prince just found out I have a fractured skull or something, and that I shouldn't dive under any condition. Please do it right away.

Love,
Abby

Abby was nervously chewing on the strap of her bathing cap. She stood at the end of the long line in Laurel's diving class. There was a sour taste in her mouth and she felt that she would be sick at any minute. "Gee, Ma. Thanks a bunch," Abby grumbled to herself. "Where are you when I need you?" With growing dread she watched the procession in front of her. Boing! off the board. Splash! into the water. One by one each girl plunged while Laurel, her sailor cap pulled way down against the sun, shouted encouraging suggestions.

In went Bonnie, legs flailing wildly.

"Try and keep those ankles *locked* together," Laurel called out.

Then Abby felt her knees collapse as Laurel focused a reassuring smile her way. "Abby, there's absolutely nothing to be nervous about. Just remember, the trick is to keep your head tucked down and the rest of your body will automatically follow." Laurel put down her clipboard and demonstrated on dry land. "Really. You're doing fine."

Sure, sure, thought Abby. They probably said the same thing to Custer. She stepped onto the edge of the board. It was like walking the plank.

"Just keep your head down." Laurel sounded so calm and reassuring. Then suddenly her voice jumped an octave. "Abby, I said KEEP YOUR—"

THWACK! Abby's entire body felt like it had been smacked with a wet sheet. Abby tried crying out, but all the wind was knocked out of her. She seemed to be sinking down, down in the water and for one horrible second she didn't think she'd surface.

"Don't panic. Just relax." Laurel was suddenly beside her in the water. She swung an arm around Abby's middle. Then Abby felt herself being dredged up onto the dock where the class hovered around her.

"You're OK. Just let yourself catch your breath," Laurel said, kneeling beside her.

"What a belly flop!" Bonnie said.

"Wow, look at her face—how red it is," said another voice.

"*See*, I *told* you!" Abby finally gasped. "I *knew* that was going to happen." She glared at Laurel who looked funny now without her sailor cap. Her wet blond hair was sticking out in all directions.

"Abby, now calm down. You were *positive* you were going to hurt yourself. So you did.

"I think you should try another dive right away," Laurel said evenly. "That's what you do if you fall off a horse—get right back on again."

Abby managed to get up and find her sweat shirt. "I don't ride and I have absolutely no intention of going near that diving board again."

"Oh no?" Laurel's voice was stubborn. "Let's get one thing straight. As long as you're in my class, I mean to see that you dive."

But by the end of the week, Abby still hadn't gone in head first.

"Come on, kid. You can do it—everyone else is," Abby would say to psych herself up. Then she'd stare down at the water. It looked so far below. Blood would begin to thrum in her head; her knees turned watery and—KERPLASH! In she jumped.

"Here she comes, ladies and gentlemen," Bonnie would shout. "Abby Kimmel! About to try another death-defying *jump*!"

Abby didn't even give Bonnie a withering look. She felt too humiliated. She didn't even blame Bonnie for making fun. If only Ma would write an excuse and get her out of this mess.

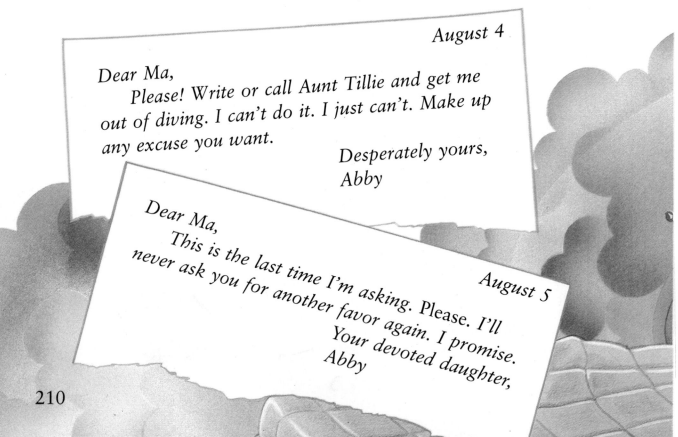

*August 4*

*Dear Ma,*
*Please! Write or call Aunt Tillie and get me out of diving. I can't do it. I just can't. Make up any excuse you want.*

*Desperately yours,*
*Abby*

*Dear Ma,*
*This is the last time I'm asking. Please. I'll never ask you for another favor again. I promise.*

*August 5*

*Your devoted daughter,*
*Abby*

Ma just *had* to come through for her. Abby was even having nightmares about diving. A couple of nights later she dreamed she was in the circus. "The amazing Abby," the ringmaster shouted while she climbed up, up an incredibly high ladder to a long and narrow diving board. Far below was a pool of water that looked no bigger than a thimble. In the audience Ma, Daddy, Emily, and Roberta were all staring up at her expectantly.

Abby tried shouting there was some mistake, but someone was poking her in the back, pushing her forward . . .

She jerked awake. Someone *was* poking her. It was Roberta.

"You were talking in your sleep," she whispered. "It sounded interesting."

"I was having a nightmare . . . a real whopper." Abby sat up, her heart still thumping. "Thanks for waking me."

The next morning when they got back to the bunk for cleanup, there on Abby's bed was a special delivery letter.

*Abby,* Ma's neat round writing said, *I am sick of hearing about diving. I certainly won't make up any crazy excuses for you, but I am mailing another special delivery letter to Aunt Tillie explaining the situation. I hope you're satisfied.*

Satisfied? thought Abby. Was she ever! "My worries are over," she shouted, tossing the letter in the air.

At lunch, the camp secretary came over to the Buttercup table and told Abby that Aunt Tillie wanted to see her in the office.

Abby chewed her lip nervously. "She's probably going to try to get me to change my mind," she said to Roberta. "But fat chance!" Abby pulled out her chair. Steeling herself for the encounter, she marched into the small office off the kitchen. She found her aunt sitting behind a large metal desk, checking over schedules. Aunt Tillie paid no attention to Abby, who stood staring uncomfortably at a wall calendar.

Finally Aunt Tillie looked up. The look of disapproval—or was it disappointment?—on her face made Abby swallow hard.

"Abby, I received your mother's letter. I've explained everything to Laurel so she won't be expecting you in her diving class from now on."

Abby shifted her weight nervously and murmured thank you.

"There's no reason to thank me—I can tell you that right now." She tapped the schedules into a neat pile.

"I've also told Karen that you will be helping her out with the Guppies for the rest of the summer."

Abby's mouth fell open. Wow! Spending every swim period with Roberta and Eileen! "You mean it?"

"Of course I mean it. Laurel tells me you're a fine swimmer and I have no intention of seeing that go to waste. And I also don't mind telling you, Abby, it bothers me to see anyone give up on getting something she wants." Aunt Tillie's sharp eyes took in Abby closely. "You did want to become a Dolphin, didn't you?"

Abby felt her cheeks burn. Aunt Tillie was being unfair. It wasn't as if she hadn't tried. "You don't understand—"

"I think I do. Now run along," Aunt Tillie said flatly.

During swim period Abby swam back and forth across the Fish Bowl, demonstrating the crawl and trying to forget the look on Aunt Tillie's face. "She was just trying to make me feel guilty," Abby told herself. Well, it wasn't going to work. Period.

"Class, I hope you were watching closely," Karen, the Guppy counselor, said when Abby had finished two laps.

"Yes, Karen," the Guppies answered in a chorus. They were spread out on the dock flat on their stomachs, kicking rhythmically and moving their arms.

"Very good. Now we'll try it for real."

There was a small tidal wave as all the Guppies jumped in the water to swim. "Eileen," Abby said patiently, "you have to use your arms and legs *both at the same time.*"

"I know, I know," glubbed Eileen, slowly sinking.

"I just don't understand it," Roberta spluttered next to her. "I swim so *beautifully* on land."

Abby spent all that week's swim periods holding onto the Guppies while they flailed and kicked and struggled just to stay afloat. It was tiring work. And hazardous, too. Roberta kicked her in the mouth by accident, and Eileen clung to her so tightly Abby was afraid they'd both drown.

"You happen to be an excellent teacher," Karen

told her after a swim period. "Some of the girls are starting to make real progress."

Abby smiled. "I never taught anybody anything before—it's fun." Then without meaning to, she caught herself staring over at the diving area. Laurel's probably really sore, Abby figured. Or maybe she's *glad* to have me out of the class. She watched Bonnie finish a dive, the best one she'd ever done. Laurel was patting her on the back.

At dinner that night Bonnie announced, "Laurel says I have a good chance of passing. What happens a lot, she says, is that you don't seem to be getting anywhere and all of a sudden it clicks." Bonnie looked pointedly at Abby. "It looks like I'll be the first—and only—Dolphin in our group."

"Rooty, toot toot," Abby said.

The next day Roberta swam, all by herself, halfway across the Fish Bowl.

"I knew you could do it!" Abby screamed from the dock.

Roberta beamed and gasped. "I feel like I just swam the English Channel."

"Didn't I keep telling you not to give up? I knew you could do it!" Suddenly her own words made Abby feel very uneasy.

Later, as Abby was leaving the waterfront, Laurel stopped her. "Can I speak to you for a sec?" she said.

"Sure, if you want." Abby avoided Laurel's eyes.

"I was scared maybe you weren't talking to me after—well, you know."

"Granted you were being a royal pain in the neck, but I've been thinking it over, and I was being pretty stubborn, too. I thought if I got tough, you'd dive and . . . well, I just hope you didn't quit the class because of me."

"It wasn't because of you, Laurel. Honest." Abby pulled on the strap of her cap. "I was just too chicken."

Laurel smiled warmly. "I wish you'd come back and give it one more try—it'd make me feel a lot better."

"I'll think about it. Really I will." But as Abby walked away, she realized she had already made up her mind.

Right before dinner she knocked faintly at the door of Aunt Tillie's office.

"Come in."

Do it and do it *fast*, Abby ordered herself. She fixed her eyes on the wall calendar. "Uh—I've thought it over, and if it's OK, I'd like to go back in Laurel's diving class tomorrow."

Aunt Tillie didn't say anything. She had her hands folded together on the desk and she seemed to be thinking about something very hard.

"That was all I came to ask," Abby said meekly.

"In that case, I'll tell Laurel to be expecting you." Aunt Tillie went over and placed a firm hand on Abby's shoulder. "Oh, and Abby. One more thing."

Abby looked at her questioningly.

"Good luck!"

"Today is your lucky day!" Roberta pranced around Abby as she and Eileen escorted her down to the lake. "I feel it in my bones."

Abby looked at them doubtfully.

When they reached the waterfront, she squeezed their hands. "This is where we part company," she gulped out, but instead of joining the other Guppies by the Fish Bowl, Roberta continued toward the diving area. "Sur-prise!" she trilled. "I asked Karen and she said it's OK for me to come with you to diving."

Abby stopped dead on the dock. "Like fun you are!" That was all she needed. An audience!

"Don't be foolish." A stubborn look came into Roberta's eyes. "I'll give you moral support."

"You'll only make me more nervous," Abby insisted. She wagged an accusatory finger. "I *know* you, Roberta. You won't just sit. You'll start winking and holding up crossed fingers and—"

"I will do nothing of the kind." Roberta sounded insulted. "And if I want to watch Laurel's diving class, I have a perfect right."

Abby clamped her hands on her hips and shot daggers at Roberta. "Well, thanks a heap!" Then she stalked off to the diving area with Roberta tagging maddeningly behind.

August 15

Dear Ma and Daddy,
Guess what? You'll never guess! I dived (dove? who cares!) All I know is I did it!

For almost the whole period I was jumping in, just like always. Then one time I was standing on the end of the board, trying really hard to get up the guts to dive. Roberta kept yelling good luck and telling me how I shouldn't be scared. I turned around to tell her to be quiet. That's when I lost my balance. All I remember is crouching my head down cause I was afraid I was going to hurt myself.

The next thing, Roberta is jumping up and down on the dock and Laurel is clapping and cheering. It was all an accident! But once I did one dive, I could do it again and again. Now I'm mad at myself for all those days I missed. Keep your fingers crossed that I pass.

Love,
Abby

## CHECK FOR UNDERSTANDING

1. What did Abby's fear of diving make her do?
2. How do you think Abby felt about her failure to dive? Explain your answer.
3. Why did Aunt Tillie allow Abby to quit the diving class?
4. What happened that made Abby want to overcome her fear?
5. Do you think Abby will behave differently if she has to face a fear again? Explain your answer.

## WRITE ABOUT *"Diving Class"*

Imagine that you are a sports reporter following Abby's progress on the diving board. Write a newspaper article telling how Abby triumphs over her fear. Make the article brief and factual.

# Skating

by HERBERT ASQUITH

When I try to skate,
My feet are so wary
They grit and they grate:
And then I watch Mary
Easily gliding,
Like an ice-fairy;
Skimming and curving,
Out and in,
With a turn of her head,
And a lift of her chin,
And a gleam of her eye,
And a twirl and a spin;
Sailing under
The breathless hush
Of the willows, and back
To the frozen rush;
Out to the island
And round the edge,

Skirting the rim
Of the crackling sedge,
Swerving close
To the poplar root
And round the lake
On a single foot,
With a three, and an eight,
And a loop and a ring;
Where Mary glides,
The lake will sing!
Out in the mist
I hear her now
Under the frost
Of the willow-bough
Easily sailing,
Light and fleet,
With the song of the lake
Beneath her feet.

"It's hard for me to fix things right because I'm all thumbs."

## Idioms

Of course, the character above doesn't *really* have ten thumbs. The expression "all thumbs" is an **idiom.** It means "awkard or clumsy."

An *idiom* is a group of words that has a very special meaning. The meaning of an idiom is different from the meaning of the individual words themselves. For example, the idiom *to let the cat out of the bag* does not mean "to free a cat." It means to give away a secret. And when you *break someone's heart,* you are not *really* "splitting a heart," you are causing great sorrow or grief.

Since idioms have a special meaning, it is important to recognize them when you read. If you are unable to do this, you will become confused about what the author has written.

In "Diving Class," for example, Abby wanted to practice diving alone. Roberta, however, insisted on watching her. When Roberta refused to leave, Abby put her hands on her hips. Then she "shot daggers at Roberta."

Think about this scene from the story. Did Abby actually *shoot daggers at* Roberta? No, "to shoot daggers at" is an idiom. It means "to glare at angrily."

Usually, you can figure out what an idiom means by the way it is used in a story. Clues in the sentence or the passage will help you find the right meaning.

Look at the sentences below. Each one contains an expression which is an idiom. Identify the idiom in each sentence. Then think of *another way* of expressing the idiom.

1. When our team lost by one point, the coach went to pieces.
2. Keep your eyes peeled for Tim; he should be arriving any minute.
3. We need all the help we can get, so we'd be grateful if you would lend us a hand.
4. When Sandra saw everyone smiling, she realized that Marie had been pulling her leg.
5. I see red whenever anyone says that I'm too short to play basketball.
6. When I began to explain about the broken bowl, Dad told me to stop beating around the bush.

Remember to look for idioms as you read.

# Melindy's Medal

by GEORGENE FAULKNER
and JOHN BECKER

||||||||||||||||||||||||||||||||||||||||

To remain calm during an emergency is necessary, but not easy. In this selection, Melindy is the first person to learn of a dangerous situation.

What emergency occurs? Why do you think Melindy acts as she does?

||||||||||||||||||||||||||||||||||||||||

*Melindy is very proud of her family. Her great-grandfather, her grandfather, and her father have all received medals for bravery. They fought in the Civil War, Spanish-American War, and World War I. Melindy hopes that someday she will win a medal for bravery as well.*

|||||||||||||||||||||||||||||||||||||||||

Nothing really extra-special happened in school for the first month. Melindy did get a little better in her numbers, and Miss Krumm, the piano teacher, gave her a new classical piece to learn, and in assembly she played the "Tramp, Tramp, Tramp" fire drill music twice.

But one day at school Melindy felt funny. Somehow she couldn't pay attention to *anything* Miss Johnson said. She mixed up her numbers worse than ever and she thought, once, that Miss Johnson was looking at her in a peculiar way. And after that, in the afternoon, her head began to hurt like anything.

Just as the children got up to march out to the assembly room, Miss Johnson said, "Come here Melindy." She put her hand on Melindy's head and said, "I think you're sick, Melindy, and I want you to go right home."

Then, even before Melindy could get out her "Oh-please-Miss-Johnson," Miss Johnson said, "Now, don't argue with me. Just go along, Melindy." And Miss Johnson and the class marched off to assembly.

Melindy was left all alone in the schoolroom, and she felt very sorry for herself. She couldn't help thinking that it would have been bad enough to have to stay home altogether. But to go to school and to almost go to the assembly hour and to almost play her new piece for Miss Krumm was just about the end of everything.

Melindy walked slowly up to her desk and started to take up her books. The first book dropped to the floor, and she just left it lying there. Then Melindy knew that she was going to cry. And because she came from brave people and couldn't let anyone see her cry, she crossed over the empty hall into the coatroom. She put her head in a coat—she didn't know or care if it was her coat or Elly's coat or Nelly's coat—and there she started to cry good and proper.

Melindy was really feeling terrible, crying there in the coatroom. She'd just come to the *boo-hoo* place, when all of a sudden, she stopped crying. She stopped crying because she thought she smelled smoke. She took another breath and she sniffed again. Sure enough, she smelled something burning. She looked around, and there, from the crack in the coatroom floor, was a little trickle of smoke coming up.

For one whole minute, Melindy didn't know what to do. She thought that maybe she should yell, and she wanted to, but then, because she'd been crying, it was hard to yell. Besides, everyone was in assembly, so there was no one to yell to. Then somehow, in that one minute, Melindy thought how once her father, without thinking twice, had acted without orders. So, she ran out of the coatroom, down the corridor, and up the stairs into the assembly hall. She ran down the side of the hall and up to the stage to play the "Tramp,

Tramp, Tramp" fire music.

Now, just when Melindy started to play the "Tramp, Tramp, Tramp" fire music, Mr. Timberlake, the principal, was making a speech. If Melindy could have seen his face she would have seen that he first looked surprised, and then he looked just plain angry.

But all Melindy could see was Billy Gumpers and Buddy Williams and Frank Alvarez in the front row and how they started to laugh, but Melindy didn't care if they laughed or not. All Melindy cared about was that Billy Gumpers and Buddy Williams and Frank Alvarez were standing up. And, although they were still laughing, they were swinging their arms and throwing out their legs and marching out right in time with the "Tramp, Tramp, Tramp."

Maybe they thought that it was just a joke. But the important thing was that they *were marching out.* And when the boys started to march out, Priscilla Marie Leroy got up and marched out, too. And then all of the girls did just what Priscilla Marie Leroy did.

Melindy played the "Tramp, Tramp, Tramp" fire music as it had never been played before. She played it loud and clear and sure. Melindy kept on playing it even though Miss Krumm came over and said, "Why Melindy!" She didn't stop when Miss Johnson came over and said, "That child's sick!" She didn't even stop when Mr. Timberlake came over and shouted at her.

And all the time the assembly room was getting emptier and emptier. The rule was that when the "Tramp, Tramp, Tramp" music started and the fire bell sounded, everybody

was to march out no matter what. Now, of course, when Melindy started playing, the fire bell hadn't sounded. It didn't sound until after Melindy had finished playing the "Tramp, Tramp, Tramp" twice. But when the fire bell sounded, it rang without stopping. And all the time it was ringing, Melindy went on playing until the room was altogether empty. Then she and Miss Krumm walked out last.

When Melindy got outside, there was a terrible commotion. People were running and the fire engines were coming down the street. Melindy could see that the school building was ablaze. But Melindy wasn't paying much attention to the fire or the fire engines or anybody. This time Melindy was crying, just as if her heart would break, right out in front of everybody.

Melindy didn't even pay at-tention when Mr. Timberlake came up and said, "The child has saved the whole school," or even when Frank Alvarez came up and said, "You did fine, Melindy."

Then Miss Johnson and Miss Krumm drove Melindy home and carried her upstairs to 3B. When they started to tell Melin-dy's grandmother about what she had done, Melindy's grand-mother didn't seem to pay at-tention. She was busy getting Melindy's bed ready. Then, af-ter Melindy's grandmother put Melindy in her bed, Melindy was sick for a long time.

While Melindy was sick she didn't know anything. She didn't know that Mr. Timber-lake came to see her every day. All Melindy could remember was that whenever she woke up, her grandmother was al-ways sitting there holding a cool cloth next to her head.

One time, Melindy thought she heard some people talking in the parlor. She thought she heard Mr. Timberlake's voice and she thought they were talking about medals. She heard Mr. Timberlake say, "The Carnegie Medal." But Melindy wasn't sure about it because everything she heard kept getting mixed up with the old dream. She kept dreaming over and over again about the ruby red and navy blue flag with the stars shining out like diamonds from its field of honor as someone carried it on, up and over the hill.

Then one day Melindy went to sleep and she slept all night through and didn't dream at all. In the morning, when she

woke up, her fever was gone and she felt very tired and sad and happy, too.

The next day her father and grandmother came into her room. In her grandmother's hand there was a brand new medal. And her grandmother said, "This is your medal."

Melindy and her father and her grandmother looked at the medal. And they thought it was the most wonderful thing in the world.

## CHECK FOR UNDERSTANDING

1. Why was Melindy so disappointed about missing assembly hour that morning?
2. Where did Melindy go when everyone else went to assembly, and why did she go there?
3. What emergency occurred?
4. Why do you think Melindy acted as she did?
5. How do you know that Melindy got the children out of assembly just in time?

**WRITE ABOUT** *"Melindy's Medal"*

The school newspaper wants to include a story about Melindy's brave actions. Pretend that you are a classmate of Melindy's and write the story. Describe what happened during assembly that Monday morning. Be sure to give your story a title.

# COMPREHENSION

## Summarizing

In the last unit, you learned that every story has a **main idea**. Part of the purpose of thinking about a story's main idea, you remember, is to get a better understanding of what the words and actions of the characters mean. But thinking about the main idea serves another purpose, too. It is a good way of remembering what a story is about.

An even better way to lock the story in your memory is to **summarize** it. Summarizing means to reduce the story to its basic elements. The basic elements of every story are:

  **a.** the **main character** or characters,
  **b.** the **setting,**
  **c.** the **major problem,**
  **d.** the **important events** leading to the solution of the problem.

Summarizing the story by listing these elements, or by writing them in paragraph form, will help make clear the main idea of the story, too.

Remember when you summarize that you are only concerned with the **major** elements of the story. If a story has a dozen characters, you probably wouldn't use all their names in your summary. You would only use the characters who play an important role in the solution of the problem. And even if a story has more than one setting, you wouldn't include them all. Instead, choose the one setting in which the most important action of the story takes place for your summary.

Think about the story you just finished reading, "Melindy's Medal." Can you think of the major problem in that story? Wasn't it the fact that Melindy smelled smoke, and there was no one nearby to tell about it?

The final part of summarizing a story is writing in your own words the events that lead up to the solution of the problem. What would you say the important events are in "Melindy's Medal"? See if your list would look like this one:

1. Melindy feels sick at school and is told to go home by Miss Johnson, her teacher.
2. She goes to the coatroom and cries, because she had wanted to play her new piano piece in assembly.
3. She smells smoke.
4. She runs to the assembly room.
5. Even though the principal is in the middle of a speech, she starts to play the fire drill music.
6. Everyone in assembly leaves the school calmly.
7. Melindy is sick for a long time.
8. Melindy gets a medal for her brave action, and her family is very proud of her.

Now think about the main idea of the story. Doesn't the summary help you to understand the main idea — that in acting quickly and in doing what she alone thought was right, Melindy saved the lives of the whole school?

★ ★ ★ **EXTRA** ★ ★ ★

# GIRL SAVES WHOLE SCHOOL

# Treasure
## at Breezy Lake

by HANS JÜRGEN PRESS

**Sometimes, if you look long and hard enough at something, you can see aspects of it you never noticed before. Detectives are trained to see clues where others might miss them. This story gives you a chance to look for clues yourself.**

**What crime has been committed? What clue gives the Fingerprint Club the best lead?**

*The Fingerprint Club meets every day after school to do their homework and pursue their hobby: solving crimes. Frank, who plays the trumpet, is the leader. The other members of the club are Angela, Ralph, and Keith W.S., who always has his pet squirrel with him. (W.S. stands for "With Squirrel.")*

*One afternoon, the club was at the police station wrapping up their last case when they learned about a new mystery. You can solve the mystery along with the Club. As you read, look carefully at the pictures. Try to discover the clues that the Fingerprint Club discovered.*

# A NIGHT VISITOR

At a quarter to three one afternoon, the door of the local police station burst open and an elderly woman stormed in.

"Sergeant, you must come with me at once. All my jewelry was stolen last night."

"I'm afraid I must ask you take a seat for a moment, madam," said Sergeant Shorthouse, turning back to the club, with a document in his hand. " 'We then told the police that the case containing the forged stamps had been lowered down the well.' Is that correct?" The Fingerprint Club nodded. "Then sign the statement, please."

"Is there no one here you can send, Sergeant?" the woman interrupted from her corner.

"I'm afraid that everyone is out at the moment, madam. May I have your name?"

"Ida Partridge—Mrs."

"Well, first you must make out a formal complaint."

When Mrs. Partridge left the police station some ten minutes later, the Fingerprint Club was waiting for her on the steps.

Frank said, "Don't worry, Mrs. Partridge, we'll help you."

Then they all went to view the scene of the crime.

"What a dreadful mess," said Angela, "but at least we know exactly what time the burglar was here."

*How did the club know when the burglary had taken place?*

# 2

# A CLUE ON THE ROOF

"Mrs. Partridge's clock stopped at exactly five minutes past midnight," Angela said. "The burglar was probably looking for a safe."

Ralph added: "He must have come in by the balcony window—look, one of the panes is broken."

The Fingerprint Club went out onto the balcony to search for clues.

"Not the smallest trace," said Ralph. He peered at the edge of the roof through his magnifying glass.

"Our cat burglar must have climbed over the roof," Frank remarked.

Keith W.S. patted his pet squirrel and lifted it onto the roof. "Here's a job for you, little friend."

After a few seconds, the squirrel began scratching in the gutter, then picked up something in its paws.

Ralph shouted, "It's a ticket. Here's our first clue."

Angela, twitching her braids, asked, "Which film had the burglar been to see?"

The Fingerprint Club bought a newspaper on their way back to their headquarters and looked at the movie listings. It wasn't an easy task. Frank was the first to work it out.

"He chose the right film," he said, doubling up with laughter.

*What was the film called?*

# 3

# THE OTHER SIDE

*Deep Pockets—Long Fingers* was the title of the movie. Angela turned the ticket over. "Look at this!" she exclaimed. The club read it out in unison: ". . . aser."

"It must be part of someone's name," said Frank. "He must have booked his seat in advance."

"He's probably a regular movie-goer," added Angela, hopefully.

That evening the Fingerprint Club went to the movie theater and loitered by the ticket office, hoping that someone would eventually ask for "aser's" tickets.

Three evenings later they were in luck. A man and a woman in motorcycle gear came up to the ticket window.

"Tickets for Fraser?" the man asked.

Once the Fingerprint Club saw the motorcyclists go into the theater, they held an urgent conference outside.

"We must find out where Fraser lives," said Ralph.

Angela asked, "How are we going to do that?"

"We'll follow him on our bikes."

The Fingerprint Club separated to cover the three exits. Frank stood guard over the parking lot.

At about half past ten the audience began to stream out, and a few minutes later came Frank's trumpet signal.

They pedaled off furiously, turning the corner onto East Street in the wake of the motorcycle. Fraser speeded up, though, and the Fingerprint Club lost him on the side streets. They could still hear the throbbing of his engine, but then the noise suddenly stopped.

"He can't be far," called Frank. "Let's go and look for the motorcycle. Its number is PXE 1314."

They soon found it parked in front of 28 Windmill Street. The Fingerprint Club looked for Fraser's name on the nameplates beside the door.

"Fraser isn't here," said Angela.

Just then Frank strolled up, looking very pleased with himself. "Fraser does live here," he said. "I've seen his name."

*Where had Frank seen the name?*

# 4

# THE BIRD FLIES THE NEST

Frank found Fraser's name on a mailbox nearby.

"Let's wait till daylight to brave the wolf in his den," Frank suggested.

When they came back to Windmill Street the next morning, the motorcycle had disappeared. They went into the house and found Fraser's room up in the attic. Ralph rang the bell. No one answered.

"He's gone away," said Angela. "What are we going to do now?"

"We know the number of his motorcycle," said Ralph.

"That's no use," Keith W.S. said, cracking a hazelnut for his squirrel.

"Look here," Frank said, "we're not giving up as easily as that. We'll keep looking, all of us."

Days went by. The Fingerprint Club searched streets, backyards, and parking lots, but found no trace. They began to comb the surrounding villages, too, but Fraser and his motorcycle had completely vanished.

Finally one afternoon as they were riding round the countryside, Frank suddenly braked his bike hard.

"Look, there," he shouted.

Half-hidden in the bushes was the motorcycle with the PXE 1314 number plate.

"The rear wheel is missing," Angela noticed.

"And where is its rider?" asked Keith W.S. "He must be near here."

The club looked around.

"Come on!" exclaimed Frank, running toward a nearby campsite. It was only a matter of seconds before he pointed toward one of the tents.

"That's our man. See what he's doing."

*What was Fraser doing?*

# 5

# THE NECKLACE

Fraser was pumping up his tire. But what on earth was he doing in a camping site near Breezy Lake?

"Do you think he realized that we were following him?" suggested Ralph.

"Anyhow, we must keep a close watch on him from now on," said Frank.

They settled down on a small hill from which they could observe Fraser's tent unseen. For two hours nothing happened. But at moonrise Fraser stole out of his tent and crept down to the shore. He threw a duffel bag, to which a rope was attached, into the lake. The club heard it splash as it hit the water. Fraser returned noiselessly to his tent.

"What was in that bag?" Angela whispered.

"Tomorrow we'll go and look," Frank answered.

The next day the club was back, equipped with flippers and masks. They dived into the lake. After several attempts, Frank spotted the duffel bag at the bottom of the lake.

When they reached the bag, Ralph struggled with the knots and Frank reached inside. At that moment there was a sharp tug on the rope and the bag vanished upward. The club realized at once that

Fraser had returned. They surfaced among the reeds.

"What a nuisance!" Ralph exclaimed furiously.

"At least we have recovered a necklace," Frank said, trying to cheer him up.

Angela inspected it. "It looks like a family heirloom," she said.

An hour later they stood outside Mrs. Partridge's door. "We may have good news for you," Angela said when Mrs. Partridge opened the door. "We have found something and we'd like you to tell us if it belongs to you. Show her the necklace, Frank."

"No need," answered Frank. "I know it is her necklace."

*How did Frank know the necklace belonged to Mrs. Partridge?*

# 6

## MOBILE UNIT

As soon as Frank pointed out the necklace in the painting, he said to the others, "Quick, let's get back to Breezy Lake. Hurry."

They were, of course, just too late. Fraser had left on his motorcycle.

"We'll have to tell Sergeant Shorthouse," said Ralph. "I'll call him."

Minutes later the squealing of brakes announced the arrival of a police car at Breezy Lake. The Fingerprint Club jumped in and they raced off again. Angela explained the situation to the sergeant as they went.

"Stop!" Angela shouted suddenly. The car drew up beside a policeman on a bicycle.

"A motorcycle and sidecar? Yes, I've seen one. It turned into Robertson's farm a little while ago."

As they entered the farmyard with the police, the Fingerprint Club saw the motorcycle. They went into the house and called, "Hello."

"Yeeees," answered a woman's voice from the kitchen.

"That's his girlfriend," whispered Frank. "The one he took to the movies that evening."

"What's your name?" asked Sergeant Shorthouse.

"Rita Fergusson. I'm the cleaning woman. The

boss and his wife have gone to town. I've been here alone all morning."

"Where's the man who rode up on that motorcycle outside?" asked Sergeant Shorthouse.

"I don't know what you're talking about."

"If that's the way you want it," the Sergeant answered, "we'll search the whole house. Show us around."

Rita pulled a chair into the middle of the room and sat down on it, saying with a scornful air, "Search if you want to. But don't expect me to help you."

Sergeant Shorthouse and the other police officers wasted no more time but searched every room in the house. Finally the sergeant came back to the club and said, "Well, we've looked everywhere . . ."

"There's one door you've missed," Angela answered. "Perhaps that's the right one."

*Which door did Angela mean?*

# THE TREASURE

Not until Angela pointed it out did Sergeant Shorthouse see the trap door.

"Get up," he said to Rita.

As he pulled the door open, she cried, "There's really no one down there."

Sergeant Shorthouse only laughed and shouted down into the cellar, "Come out of there, no one."

A crash helmet slowly emerged and under it, a face.

"Fraser!" exclaimed the club with one voice.

Sergeant Shorthouse put the handcuffs on him and asked, "Where's the loot?"

But Fraser struggled furiously and said, "I'll sue you. I'm an honest citizen."

"That remains to be seen." The second police officer climbed down to the cellar and returned with the duffel bag. "There's nothing else suspicious," she said.

Sergeant Shorthouse reached into the bag. It was empty.

Meanwhile, the Fingerprint Club had slipped quietly away into the cellar.

Ralph, squinting in the gloom, suddenly exclaimed, "I've found it. Look, all of you, there's the stolen jewelry!"

*Where was the jewelry?*

249

## CHECK FOR UNDERSTANDING
1. What crime had been committed?
2. Why did Mrs. Partridge let the Fingerprint Club help her?
3. What clue gave the Fingerprint Club the best lead?
4. What information helped the club find Fraser several times during the story?
5. Why did Fraser throw the duffel bag into Breezy Lake?

## WRITE ABOUT *"Treasure at Breezy Lake"*
Pretend that Fraser kept a journal. Write a few sentences for each day that the club made a move toward solving the case. For each day, include a sentence or two telling what Fraser planned to do next. Begin with the night that the club saw Fraser at the movie theater.

# Sunken Treasure

What would you think if you found a silver coin at the beach dated 1715? What would be your reaction if you found more silver coins, and even a gold one? If you are like Kip Wagner, you would want to solve the puzzle of where the coins were coming from.

Where did the treasure come from, and how did it end up where it did? What was the most important discovery Kip made in order to find the treasure?

by JUDY DONNELLY

## A FAILED MISSION

July 30, 1715. Eleven ships sailed slowly along the coast of Florida. They were heavy with silver and gold. About 2000 sailors were on board. The ships had to take their treasure all the way back to Spain—about 5000 miles away. The voyage would be full of danger. Pirates sailed the ocean. Hurricanes struck without warning. And the sea was full of reefs—hard jagged ridges hidden just underwater. If the bottom of a ship scraped against one, it would be torn open.

The sea was very still. The ships were barely moving. Then the sky grew dark and rain began to fall. The winds howled and giant waves crashed down. The storm grew worse; now the waves were like mountains. Men were swept overboard. Wood cracked, sails tore, tons of water poured down. The ships were pushed toward the reefs. One ship sank to the bottom. Then another and another. Ten ships went down in the terrible storm. A thousand men died. A fortune in treasure was lost.

## A MODERN DISCOVERY

Almost 250 years later, a man was walking along a Florida beach. His name was Kip Wagner, and his job was building houses. He had moved to a nearby town to build a new motel.

Kip was looking for old coins. He had been looking for years. He had heard stories about Spanish coins turning up on the beach—pieces of eight that came from sunken treasure ships. When a friend finally showed him some pieces of eight, Kip was surprised. They weren't round. They weren't shiny. They weren't anything like the coins in his pocket. They were oddly shaped and blackened by the sea. If he had seen one, he would never have bothered to pick it up.

Even knowing what to look for didn't help Kip. He never found anything. Sometimes he thought he never would.

Kip used a metal detector. He would sweep the rod back and forth over the beach. If there was any metal under the sand, the detector would make a special noise. A beep.

Often the metal detector beeped. Kip would dig in the sand, and what would he find? A tin can.

Then one day the detector beeped the way it always did. Kip brushed away the sand. This time he saw a black, strangely shaped piece of metal. He couldn't believe it! An old silver coin! He had finally found one!

Kip picked it up. Pirates had killed for these coins. Treasure hunters had died trying to find them. And now he held one in his hand.

Kip decided something. He would never give up searching until he found a great treasure.

## THE SEARCH FOR A SHIP

Kip went back to the same beach again and again. He found more silver coins, even some gold ones. He began to call the place his "money beach."

He had one big question: Where had all these coins come from? He felt sure they had washed up from the sea. Somewhere, probably nearby, was the wreck of a great treasure ship.

Kip swam out to look for the wreck. He cut himself on the sharp edges of the reefs, but he found nothing. He borrowed a boat, cruised through the waves, and stared down into the water. Still nothing.

He was never going to find any treasure this way. He had to know where to look. He decided to stop searching the ocean; instead, he would search for the answers in the library!

Kip had one important clue: The coins from the beach had dates on them, and no coin was dated later than 1715. He heard that some treasure ships had gone down in a hurricane in 1715, but no one knew where they had sunk.

Kip tried the biggest library in the country, the Library of Congress, in Washington, D.C. The library had a very rare book. It was 200 years old. Sure enough, it told about the shipwrecks of 1715! There was even a map! The map showed that the treasure ships had gone down within a few miles of his money beach!

Kip took to the ocean again. This time he made himself a special surfboard with a glass window in it. He would paddle along and see down into the water. Time after time Kip looked.

Then one day he saw strange shapes. He paddled closer. They were cannons from a ship.

Nearby was a huge anchor. Suddenly he knew: He had found the wreck! He had expected to see a whole ship lying on its side, but a wooden ship would be rotted away after almost 250 years in the ocean. Only the metal parts would last.

And the treasure? Kip was sure it was still there. But it must be scattered and buried under the sand.

Kip got special permission from the Florida government to search for the treasure. He promised to give Florida part of any treasure he found. He bought an old boat and machines to move sand. He spent a year getting a team of eight men together. He liked and trusted every one of them. One morning, in January 1961, he set out for the wreck.

The team was excited. Kip was nervous. Storms made the sand at the bottom of the ocean move so that what you saw one day might be covered up the next. Would he be able to find the wreck again?

255

The sea was rough. Kip had to steer the boat close to two dangerous reefs—the same reefs that had sunk the treasure ships.

The boat made it. The water was very cold. Only two of the team had special diving suits to keep them warm. Down they went.

Then one diver broke through the water. He waved a handful of silver coins. "They're down there by the bushel!" he cried. He left the coins on the deck and disappeared. Then he was back, pushing what looked like a big black rock onto the ship. It was a mass of silver coins—all stuck together. There had to be a thousand of them!

Everyone began to laugh and shout. And they all dived in! Nobody cared how cold the water was! For the rest of the day, they picked treasure off the bottom—some $80,000 worth.

And this was only the beginning. Later they found gold coins, jewelry, silver candlesticks. Their discoveries surprised the world. They found a gold chain 10½ feet long! They found a wooden treasure chest that was loaded with 3000 coins. How had a wooden chest lasted after 250 years in the sea? No one could believe it. They found something even stranger—28 priceless cups and saucers from China. Not one was even cracked.

That wasn't all. Kip led his team to seven more treasure wrecks! They found more than $3 million in treasure!

Kip had made his dream come true. He was famous. Reporters followed him. He was invited all over the world. He was on television, in magazines. Treasure hunters everywhere tried to do what he had done.

And this was the man who thought he would never find even one silver coin!

## CHECK FOR UNDERSTANDING

1. Where did the treasure come from? How did it end up where it did?
2. What did Kip Wagner use to find his first silver coin?
3. What was the most important discovery Kip made in order to find the treasure?
4. What did Kip make to look for the ships? What were the shapes he saw?
5. What did Kip have to get from the state of Florida? What did he have to give the state?
6. What did Kip find that was neither silver nor gold, but priceless?

## WRITE ABOUT *"Sunken Treasure"*

Make up an interview with Kip Wagner. Write ten questions you would like to ask him about his experiences in finding sunken treasure. Write the answers you think he would give, using information in the story.

## Reading Math Problems

Sometimes a math problem is given to you in the form of a story. The facts you need to know to solve the problem are given to you in the story. And the problem you have to solve is asked in the story. We call this kind of math problem a **story problem**.

How do you solve a story problem? The best way is to follow certain steps. There are four steps.

### Step 1: Read

The first thing you do is **read.** Read the story problem from beginning to end. This will give you a general idea of what it's all about. As you read, you should ask yourself two things:

> *What is the story problem* **telling** *me?*
> and
> *What question is the story problem* **asking** *me?*

There is something else you must do. Although a story problem is in the form of a story, you should not read it in the same way that you read a regular story.

You read it much more carefully. Even the small words are important — words that you may often skim over when you read. Words like *all, every,* and *each*.

In fact, sometimes these small words are *most* important.

In the story we have read, "Sunken Treasure," Kip and his crew find old Spanish coins called *pieces of eight.* Let's do a story problem about these coins. As we do it, we will see how important the small words can be.

Kip found twenty pieces of eight. This was another name for the Spanish coin, the *peso*. Long ago, pieces of eight—old pesos—were worth the same as an American dollar. But Kip knew that because of their historical interest, each one is now worth ten times its original value. What is the value today of all the coins Kip found?

You have read the story. You know what it is about. As you read, you have asked yourself the two questions:

*What is the story problem **telling** me?*
and
*What question is the story problem **asking** me?*

The problem you are to solve is usually at the end of the story problem. Here it is:

"What is the value *today* of *all* the coins Kip found?"

Although *all* is a small word, it is a very important word in the question. Why is it important? Suppose that one word *all* were changed to *each*. The question would then read: What is the value of *each* coin found?

It is a different question. The problem is different. And the correct answer would be different.

Do you see how important a small word can be?

Now we go to our other question:

> *What is the story problem* **telling** *me?*

This is a good time to go back and look again at the story problem. It tells you a lot of different facts. But now you know the question you have to answer. And so you are better able to pick out the facts that will help you solve the problem.

What are the facts?

An important fact is about the value today of the pieces of eight. Again we see how important one word can be. What does the question ask? It does not ask you for the value of the coins long ago. It asks for *today's* value. If you did not read carefully, if you did not pay attention to the word *today*, you would not get the correct answer.

## Step 2: PLAN

You know the problem you must solve. And you know what facts are needed to solve it.

Now you ask yourself: What should I do with these facts? You must **plan** what to do with them. It might be a help to jot down the facts you need.

> Old Value of each coin = $1.00
> Today's Value = 10 times old value

To get today's value you have to multiply $1 by 10.

The question asks for the value of **all** the coins. How many coins were found? **20**. **20** is another important fact.

To get the value of all the coins, what will you have to do? Again, you can see you will have to multiply *today's value by the number of coins.*

Now you have all your facts.

You have written them down.

And you have made your plan. You know what you are going to do with them.

Now is the time for the third step.

### Step 3: SOLVE

You are ready to **solve** the problem.

$$\$ 1.00 \quad \$10.00 \qquad \text{(today's value of each coin)}$$
$$\underline{\times 10} \quad \underline{\times 20} \qquad \text{(number of coins)}$$
$$\$10.00 \quad \$200.00$$

This is your answer. This is the solution to the story problem. The value *today* of *all* the coins found is **$200**.

There is one last step when you do a story problem. You ask yourself one more question. *Am I sure this is the correct answer?* How can you tell? It is time for Step 4.

## Step 4: CHECK

**Check** your answer.

How do you do that?

First, look back at the question. Pay attention to the exact words. Remember — *every* word, even the smallest, is important.

Now ask yourself this: *Did I answer the question that is asked? Did I tell them the value* **today** *. . . of* **all** *the coins Kip found?*

*Now* **double-check** your facts.

Do you have the correct number of coins found?

Do you have the correct value of each coin, not long ago, but *today*?

Now you feel your facts are correct.

You feel you are answering the right question.

Now go over something else. Was your plan right?

Was the multiplication the right thing to do? Not adding? Not dividing?

If your answer is yes, there is one more thing to do. Check your math. Did you do it correctly?

Word problems are not harder or easier than math problems. But they are different. In a word problem, your facts are not handed to you. In a way, you have to find them. You have to pull them out of the story and it's up to you to figure out what to do. Because you are not told to add, to divide, to multiply.

The best way to do a story problem is to follow the four steps:
1. Read
2. Plan
3. Solve
4. Check

## Using What You Have Learned

Solve this story problem.

Jack and Nancy went on a hike. They left from Nancy's house, which was at the beginning of the trail. They hiked two miles, then took a rest. They then hiked another mile when Jack discovered that he had lost his canteen. So they turned around. They walked back half a mile, where they found it on the trail. How far were they now from Nancy's house?

## Expanding Your Skills

Make up a simple story problem. Check your facts. Check your question. Make sure it can be answered from the facts you have given. Exchange story problems with another student.

# The Tiger and the Rabbit

by PURA BELPRÉ

Cleverness is not just thinking well, it is thinking fast. But what if the problem you are trying to solve with quick thinking is how to save your own life? Fortunately for the Rabbit in this story, his brain is always far ahead of the Tiger's mouth.

How does the Rabbit manage to get the Tiger tied to a tree? What other things besides the Rabbit's cleverness allow him to always get the better of the Tiger?

Long, long ago, all the animals were friends and lived at peace with one another, except the Tiger. For the Tiger had promised himself to eat small animals, especially the Rabbit, if they ever crossed his path.

But the Rabbit was very clever and known for his quick wit. He knew that the Tiger wanted to eat him, and though he considered the beast stupid,

264

clumsy, and a fool, he managed to keep away from his path. But this was not always possible, since they both liked to roam about.

One day, when the Tiger was bringing home a coil of rope, he met the Rabbit resting under the shade of a tamarind tree. The Tiger dropped the rope and, rushing up to the Rabbit, said, "Aha! Today you shall not escape me. I will eat you up."

The little Rabbit was at once on the alert, but answered calmly: "You might as well. I have been trying to die, for if you knew what is going to happen, you wouldn't care to live, either. Eat me up and be done with it. But for you, ah! I am sorry."

Eager as the Tiger had been to eat the Rabbit, the fear of what was going to happen got the better of him, and the idea of saving himself was foremost in his mind. The Rabbit saw his confusion and waited patiently for the question he was sure would come.

"What is going to happen, Rabbit?" the Tiger asked.

"Why, haven't you heard?" answered the Rabbit. "A terrible hurricane is coming on, stronger than any we have ever had."

Now, there was nothing the Tiger feared more than hurricanes. He shivered at the thought of the howling of the wind, the crashing of trees, and the downpour of rain.

"Oh, little Rabbit," he said, "what am I to do? You are so small that you can hide anywhere. You are so light on your legs that you can run miles away, but what about me? Help me, please."

The Rabbit remembered the rope the Tiger was carrying home, and looking up at the large tamarind tree under which he stood, a plan came to his mind.

"There is only one thing," he said, "only one thing to do. I must tie you to this tree. It has stood several hurricanes and will no doubt stand this one, too."

"Tie me quickly," answered the Tiger.

So the Rabbit tied him with the coil of rope and firmly wound the rope around the thick trunk of the tamarind tree. Then he climbed into the tree so that he could watch the Tiger.

Pretty soon a number of small goats passed by, and when they saw the Tiger stretched on the grass firmly tied to the tree, they bleated for joy.

"You wouldn't bleat so happily," said the Tiger, "if you knew what is going to happen."

"What is going to happen?" asked the little goats, who for the first time found themselves speaking to the Tiger.

"A terrible hurricane is coming on, stronger

than any we have ever had," he said.

"Ha! Ha! Ha!" laughed the goats. "A hurricane indeed! We come from all up and down the mountain path, and from the green pastures on the hills, and nowhere have we heard such news. There is no hurricane coming."

Gone were the Tiger's fears, and at once he noticed how fat the little goats were and what a tasty morsel each one would make.

"Untie me, please," he pleaded.

But the little goats scampered away to tell the other animals that they could rejoice free of care, for the Tiger was tied firmly to a tamarind tree.

The Tiger wriggled and wriggled, and tried in vain to free himself. Up in the tree the little Rabbit was enjoying the sight below. Just then, a monkey swung down from a tree nearby. When he saw the Tiger, he let out a screech that brought down a large number of his friends.

"Untie me, please," pleaded the Tiger again.

"If we do, you will eat us up," answered the monkeys.

But the Tiger promised not to eat them up, and the monkeys began to work at the ropes. They gnawed at the knots until, little by little, they finished the work and set him free. No sooner done, the Tiger turned upon them, clawing and biting the poor monkeys who, taken by surprise, began to jump and screech with all their might. Some ran wildly through the forest, while others climbed the nearby trees. All but one escaped, and the Tiger now turned fiercely upon him.

Just then, the Rabbit called down: "Tiger, that is not the way one eats a monkey. I certainly wouldn't do it that way."

"How would you do it?" he called back.

"Ah, I would throw the monkey up and catch it in my mouth," answered the Rabbit.

"That is easy enough," said the Tiger. So he
threw the monkey up into the air, but his aim was
so poor that he threw him right on the branches of
a tree. The Tiger stood with his mouth wide open
waiting for the monkey to drop.

The Rabbit then shook a branch of the tamarind tree, and down dropped a large number of tamarind pods, right into the Tiger's mouth.

Poor Tiger, half choking and shaking his head to

free his mouth of the fruit, ran through the forest, vowing more than ever that he would eat up the Rabbit the very next time he met him.

Long after his adventure with the Tiger, the Rabbit paid a visit to his friend the Fox, and the conversation fell on the subject of the Tiger. The Fox was a great admirer of the Tiger and thought he was very clever and intelligent. He said the Tiger could do anything he wanted; nothing ever stood in his way. The Rabbit, who knew better, began to laugh.

"He is a fool, that's what he is," he said. "A big fool. Why, he is such a fool that he lets himself be used as a horse by his friends."

"I don't believe it," said the Fox.

"I will prove it to you," answered the Rabbit, "and when I do, I hope you will be at your door to answer my greeting."

Time went on, and the Fox forgot the Rabbit's foolish talk. One Sunday, he decided to invite some of his friends for a feast. He prepared special things to eat, but was discouraged because he had not been able to get music for entertainment. Just then the Tiger arrived, and wishing to help him, offered to bring the best guitarist he could find. It so happened that the Rabbit was the best guitarist in the place and the only one available at the time, so the Tiger decided to look him up.

He came to his house and knocked at the door.

"Who is there?" asked the Rabbit.

"It's the Tiger. I have come to get you to play at the Fox's feast."

"Go away," answered the Rabbit. "I am sick and cannot go."

"But you must come," said the Tiger. "There is no one to play, and I have promised the music."

"Aha!" thought the Rabbit. "This is my chance."

"If you come," said the Tiger, "I won't ever try to eat you up—I promise."

The Rabbit wrapped a handkerchief around his head and, leaning on a cane, opened the door.

"I cannot walk, as you well see," he said.

"I will carry you on my back," offered the Tiger, who did not want to disappoint his friend, the Fox.

The Rabbit climbed on his back, but no sooner did he climb up than he slid down again.

"Oh! Oh!" he cried. "I can't sit on your back unless I have a saddle. Now I have a little one here. . . ."

"All right," said the Tiger. "Bring it out, but only hurry, hurry."

Along with the saddle came a bridle and a pair of spurs. When the Rabbit finished harnessing the Tiger, he limped into his house again and came out with his small guitar. Pretending he was very sick, he took some time to climb on the Tiger's back, groaning feebly.

"Let us go, Tiger," he said at last, picking up the reins.

On trotted the Tiger, and pretty soon they came into view of the Fox's home. The Rabbit quickly cast off the handkerchief from his head and set the spurs to the Tiger's flanks. Up went the Tiger's legs; he reared like a horse, and sped along past trees and shrubs and finally past the Fox's house.

"Adíos! Good-by Fox!" called the Rabbit, as he sped by.

Great was the Fox's surprise as he recognized the Rabbit on the Tiger's back. Like a flash, the Rabbit's promise came to his mind. The Rabbit was correct. "The Tiger is a fool, a great fool," he said.

By that time the Rabbit had come back and now stood at his door, laughing—and the Tiger followed him.

272

"Fox," Rabbit called, "I did prove it to you! Didn't I?"

That day, he played better than ever. And now the Tiger realized how clever the Rabbit was and, before the feast ended, they became the best of friends.

## CHECK FOR UNDERSTANDING

1. How did the Rabbit manage to get the Tiger tied to a tree?
2. Why did the goats bleat with joy when they saw the Tiger?
3. How did the Rabbit save the Monkey's life?
4. What other things besides the Rabbit's cleverness allowed him to always get the better of the Tiger? Explain your answer.
5. What change took place in the Tiger that resulted in his becoming friends with the Rabbit?

## WRITE ABOUT *"The Tiger and the Rabbit"*

Pretend that you are the Tiger and write a letter to a newspaper advice column. Ask for hints on how to control your appetite, particularly when you are with the Rabbit around dinner time. Write the letter you think the advice columnist would send in reply.

# LITERATURE

## Elements of Plot

Have you ever started to write a story of your own and asked yourself, "Where do I begin?" and "Where will I end?" These are important questions every author asks before writing. They are particularly important for a story that is realistic, and perhaps based on a real experience.

These questions are important because they are questions about the basic form the story will take. The form of a story serves the same purpose a skeleton does to a human being, or a framework does to a house. The skeleton, or framework of a story, is called the **plot.**

The plot is more than the beginning and the end of a story. The plot consists of all the major events that move the story from the beginning through the middle to the end.

The beginning of a story introduces the ingredients of the story. In this introduction, you learn the setting, or where and when the story takes place. You also meet the important characters in the story. Finally, part of the purpose of the story beginning is to introduce the **conflict,** or problem, of the story.

The conflict is probably the most important part of the plot. The conflict is the problem around which all the actions and events of the story take place. The conflict can be defined as whatever forces a character to do something that is not part of his or her ordinary life.

Think about the story "Diving Class." The beginning of the story, which is a letter, reveals the setting and introduces the characters and the conflict.

*July 31*

Dear Ma and Daddy,

Everything's fine at camp except I'm really scared about my diving test. It's the only one I have left for Dolphin. I'll never be able to do it. Never. Do you think you could please call Aunt Tillie, the camp director, with an excuse?...Please do it right away.

Love,

Abby

The middle of a story consists of the actions or events in which the character tries to **solve** the problem. In "Diving Class," the middle of the story consists of Abby's attempts to *avoid* the diving test. None of her attempts really solve the problem, or resolve the conflict.

Part of every plot is the **turning point.** This consists of the moment in the story when some important change takes place that finally leads to a real solution of the problem. For Abby, the turning point comes when she gives a younger swimmer the confidence she herself needs to take the diving test. When Abby goes into Aunt Tillie's office, the turning point is complete.

The final element of the plot is the story's **ending.** In the ending, the story shows the result of the change that took place in the turning point. In the ending, the reader gets to see exactly how the problem has been worked out once and for all. In "Diving Class," you learn in the ending just how Abby actually made her first dive.

Of course, you shouldn't think about the elements of the plot as you read a story. But if you think about the **conflict,** the **turning point,** and the **ending** after you are finished, you will gain a better understanding of the story.

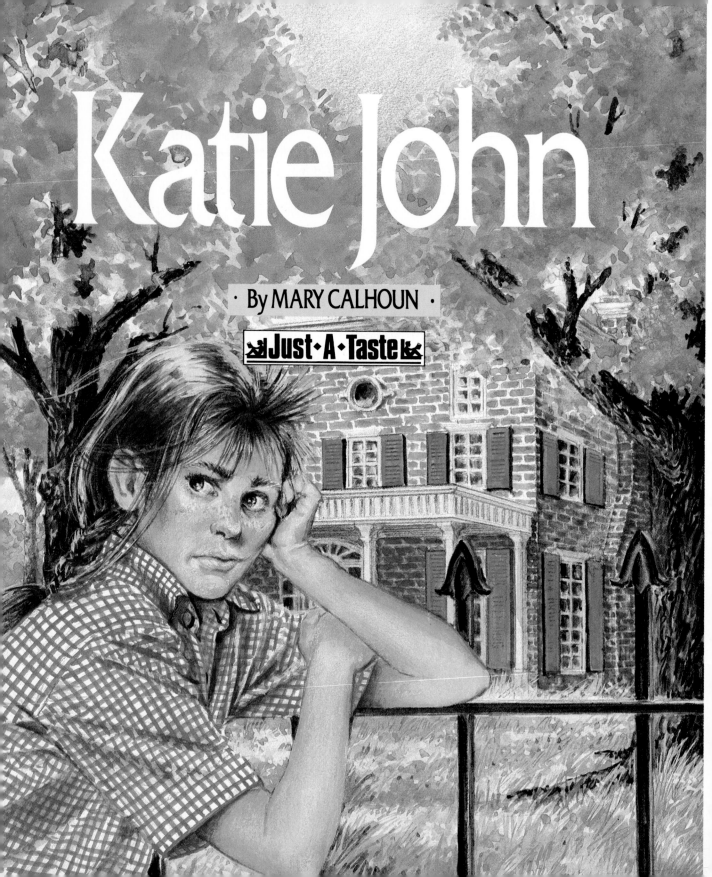

One of the problems of moving to a new place is making new friends. But what do you do when the first friend you make says your new house is haunted? You might do what Katie John does: investigate and find a solution.

How does Katie John feel about her new house? How do you think Katie John will feel about the house by the end of the summer?

# The Mysterious Voice

Morning. Katie John opened her eyes and looked at the strange room. Yes, they were here, all right. She pulled on her blouse and shorts and ran out of the house. Did it really look as horrible as it had when they arrived last night?

Oh, worse. Katie John groaned. It was nothing but an ugly old red brick house, squatting in the sunlight.

Square as a box, flat roof, not even a bit of ivy on the walls to soften the sharp corners. It was three stories high, and little hooded windows rimmed the top of the house, like beady eyes. The ugly box was glaring at her.

"So, hah!" Katie John glared back.

Using all her fingers, Katie made a ferocious face at the

house. She stretched her eyes and mouth down, shoved her nose up, and crossed her eyes.

"Gaaaah, you old house!"

When Mother had first told her about the house in Missouri, Katie had comforted herself that it might be a beautiful old southern mansion, with huge white pillars on the porch. Well, the house was old, and it had a porch, but the posts were spindly and dirty gray. And it certainly was no mansion. Katie John kicked a post and flopped down on the steps.

Mainly she was mad at the house because it had ruined her whole wonderful summer. If it weren't for the house, she'd be back home in California right now, getting ready to go to the camp up in the Sierras. Seemed as if she'd waited all her life to be old enough to go to camp, and now when she was—*whack*, Katie banged the step with her heel—here she was in the backwoods of Missouri. Why, this poky little town wasn't even on a main road.

"I bet they don't even *have* any camps around here," she muttered. "I bet nothing ever *ever* happens here."

It had all come about because Great-Aunt Emily—*poor* Great-Aunt Emily, Katie corrected herself—had died and left the house to Mother. So she and Dad and Mother had driven back East to Barton's Bluff to sell the house.

It might take all summer, Mother said.

Impatiently, Katie ran her fingers up through her thick, straight bangs, making her hair stick up in spikes. Then she propped her chin on her hands and stared toward the street. At least this yard wasn't bad. It was big and grassy, and maple trees lined the street beyond the fence.

Katie John studied the fence. It was different from the

redwood or neat white picket ones back in California. This was an old-fashioned black iron fence, with iron bars rising to upside-down V's, like a row of jagged teeth. The fence went all across the front of the yard and around the corner, down the side hill. Another iron bar ran under the row of teeth, with enough space in each tooth for a foot.

Katie brightened. Wonder if she could walk the fence?

She ran over to it and swung up, balancing easily. Her head brushed the lower branches of a tree, and down the steep hill she could see the Mississippi River, sparkling blue. Later today she'd go down there, Katie promised herself. But right now, the fence. Katie began to edge sideways, one foot following the other.

"Your Great-Uncle Dick broke his wrist doing that," a voice said calmly.

Katie jerked, caught her balance, and saw a girl standing on the sidewalk. The girl had a round face, with hair smoothly drawn back into pigtails. Katie suddenly remembered that she hadn't combed her hair this morning, and she'd worn these shorts for the whole trip.

"How do you know?" Katie demanded. "What happened?"

"I know because your Great-Aunt Emily told me," the girl said. "When he was a little boy he walked the fence and fell off and broke his wrist. So you'd better get down."

Something about the girl made Katie John feel contrary. The girl seemed so safe and sure, as if she'd never made a mistake or been scolded in her life. Anyway, Katie had made up her mind to walk this fence, and she was going to do it.

"Well, I'm sorry about Uncle Dick," she said, "but he was probably lots younger. I'm not going to fall."

She sidestepped along the fence toward the corner. The girl followed.

"I'll catch you when you fall," she said. "I'm Sue Halsey. I live three doors down the street. I know all about you, too."

Katie stopped. "Who am I?"

"You're Katie John Tucker, and you're ten, same age as me. You live in California, you've come to sell the old Clark house, and I know because—"

"No, I'm not," Katie interrupted. "Katie's in the house."

Sue looked so uncertain that Katie laughed.

"You're right. I'm Katie John. Come on up." She stretched out a hand to Sue.

"No." Sue started to walk away.

Katie felt a little ashamed. She hadn't meant to hurt the girl's feelings.

"I'll tell you something I'll bet you don't know," she offered.

Sue stopped. "What?"

"When we sell the house, we're not going back to California," Katie said, struggling past a bush that threatened to push her off the fence. She turned the corner and started downhill. "We're going to New York City and live on the house money while Daddy finishes the book he's writing."

Privately Katie didn't think much of the idea. In fact, she hated the thought of moving. There wasn't much to do in her hometown, but that was where she'd grown up, and that was where all her friends were.

"My!" Sue was sighing. "All right then, I'll tell you something, Katie John Tucker. This old house is haunted!"

"What?" Katie stopped to look at Sue. "Now you're teasing me."

"No, really," Sue insisted. "I heard voices in there."

Sometimes when Miss Clark—Great-Aunt Emily—had been out in the yard, Sue had stopped to talk with her, she explained, but she'd never been in the house. Then one day Miss Clark had asked her to come in because she wanted to give Sue an old doll. Sue had waited in the parlor while Miss Clark had gone to find it.

Sue's voice dropped. "And while she was gone I heard someone humming and talking softly *right in that room*!"

"Oh, you probably just heard Aunt Emily."

"No, she was way off upstairs," Sue said. "And the voice was right near me. I ran out to the yard and I've never been in that house since."

Voices! Haunted house! Katie John stared at the house. Now that she was around at the side of it, she saw that it wasn't a simple box, after all.

It rambled all over the hill at the back, and there were big brick stables behind it.

"Well, you're going in that house now! Show me where it happened," Katie commanded.

Katie jumped down from the fence and ran around to the front door. Sue followed reluctantly. Inside, the hallway was dim after the sunlight. Katie stopped short. "Oh!" A huge animal was looking at her. Then she saw it was only a stuffed moose head on top of a hat and coat rack.

She hadn't seen the inside of the house at all. Last night when they'd arrived, she'd been half-asleep, and her dad had tumbled her into a bed. Now she saw that a long stairway with a polished banister rose to the second floor. On the left of the staircase was the room she'd slept in. On the right was a closed door.

Sue opened it. "This is the parlor. It was in here." She stood back. "I'll wait outside."

Katie pulled her arm. "Come on. A voice can't hurt you."

Nevertheless, Katie John tiptoed as they entered the room. Brown inside shutters were closed at the windows, and in the dark the furniture loomed under shapeless covers. Thick tapestry draperies covered one wall.

"It was over by the piano that I heard it," Sue whispered. "I was sitting on the piano bench."

Katie turned, caught a glimpse of movement across the room, and gasped. A face! Then she let out her breath. It was her own face, reflected in a mirror set back in a tall carved bureau—or something. Anyway, it had mirrors and cupboards and shelves cluttered with vases and ornaments.

"Look out!" She poked Sue and pointed toward the bureau.

Sue looked, gasped a little shriek, and crumpled to the floor, hiding her eyes.

"Oh heee!" Katie gurgled with giggles. "Ha-ha-heee!" She collapsed on top of Sue, breathless with laughing. "It's just a mirror!" Still, she whispered through her giggles. It was all so shadowy and sort of secret in here.

Sue started to get mad, but Katie whispered, "I'm a ghost!" in such a silly voice that Sue caught the giggles, too. They flopped in a heap, squealing with laughter every time they tried to get up.

At last they got untangled, and Katie led the way to the piano. "All right now, let's listen." They hushed down and sat on the piano bench. Katie waited for a moment, but she didn't hear anything.

"Maybe it was something in the piano that you heard."

She lifted the folding lid and touched a black key. *Pon-n-n,* the musical note sounded softly in the still room. But when it died away there was no other sound. The girls watched each other with listening eyes.

And then, "I hear something! Shh!" Katie whispered.

There was a little murmur and—yes—a laugh! Now a deeper rumble.

Sue clutched Katie's arm. "I'm leaving!"

"No, you're not! Maybe it's my folks in the hall."

Katie stepped toward the door, but the sound faded immediately. She moved back to the piano bench, and there was the mutter-mutter again. It was a voice, all right! But she couldn't make out the words. Katie slid to the end of the bench, next to the wall, while Sue watched her from the middle of the room. Now the voice was louder. Katie leaned her head against the wall.

And she heard the voice saying, "I'll go see whether Katie's awake."

It wasn't a ghost at all. It was her mother's voice!

"It's my mother!" Katie laughed in relief. "She's talking to Dad."

"But—but that's an outside wall you're listening at." Sue's voice trembled.

Katie looked at the wall, and it was then that she noticed the hole. There in the wallpaper was a small hole, rimmed with china.

"Come here." She motioned to Sue and put her ear against the hole.

Quite clearly she heard her father say, "Now where's my other shoe?"

"Sue, it's my folks talking in a bedroom somewhere!" Katie cried. "This must be some kind of old telephone system in the walls."

Immediately she stuck her finger into the hole. With her

fingertip she felt a little metal passage, and she pushed her whole finger in, trying to feel farther.

"I'll call my folks through here," Katie giggled. "Won't I give them a surprise!"

But when she tried to pull her finger out, she couldn't. It was stuck in the small opening.

"Sue, I'm stuck. Help pull."

"A speaking tube! So that's all the voice was," Sue chattered. "Here, try to twist your finger—I should have known. Mom says Miss Clark had all kinds of funny gadgets built into this house . . . Can't you pull?"

But Katie's finger was stuck tight and swelling.

"Hurry, go get my mother," Katie half-giggled, half-sobbed, "before I grow fast to this crazy old house."

Sue ran to the hall and shouted up the stairs, while Katie tried to call into the speaking tube. Her finger had plugged the hole too neatly, however, for her voice to get through.

Katie's mother ran down the stairs in her bathrobe, crying, "What—what—who?" at the sight of a strange girl in the hall. "What's the matter?" Katie's dad called, clattering down behind her. They hurried into the parlor, where they saw their daughter hooked to the wall by one finger.

"Katie John Tucker!" exclaimed her mother. "Are you in trouble before I can even get up in the morning?"

"Mother, I'm sorry, it was—"
"Ghost . . . voices," Katie and Sue talked at once. "Speaking tube in the wall and then—"

Katie's mother threw up her hands. "Never mind! Stop! Let me get you loose and then you can tell me."

She hurried away and brought back soap and a wet

285

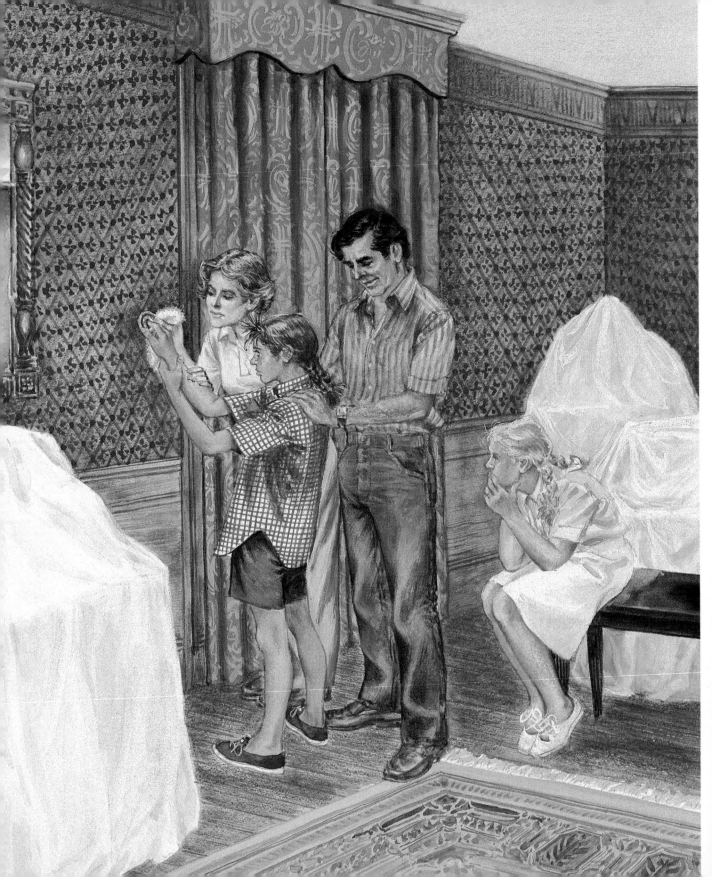

washrag. While she soaped Katie's finger, Katie's dad grinned down at her.

"Stop wiggling," he told her mildly. "The old house likes you. It was just trying to get a good hold on you."

Katie laughed as her sore finger slipped out of the hole, but she set her chin. "Well, it hasn't got me yet!"

*The enormous old house is full of exciting surprises for Katie John. Read about her further adventures that summer in the novel* Katie John *by Mary Calhoun.*

## CHECK FOR UNDERSTANDING

1. How did Katie John feel about her new house? Why did she feel that way?
2. Why had Katie John and her family moved to a house in Missouri from their house in California?
3. What was the first thing Katie John found that she liked about the house?
4. What do you think made Katie John feel "contrary" toward Sue?
5. How was the mystery of the voices solved?
6. How do you think Katie John will feel about the house by the end of the summer? Explain why you think as you do.

## WRITE ABOUT *"The Mysterious Voice"*

Sue Halsey mentioned that Great-Aunt Emily had other gadgets built into the house. Describe what one of the other gadgets might have been and what its purpose was. Use your imagination. It can be a real gadget or a fantasy one.

# THINK ABOUT IT

Think about the characters in the stories you have read. How is their solving one problem linked to the solution of a larger problem?

- Why was Abby's first solution to the problem really no solution at all?
- How did Melindy compare herself to other members of her family?
- How good were you at solving the mystery of the treasure at Breezy Lake?
- What were the main obstacles facing Kip Wagner in his hunt for Spanish treasure?
- What animal was a problem to the other animals, and what animal was a problem to him?
- How did the mysterious voice help solve another problem for Katie John?

After reading and thinking about these different solutions to problems, what do you think life would be like without problems to solve?

# WRITE ABOUT IT

Write a paragraph describing a problem that you solved recently, all by yourself. In your paragraph, tell how solving the problem made you feel. Tell also whether you think some good feelings only come from solving problems, and are not felt for other reasons.

# READ ABOUT IT

*Henry and the Clubhouse* by Beverly Cleary. William Morrow & Co., 1962. Ramona deliberately locks Henry into his clubhouse and he must find a way out, without telling Ramona where he hides the key.

*The Great Brain* by John D. Fitzgerald. Dial Books for Young Readers, 1967. No problem is too big for Tom Fitzgerald, the Great Brain of Adenville, Utah. He is quick to share his wild schemes with anyone in Adenville—for a small price, of course.

*Pippi Longstocking* by Astrid Lindgren. Viking Press, 1950. No one can get the better of high-spirited, red-headed Pippi, who is so strong she can lift people up! She has many adventures, as she lives with her horse and monkey in a little town in Sweden.

*Sidewalk Story* by Sharon Bell Mathis. The Viking Press, 1971. Tanya and Lilly Etta, neighbors and friends, find themselves in a difficult situation when Tanya is forced to move. Lilly Etta contacts the local television station and resolves the problem.

*Soup in the Saddle* by Robert Newton Peck. Alfred A. Knopf, 1983. Soup and Rob ride right into trouble when they learn that the celebration honoring their teacher is destined for disaster. The boys enlist the aid of an old racehorse, the school nurse, and mean Janice Riker to carry out their scheme to save the day.

# CLUES AND DISCOVERIES

**4**

*Discovering a new land, an unknown island, or buried treasure is an exciting experience. But these aren't the kind of discoveries most people make. There is another kind of discovery people make all the time, and in some ways it's even more exciting. They discover themselves.*

*As you read this unit, ask yourself what the characters discover about themselves in the selections. Think about what other discoveries they make along the way. How may the discoveries the characters make in these stories change their lives in the future?*

# Paddington Turns Detective

A Play by ALFRED BRADLEY and MICHAEL BOND

There are some people who, whenever they try to be helpful or kind, end up doing just the wrong thing. In this story, Paddington shows that he is exactly that sort of person—or, actually, that sort of *bear*.

What helpful deed does Paddington try to do?

What goes wrong with Paddington's efforts?

## CAST OF CHARACTERS

| | |
|---|---|
| Mr. Brown | Police Officer |
| Mrs. Brown | Mr. Curry |
| Mrs. Bird | Judy Brown |
| Paddington | Jonathan Brown |
| Mr. Gruber | |

# Scene 1

[*The Browns' sitting room. Mr. and Mrs. Brown are talking.*]

MR. BROWN: I can't think who would do a thing like that.

MRS. BROWN: Nor can I, Henry. It's never happened before.

MR. BROWN: I suppose it's too late to do anything about it now. It's very disappointing.

MRS. BIRD [*coming in from the kitchen*]: What's the matter, Mr. Brown?

MR. BROWN: Someone's stolen my prize squash.

MRS. BIRD: When did that happen?

MR. BROWN: I don't know for sure. It was there on Wednesday. They must have stolen it during the night.

MRS. BIRD [*after exchanging a look with Mrs. Brown*]: Well, you've got several more.

[*Paddington comes in.*]

MR. BROWN: That isn't the point.

PADDINGTON: Good morning, everybody.

MRS. BIRD: Good morning, Paddington.

PADDINGTON: Is anything the matter, Mr. Brown?

MR. BROWN: Somebody has stolen my prize squash. I've several more, of course, but they'll never be ready in time for the show.

PADDINGTON: Oh, dear! I'm sorry to hear that, Mr. Brown.

MR. BROWN: It's the biggest I've ever grown. I felt I was sure to win a prize. I've a good mind to offer a reward to anybody who tracks down the culprit. [*A thoughtful look comes into Paddington's eyes, and he makes for the door.*]

MRS. BROWN: Aren't you having any breakfast this morning, Paddington?

PADDINGTON: No, thank you, Mrs. Brown. I want to see Mr. Gruber about something.

MRS. BROWN: What's that?

PADDINGTON: I'm not sure until I see him. [*He puts on his hat and goes.*]

MR. BROWN: *Now* what has he got on his mind?

MRS. BIRD: I don't know, but I noticed a funny look came into his eyes when you mentioned a reward . . .

# Scene 2

[*Mr. Gruber's shop. Mr. Gruber puts down the book he is reading as Paddington comes in.*]

PADDINGTON: Good morning, Mr. Gruber.

MR. GRUBER: Good morning, Paddington. You're early today. It's only ten o'clock.

PADDINGTON: Yes. I've got a problem and I wondered if you could help me.

MR. GRUBER: I'll do my best. Tell me about it.

PADDINGTON: It's a flashing light.

MR. GRUBER: A flashing light?

PADDINGTON: In the garden at Number Thirty-Two, Windsor Gardens—and Mr. Brown's squash.

MR. GRUBER: You'd better begin at the beginning.

PADDINGTON: Yes, I suppose I had. You see, I've got a new flashlight and last night, when I was in bed, I shined it at the window by mistake.

Then I noticed that somebody was flashing a light outside in the garden—like a signal. So I flashed my light on and off three times and the light outside the window flashed three times as well.

MR. GRUBER: What did you do?

PADDINGTON: I pulled the bed-clothes over my head and went to sleep!

MR. GRUBER: I see.

PADDINGTON: Then, when I came down to breakfast this morning, Mr. Brown told me that somebody had stolen his prize squash.

MR. GRUBER: And you think that the two things are connected?

PADDINGTON: That's right and I thought I would like to catch whoever it is. Not just for the reward . . .

MR. GRUBER [*twinkling*]: Oh, there's a reward, is there?

PADDINGTON [*casually*]: Mr. Brown did mention it. Do

297

you remember that book you showed me once about the famous detective?

MR. GRUBER: Sherlock Holmes? Yes.

PADDINGTON: I would like to be able to catch criminals like he did. But I may need to disguise myself. It'll make things a lot easier.

MR. GRUBER: I think I can help you there, Mr. Brown. [*He takes down a cardboard box.*] Somebody sold this to me a long time ago. You can borrow it if you like.

PADDINGTON [*reading from the lid of the box*]: Master Detective's Disguise Outfit. Thank you very much, Mr. Gruber. May I look inside?

MR. GRUBER: Of course.

PADDINGTON: It looks very interesting. [*He takes out a magnifying glass.*] What's this, Mr. Gruber?

MR. GRUBER: That's a magnifying glass to look for clues.

PADDINGTON: Very useful. And here's a police whistle and some bottles and a pad.

MR. GRUBER: They're for fingerprints, and one of the bottles is full of invisible ink.

PADDINGTON: And a beard! Just what I need.

MR. GRUBER: Here. Try this old coat. It may be a bit big.

[*Paddington slips it on. It trails behind him.*]

PADDINGTON: Thank you very much, Mr. Gruber. [*He hooks the beard over his ears.*] How's that?

MR. GRUBER: Splendid!

PADDINGTON [*putting his bush hat on*]: I don't think anybody will recognize me now.

MR. GRUBER [*as Doctor Watson*]: Do you think it will be a difficult crime to solve, Mr. Holmes?

PADDINGTON: On the contrary. Elementary, my dear Watson. [*He tucks the disguise outfit under his arm and sails out.*]

# Scene 3

[*The living room at Number Thirty-Two, Windsor Gardens. There is a knock on the door. Mrs. Bird goes to answer it.*]

PADDINGTON [*in a deep voice*]: Good morning.

MRS. BIRD: Oh, hello, Paddington. I didn't expect you back so quickly.

PADDINGTON: I'm not Paddington, Mrs. Bird. I'm Sherlock Holmes—the famous detective.

MRS. BIRD: Yes, dear. Don't forget to wipe your feet.

MRS. BROWN [*coming in from the kitchen*]: Is Paddington back already? I thought he would be having lunch with Mr. Gruber.

MRS. BIRD: He's up to something, but I don't know what. He's just come back in a long overcoat, hidden behind a beard, and he looked very thoughtful.

MRS. BROWN: Oh, dear! Something always happens when he's like that.

[*Paddington enters, minus his disguise.*]

PADDINGTON: Hullo, Mrs. Brown.

MRS. BROWN: Hallo, Paddington.

PADDINGTON: I wonder if I could have a new battery for my flashlight?

MRS. BROWN: Is the other one dead already?

PADDINGTON: Yes. I've had to use it rather a lot lately.

MRS. BROWN: Here you are.

PADDINGTON: Thank you very much, Mrs. Brown. [*He goes into the hall.*]

MRS. BIRD: I wonder why he needs his flashlight?

[*Paddington comes back suddenly, making them jump.*]

PADDINGTON: Mrs. Brown, do you happen to have some rope I could borrow?

MRS. BROWN: I don't think I have any rope, but I've a plastic clothesline. Would that be any good?

PADDINGTON [*gravely*]: That would do very well.

MRS. BIRD: Here you are. [*She gives him the clothesline.*]

PADDINGTON: Thank you. [*He goes into the hall again.*]

MRS. BIRD: And what does he need those things for?

MRS. BROWN: I shudder to think.

PADDINGTON [*coming back suddenly again*]: There's just one more thing.

MRS. BIRD [*wearily*]: Yes, Paddington?

PADDINGTON: I wonder if I could take my lunch to my room today. I'm not very hungry at the moment, and I may feel like a marmalade sandwich later.

MRS. BROWN: Here you are, all ready and waiting for you. [*She hands him the sandwiches on a plate.*]

PADDINGTON: Thank you very much. [*He goes off as Mrs. Brown and Mrs. Bird shake their heads in amazement. After a moment they go off, too.*]

[*Blackout. After a moment the alarm clock sounds in the distance.*]

[*Paddington yawns as he enters.*]

PADDINGTON: Midnight, that's the best time to catch criminals. [*He switches on his flashlight and shines it through the window.*] Nothing there, but I'd better be prepared. [*He puts on his beard, overcoat, and hat and picks up his case.*] I'll go and hide in the greenhouse.

[*He goes off. A moment later, a shadowy figure appears at the front of the stage. He is carrying a lantern, but is muffled up in a scarf so we don't see his face. As he reaches the front door, Paddington comes along carrying the clothesline and pillowcase. The figure walks away and Paddington creeps up behind him. The figure turns round suddenly, but Paddington ducks and isn't noticed. The next time the figure turns away Paddington seizes his opportunity, pops the pillow-*

*case and lasso over his head and runs around him with the clothesline, pinning his arms to his sides so that he can't remove the pillowcase. When he is secured, Paddington blows his whistle.*]

PADDINGTON: It's no good struggling. You've met your match! [*The figure answers with a muffled snort and struggles to get free.*] Be quiet, you will have your chance to speak when the police get here. [*Paddington leads him indoors just as the Police Officer arrives on the scene.*]

POLICE OFFICER: Hullo. Hullo. What's going on here?

PADDINGTON: Good evening, Officer, that was quick.

POLICE OFFICER: I just happened to be passing, sir, and I heard your whistle. What's the trouble?

PADDINGTON: I've captured a burglar! I think he's the one who took Mr. Brown's squash.

POLICE OFFICER: Mr. Brown's squash?

PADDINGTON: That's right. I thought I saw a flashing light. Then I saw a shadowy figure. I couldn't see his face but from the way he walked, I'm sure it had a nasty look on it.

POLICE OFFICER: Well sir, let's see, shall we? I'll switch the light on. [*He switches on the light and then jerks the rope which Paddington has been holding. The figure spins round until he comes to the end of it. The Police Officer undoes the lasso and the figure wrenches the pillowcase from his head.*]

PADDINGTON: Oh, dear! [*He puts his flashlight down.*]

MR. CURRY: What is the meaning of this assault?

POLICE OFFICER [*to Paddington*]: You were right. He *has* got a nasty look on his face. You are accused of acting in a suspicious manner.

MR. CURRY: Suspicious manner! I was going about my own business.

POLICE OFFICER: At midnight? With a lantern?

MR. CURRY: I happen to collect moths and the light of the lantern attracts them. [*He suddenly sees Paddington.*] Bear! I might have known you would be at the bottom of this.

PADDINGTON: I'm sorry, Mr. Curry. [*He takes off his beard.*]

MR. CURRY: Not as sorry as you will be!

POLICE OFFICER: Hmmmm. And what were you doing prowling round the house in disguise, young fellow—I mean, bear?

[*Mr. and Mrs. Brown, awakened by the noise, come onstage.*]

POLICE OFFICER: Unless you can explain yourself . . .

MR. BROWN: Whatever is the matter?

PADDINGTON: Well, I'm afraid it's a bit complicated. You see, it all happened because of your squash, Mr. Brown . . . the one you were getting ready for the show. I was trying to catch the thief.

MR. BROWN: I don't see how my squash has anything to do with this noise.

MRS. BROWN: I think I'm beginning to understand. . . . Paddington was trying to catch the person who took it. But I'm afraid he didn't stand a chance.

POLICE OFFICER: Why not, madam?

MRS. BROWN: I was going to tell you sooner or later, Henry. It's my fault really, you see . . . I cut your squash by mistake!

MR. BROWN: You did? You cut my prize squash?

MRS. BROWN: Well, I didn't realize it was your prize one. And you know how fond you are of stuffed squash. We had it for dinner on Thursday.

MR. BROWN: We had it for dinner? How could you?

POLICE OFFICER: Here, not so fast, sir, I can't get it all down. Has anybody else anything to say?

MR. CURRY: Yes, I have. I demand that this bear is punished. Springing out on an innocent member of the public. I shall demand damages.

[*Paddington is very unhappy at the trouble that he has caused. He decides to creep quietly away before anybody notices.*]

POLICE OFFICER [*to Mr. Brown*]: What do you say to that, sir?

MR. BROWN: As my squash seems to have caused all this trouble, perhaps I had better try to find a solution to the problem. This morning I promised a reward to anybody who found out who took the squash. Now, through you, Mr. Curry, we have actually found the culprit. [*Mrs. Brown looks guilty.*] Suppose I gave the reward to *you*. Would that satisfy you?

MR. CURRY: Well, I don't know—

MR. BROWN: Say five pounds?

MR. CURRY [*after a moment's hesitation*]: Very well, but it mustn't happen again. And I demand an apology.

MR. BROWN: I'm sure Paddington didn't mean any harm, but of course, he will apologize.

MRS. BROWN: Where is he?

[*Judy and Jonathan, who have appeared by this time, begin to look for him.*]

MRS. BIRD [*enters*]: Whatever is going on here?

JUDY: It's Paddington. He's missing.

JONATHAN: He isn't in his room. I've just looked in there.

JUDY: And all his things have gone.

JONATHAN: His suitcase . . .

JUDY: His clothes . . . and his picture of Aunt Lucy . . .

JONATHAN: Everything!

MRS. BROWN: Where on earth can he have got to?

MR. BROWN: There's only one thing for it, we must organize a search party. [*He picks up the flashlight.*]

MRS. BROWN: But where can we look? We don't even know where to start.

MRS. BIRD [*grimly, as she puts on her coat*]: I do . . . follow me. If you want my opinion, there isn't a moment to lose. [*Mrs. Bird hurries out, followed by the rest of the family.*]

MR. CURRY: Hey! Hold on! Wait for me! [*He hurries after them.*]

# Scene 4

[*Paddington Station. It is set with luggage and parcels. There is an announcement: "The train about to leave from Platform One is the Boat-train Special." A guard's whistle sounds. The Browns rush across stage, but the train is already moving off. A moment later they walk sadly back on.*]

JUDY: Too late!

MR. BROWN: We don't *know* he was on it.

JONATHAN: I bet he was. I bet Mrs. Bird was right.

JUDY: She usually is. Besides, you heard what they said.

JONATHAN: It was the Boat-train Special!

MRS. BROWN: Goodness knows where he'll end up.

MRS. BIRD [*following on behind*]: If only I'd thought of it before.

JUDY: Can't we ring up the station at the other end?

MR. BROWN: We can. But knowing Paddington, he might get off anywhere.

MRS. BIRD: Things just won't be the same without that bear.

MR. BROWN: You can say that again! [*He turns to leave, and as he does so, Paddington pops up from behind the parcels and raises his hat. Mr. Brown sees him and shines the flashlight in his direction.*] Paddington!

PADDINGTON: Hullo, Mr. Brown.

THE BROWNS [*chorus*]: Paddington!

JUDY: You didn't go after all!

PADDINGTON: I did. But I missed the train. I seem to cause so much trouble that I thought you wouldn't want me to stay any more, so I thought I'd better go back to Darkest Peru. [*He reaches behind the parcels and takes a jar of marmalade, which he puts in his suitcase. Then he holds up his picture of Aunt Lucy.*] I haven't even had time to pack properly.

MRS. BROWN: Not want you to stay?

MRS. BIRD: Of course, we want you to stay.

JUDY: Even Mr. Curry wants you to stay. Don't you, Mr. Curry?

MR. CURRY: Well, er . . . Hmmmmmmmph.

MR. BROWN [*waving his flashlight in the direction of Paddington's photograph frame as he talks*]: Besides, if you go, who's going to eat all the marmalade?

MRS. BIRD: Exactly! The cupboard's full.

PADDINGTON [*peering at the glass on the photograph excitedly*]: Would you mind doing that again, Mr. Brown?

MR. BROWN: Do what again?

PADDINGTON: Wave your flashlight about.

MR. BROWN: You mean . . . like that? [*He repeats the action.*]

PADDINGTON: That's it! That's what I saw the other night! Oh, dear!

JUDY: Can anyone join in?

JONATHAN: Or is it a secret?

PADDINGTON: It's a reflection, Mr. Brown. You see, when I shone that flashlight at my bedroom window the other night, I thought I saw someone signaling back at me. Only it wasn't. . . . I thought it was the man who'd stolen your squash. But it must have been the reflection from my flashlight all the time. . . .

MRS. BROWN [*looks at the others*]: Paddington . . .

PADDINGTON: Yes, Mrs. Brown?

MRS. BROWN: You're incorrigible!

PADDINGTON [*hotly*]: I'm not, Mrs. Brown. I'm a bear!

JUDY: And a jolly good bear at that. [*She takes his paw.*]

JONATHAN: Hear! Hear!

## CHECK FOR UNDERSTANDING

1. Why was Mr. Brown upset?
2. How did Mr. Gruber feel about Paddington?
3. What helpful deed did Paddington try to do?
4. What went wrong with Paddington's efforts?
5. What sort of man was Mr. Curry?
6. Why weren't the Browns angry with Paddington?
7. Do you think Paddington learned a lesson from this incident? Explain your answer.

## WRITE ABOUT *"Paddington Turns Detective"*

After a crime is committed, the police must write a report telling about it. Write the report given by the policeman whom Paddington summoned. Make your report factual, describing the setting, the crime, the people involved, and the outcome.

## Compound Words

When Paddington was in bed, he saw a light in the garden *outside* his window. He flashed his *flashlight* three times. Then he pulled the *bedclothes* over his head and went to sleep.

How are the words *outside, flashlight,* and *bedclothes* alike? As you can see, each of these words is made up of two smaller words. The word *outside* contains the words *out* and *side.* The word *flashlight* contains the words *flash* and *light. Bedclothes* contains the words *bed* and *clothes.* These three words are known as **compound words.**

A compound word is a word that is made up of two smaller words. Often, you can figure out the meaning of a compound word by combining the meanings of the smaller words it contains. Therefore, it is important to recognize compound words when you see them.

For example, did you know the meaning of *bedclothes* when you first saw this word in the story? By finding the words *bed* and *clothes,* you may have figured out that *bedclothes* are the sheets and blankets on a bed.

If you cannot figure out the meaning of a compound word by combining the meanings of the words, or by the context, then you should use a dictionary.

> When Paddington turned detective, he wore a long *overcoat* as a disguise. He also used some bottles and a pad for *fingerprints.*

The words *overcoat* and *fingerprints* are compound words. What are the words that make up these compounds? Show how you can figure out the meaning of *overcoat* and *fingerprints* by combining the meanings of the shorter words.

Below are two sentences from the play. Find the compound words in these sentences. What are the shorter words that make up the compounds?

Paddington seizes his opportunity, pops the pillowcase over his head and runs around him with the clothesline.

He reaches behind the parcels and takes a jar of marmalade, which he puts in his suitcase.

Sometimes compound words are not written together. They are written as two separate words. For example, *book club, high tide,* and *ground crew* are compound words. You may remember that Paddington used a *magnifying glass* to look for clues. *Magnifying glass* is a compound word, too.

There is one other kind of compound word. It is created by using a hyphen. *Hand-me-down* and *air-cooled* are examples of this kind of compound.

The next story you are going to read is "The Indianapolis Ten-Mile Bicycle Race." In the story, you will discover the following compounds. Figure out the meaning of each by combining the meanings of the words in the compounds.

| | | |
|---|---|---|
| sidewalk | grandstand | finish line |
| headstand | gateman | halfway |

# THE INDIANAPOLIS TEN-MILE BICYCLE RACE

by MARY SCIOSCIA

People are often surprised at what they can do if they only try. Marshall Taylor always wins whenever he has a bicycle race with his brothers. He also enjoys doing bicycle tricks. But, in this story, he is amazed by how much more he is capable of doing.

What does Marshall do that surprises even him? What is the result of his action?

" 'Hay and Willit's bicycle store. Best in Indianapolis. This gold medal will go the winner of the ten-mile race. May 10, 1892,' " Marshall Taylor read.

"I bet you could win that race," said his little brother Carlton.

"Not me," said Marshall. "I'm not that fast. Hey, Carlton. Look how wide the sidewalk is here in front of the store. Want me to show you some of the bike tricks now?"

Carlton clapped his hands. "Yes. Show me, Marshall."

Marshall lay on the bicycle seat and pushed the pedals with his hands. He helped Carlton do the same trick. People walking past the store stopped to look.

Marshall squatted on the bicycle seat and juggled three pennies. Carlton tried squatting on the seat, too. He couldn't do it. Marshall did the trick again.

More people stopped to watch.

A tall thin boy said, "That's a stupid trick. I bet you fall on your head."

A small girl said, "George Pepper, mind your manners."

"Go lay an egg!" said George Pepper.

More people stopped to watch. A coachman pulled his carriage over to the curb to see Marshall's tricks.

Marshall did a headstand on his bicycle seat. Then he rode his bicycle backward. Suddenly, the

bicycle shop door opened and Mr. Hay stood in the doorway.

"Now you're in for it," jeered George Pepper. "You're in real trouble now!"

"Young man," called Mr. Hay. "I want to speak to you."

Marshall walked the bicycle over to Mr. Hay.

"Yes, sir?" said Marshall.

"Where did you learn those tricks?" asked Mr. Hay.

"I made them up, sir. I was just showing my little brother. He likes to see them."

"I don't wonder," said Mr. Hay.

"I'm sorry, sir, if we disturbed you."

"Disturbed us! Not at all! Those are the best bicycle tricks I've ever seen. My partner and I could use a boy like you. How would you like a job? We need someone to dust and sweep the store every day and to put coal in the potbellied stove. You could come here after school and on Saturdays to do those jobs. And if there is time, you could do your bicycle tricks in front of our store. It will make people want to come to this bicycle shop."

"Yes, sir!" cried Marshall.

"Start Monday after school," said Mr. Hay.

"I'll be here!" said Marshall.

Marshall liked his job. He didn't even mind the dusting. Every day he took the medal out and polished it carefully. Once, when he was alone in the

store, Marshall unpinned the gold medal and stuck it onto his shirt. He looked at his reflection in the glass case. He turned a little so the light glinted on the gold.

It was fun to pretend that Mr. Hay had given him the medal because he could ride faster than anybody else.

"But what if Mr. Hay sees me wearing this medal?" Marshall thought. "He might get angry."

Marshall put the medal back into the case.

One Saturday Mr. Hay said, "Today you and I are going to spend the day at the bicycle race track. I need your help taking bicycles, extra wheels, and riding clothes out to the track. We usually sell quite a few items on racing days. Mr. Willit and I thought you'd enjoy working there with me. And you'll be able to see the big ten-mile race, too."

Hundreds of people were in the grandstand. Children stood by the fence at the edge of the track and looked through the metal crisscrosses. Mr. Hay gave his tickets to the gateman, and he and Marshall walked inside to a booth near the edge of the track. They set out the wheels and shirts and shorts on the counter. Mr. Hay leaned the bicycles against the side of the booth.

More than a hundred racers in bright jersey tops and black shorts stood near the starting line. Beside every racer there was someone holding the bicycle.

"Each rider needs someone to push him off," said Mr. Hay.

"Can't they push off with one of their own feet?" Marshall asked.

Mr. Hay shook his head. "Racers' feet have to be clipped to the pedals. And they have a fixed gear."

At the judges' stand, a man stood up and shouted through a huge megaphone, "Attention, everyone! All those entering the one-mile race, line up at the starting line."

"One-mile race?" said Marshall. "Isn't it ten miles?"

"There will be several short races before the main event," said Mr. Hay.

"I see a lot of our customers lining up to be in the race," said Marshall.

"Land's sakes, Marshall! You just gave me an idea. You should ride in one of the short races. It would remind people of our store."

"Would they let me?"

"I'll ask the judges," said Mr. Hay.

When Mr. Hay came back, he said, "You can ride in the next one-mile race. Come with me to the dressing room and put on those shorts and this yellow shirt. Choose any one of the bikes we brought."

✳  ✳

At the starting line, Mr. Hay said, "Each time around the track is one lap. Five laps make a mile. Don't worry if you forget how many laps you've gone. When you hear the bell ring, you know it is the bell lap. That means one left to go."

Marshall got on the bicycle. Mr. Hay held it steady while Marshall clipped his feet onto the pedals. A tall thin boy in a red shirt got in line next to Marshall.

"George Pepper!" thought Marshall, wishing George weren't right next to him.

"What are you doing in this race?" said George. "You won't last one lap."

"Come on, George, leave him alone," said another racer. "That's the boy who does those good tricks at the bicycle shop."

"You mean those stupid tricks," said George. "I hope he gets thrown out of this race."

The man in charge blew a whistle. All the racers leaned over their handlebars. Their helpers held the bicycles steady. The man raised his pistol in the air.

"One! Two! Three!" the starter shouted.

*Bang!* went the pistol.

Mr. Hay gave Marshall a strong push. He shot ahead of George Pepper. A tall boy got ahead of Marshall. Four more people got ahead. Marshall rode past one of them. George came up even with Marshall.

"I'm warning you," said George. "You better stay behind me if you know what's good for you."

Marshall pushed his legs as hard as he could. But George got ahead.

Around and around the racers went. Now there were seven people ahead of Marshall.

*Ding, ding, ding,* the bell rang.

One more lap to go for the mile. Marshall speeded up. A racer crossed the finish line. Two more. Another. Next was George Pepper in the red shirt. Right after George came the tall boy.

Then Marshall crossed the line. Mr. Hay hurried over to help Marshall stop.

"You came in number seven. That's great!" said Mr. Hay.

"It wasn't very good," said Marshall. "Six people beat me."

"But you beat over forty people. And you've never even been in a race before. You're good enough to try the ten-mile race."

"Oh, no," said Marshall. "I could never win that."

"No," agreed Mr. Hay. "You couldn't win. But I think you could finish. Try it, Marshall. If you get too

320

tired, you just stop. Many racers will drop out before the fifty laps are done."

During the next race, Mr. Hay spoke to the judges again. Marshall rested with the other riders in the grassy center of the track.

"Good news," said Mr. Hay, joining Marshall. "You can try the ten-mile race."

Marshall wheeled his bicycle over to the starting line.

"Don't try to go too fast at first," said Mr. Hay. "Just keep up with the others, if you can. Save your energy for the sprints."

"What is a sprint?" asked Marshall.

"A sprint means going extra fast for one lap. Whoever passes the finish line first gets points toward winning."

"How will I know when it's time to sprint?"

"The bell rings at the start of the fifth lap. Each mile there will be a sprint race on the fifth lap."

Marshall looked at the riders lining up. "Whew!" he said. "It looks as if all the racers entered this race."

Mr. Hay nodded. "A hundred and seventeen bike racers are in the ten-mile race."

Marshall's bicycle wobbled a little as Marshall bent down to clip his feet onto the pedals. Mr. Hay steadied it.

Marshall could feel his heart thumping hard. His hands felt slippery on the bicycle handles.

"Here," said Mr. Hay. "Use my handkerchief to dry your hands."

The whistle blew. Marshall's legs felt shaky.

"One!" shouted the man. "Two! Three!"

*Bang!*

Mr. Hay shoved Marshall's bicycle so hard, Marshall could smell the dust that flew up. Marshall pushed his legs down. Around and around went the wheels.

The riders rode in a close pack. Two bicycles bumped and one fell. Marshall swerved around the fallen bicycle and rider. He almost hit another bicycle. Marshall swerved again. It was George Pepper's bicycle.

"Hey, you," shouted George. "Out of my way. If you touch my bike, you're dead!"

*Ding, ding, ding!* The bell lap!

Marshall pulled ahead of the pack for the sprint. George Pepper passed him. Three more riders passed him. Then two more. Marshall pushed his legs hard. He passed one rider, then another. He crossed the finish line.

The first sprint was over. He could hear the crowd cheering. Nine more miles to go! Marshall wondered who had won that sprint. It was hard to know who was ahead, because the riders kept going around and around the track. When Marshall passed someone, he wondered if that person had already done more laps than he had.

Around and around they all went. Marshall's legs ached. His chest felt tight.

"I hope I can finish the first half of the race," he said to himself.

*Ding, ding, ding!* Another bell lap. Everyone pushed harder. Marshall shot forward. He passed George Pepper.

George caught up with Marshall and passed him. George crossed the finish line just ahead of Marshall, but it was impossible for Marshall to know who had won the sprint. The racers were no longer riding in a close pack. They were strung out along the whole track. A few riders had dropped out.

Around and around. Around and around.

When the bell rang, Marshall couldn't remember which sprint it was. His breath came in noisy puffs. More riders dropped out of the race.

Marshall's throat felt dry. His mouth tasted dusty. His legs hurt.

"I want to drop out," Marshall thought. "I can't make the halfway mark."

Someone shouted, "Hurray, Marshall Taylor!"

It made Marshall feel glad. He felt stronger. "Maybe I can finish a few more laps," he thought.

His bicycle went faster. Around the track. Around and around. There were more bell laps and more sprints. Marshall lost count. Around and around. His damp shirt stuck to his back. His legs ached. His back was sore from being bent over the handlebars.

The people in the grandstand stamped their feet and cheered. He heard Mr. Hay, standing at the edge of the track, shout, "Last lap coming up next!"

*Ding, ding, ding!*

Marshall pushed with all his strength. The wheels seemed to say, "Got to finish. Got to finish."

*Scrunch.*

He heard the sound of clashing metal and felt his rear wheel being pushed.

"Out of my way," shouted George, trying to knock him down.

A man at the edge of the track blew his whistle.

"Foul!" he shouted. "George Pepper. Over to the side!"

George pretended he didn't hear. He tried to get ahead of Marshall. The man blew his whistle again. Marshall rode past George. Several riders seemed to be riding exactly even with one another. Marshall speeded over the finish line. Everyone was so close, he couldn't tell who was ahead or behind. His bicycle was going so fast he couldn't stop. He went around another lap to slow down.

Marshall heard the crowd shout something that sounded like "Marshall Taylor! Marshall Taylor!" Hats and programs flew into the air.

Mr. Hay hurried over to Marshall to hold his bicycle. He hugged him.

"You won, Marshall. You won!"

"Who? Me!" said Marshall.

The judges held up their hands to quiet the crowd. Then a man with a megaphone shouted, "Marshall Taylor, the winner by sixteen seconds! Marshall Taylor has won the annual Indianapolis ten-mile bicycle race!"

The crowd cheered and clapped and stamped their feet.

Mr. Hay and Marshall walked to the judges' platform. A judge gave Marshall the gold medal.

A thunder of applause came from the audience.

Marshall felt as if he were in the middle of a dream.

## CHECK FOR UNDERSTANDING

1. How did Marshall get the job at the bicycle store?
2. Why did Mr. Hay want Marshall to ride in the one-mile race?
3. What did Marshall do that surprised even him?
4. What was the result of his action?
5. What character traits did Marshall possess that made it possible for him to win the race?
6. What do you think George Pepper will say to Marshall after the race?

## WRITE ABOUT *"The Indianapolis Ten-Mile Bicycle Race"*

Imagine that you are a sports reporter reporting on the Indianapolis bicycle race. Write a news article telling what happened in the race. Keep your article factual and brief.

# On Our Bikes

by LILLIAN MORRISON

The roads to the beach
      are winding
  we glide down
      breeze-whipped
curving
      past hills of sand
  pedal and coast
      through wide smell of the sea
      old familiar sunfeel
  windwallop.

Race you to the water's edge!

## Multiple Causes of an Event

Why are you in school today? If you were asked that, you would probably give one answer. It might be, "because school is important," or it might be, "because my parents want me to learn."

Actually, there are probably several different causes for your sitting in school reading this right now. Some of them are easy to think of, and others aren't. For example, one cause of your being in school right now is that there *is* a school. You wouldn't come to school if there were no teachers or classroom. Another reason you are in school today is that you have some way to get there. If you took a bus, for example, one cause of your being in school is the bus and the driver who brought you to school.

Behind every human action is not just one cause, but many. Behind every bite of scrambled eggs you eat, there is a chicken, a farmer, an egg truck, a grocer, a cook, and an appetite. Because this is true of real life, most stories show more than one cause for an important action or event. Some of the causes in a story are easy to see, while others are not. To understand why things happen in a story the way they do, it is important to figure out all of the causes. In some stories, it is not one cause by itself that is more important than any other. Instead, it is the addition of many small causes that finally add up to the event occurring.

One way to find out all the causes of an event or action is to ask yourself this question: What things had to exist or happen to make this possible?

Think about the story you just read, "The Indianapolis

Ten-Mile Bicycle Race." Would you say that there is just one cause for Marshall's entering the bicycle race? What things had to exist or happen to make it possible for Marshall to enter the race?

- Would he have entered the race if he hadn't been so interested in winning the trophy?
- Would he have entered the race if he hadn't been hired by Mr. Hay?
- Would he have entered the race if Mr. Hay hadn't needed his help at the race track?
- Would he have entered the race if Mr. Hay hadn't suggested it?
- Would he have entered the race if Mr. Hay hadn't given him a bike and riding clothes?
- Would he have entered the race if Mr. Hay hadn't encouraged him after the one-mile race?
- Would he have entered the race if the judges hadn't let him come in as a late entry?

The answer to all of these questions is no. You understand the accidental way Marshall entered the race when you look at all the small reasons for his doing so.

The next selection you are going to read is about Lee Trevino, the famous golfer. As you read it, think of all the causes that led to Lee Trevino's winning his first U.S. Open Championship.

# I Never Had a Lesson

by LEE TREVINO and SAM BLAIR

Often people must work hard to overcome great difficulties on the way to success. This autobiographical selection tells of Lee Trevino's struggle and ultimate triumph in the world of golf.

What was the biggest difficulty that Lee Trevino had to overcome? How did he overcome it?

Most young people today first watch golf on television. But my first view of the game was from a field in Dallas, Texas.

When my grandfather moved us into an old house in the pasture off Walnut Hill Lane, I noticed people doing something but had no idea what it was they were doing. I didn't know they were playing golf. I always figured you spent your time outdoors farming, fishing, or hunting.

That was 1947 and I was seven years old. Lee Buck Trevino, country boy, had moved to the big city of Dallas. I didn't know Ben Hogan and Byron Nelson, the world-famous Texas golfers, from the Lone Ranger and Tonto.

But there I was, living 100 yards from the seventh fairway at the Dallas Athletic Club course, and after a lot of watching, I did figure out one thing. There was a rough on the right side of No. 7. I went over there and started finding golf balls.

One day a guy came over and asked, "Have you got any golf balls?"

"Yes, sir," I said. He took the five I showed him and handed me a dollar bill. That excited me.

I told myself, "Maybe I can make some money in this game."

Pretty soon I walked across Coit Road to the clubhouse. I hung around the caddy shed and began to learn about the game. I met Big Mac, the caddy master, and by the time I was eight I was carrying a bag. It was a lot different from the life I knew on the farm, but it was fun. And the money I made caddying helped put food on the table. My mother and grandfather needed anything they could get.

I never knew my father, but my grandfather was the best

father I could have ever had.

When I was very young he was a tenant farmer, working for a man who owned some land near Garland. (Garland is a suburb east of Dallas and a good-sized city, but then it was just a country town.) My grandfather was born in Monterrey, Mexico, but moved to Texas as a young boy. He worked hard all his life for little money.

By the time I was five, I was out in the fields, too. I thought hard work was just how life was.

When the cotton was ready for harvest in September, I pulled a bag through the fields, filling it with bolls. Then we planted onions. Whew! That was the worst smell in the world! When we had a hailstorm, it would beat down those onions so much we'd cry for a month.

When I was just big enough to walk, my grandfather took me out with him, hunting rabbits and crawdad fishing. We'd bring a batch of crawdads in and my mother would serve us fried tails for supper. We thought we were just surviving, but today that's an expensive delicacy.

We had an old 1929 Model A Ford, a two-seater with a tar top, and one day we were caught in a storm. We jumped in the car, but hailstones tore right through that roof and my grandfather covered me with his body. It's strange, but that's one of the things I remember most about him.

A good friend named Joe Valle worked in Dallas, and he told my grandfather there were jobs open at Hillcrest Cemetery. Soon we were packing to leave the farm. My grandfather was going to work as a gravedigger.

The pay wasn't much. When he retired years later he still wasn't making over $40 a week. But the work was steady and a house was included.

I'll never forget going to that old, unpainted house. It was just a four-room shack with some cottonwood trees and a lake out front. There was no plumbing, electricity, or wallpaper, and there were no windows. One room, which turned out to be the kitchen, didn't have a floor. It was surrounded by sunflowers and grass six feet high, with cattle roaming about. It was ugly, but it was something new. It was home.

We lived north of Northwest Highway, and there wasn't much nearby. The cemetery was a mile south, and there were a couple of houses on Hillcrest about a mile west. Then there was DAC Country Club, which became Glen Lakes Country Club a few

years later when DAC moved to a new location. Today this is in the heart of booming north Dallas. Northpark Shopping Center sprawls across the field where I hunted rabbits, and there are high-rise office buildings in all directions. The golf course where I learned to play is gone and so is our shack.

DAC was one of the top clubs in town. Graham Ross was the pro and Dick Carter the assistant, and they had a lot of players out there. Big Mac, the caddy master, often had as many as 130 caddies working on Saturday. I caddied primarily for the same men all the time. They seemed to like me. I was a good caddy, a hustling kid who didn't mind the work. If they wanted to hit balls late, I went out and chased them until dark.

That course is where I started my game. There were three holes behind the caddy shed—one about 100 yards, another about 125, and another about 60. We'd find some old clubs and start hitting. I'd hit a shot and throw the club 50 yards to another guy where he could hit. As soon as he'd hit, he'd throw the club to another guy. It might take 30 minutes to play one 100-yard hole with clubs flying around like that, but it was great experience. It sharpened my game and my competitive spirit.

From playing back of the caddy shed to winning the U.S. and British Opens was a long, long trip. But I made it, and I never had a lesson. Jack Grout taught Nicklaus how to play. Stan Thirsk taught Watson how to play. *I* taught myself how to play.

My favorite hangout was Hardy's Driving Range. It was a couple of miles from my house, on Lovers' Lane near Greenville, and I first went there one night to hit golf balls when I was eight. I was barefoot and wearing some old tattered jeans and a T-shirt. I went with Jack Shawver, a real tall kid about twelve years old. He played golf all his life and couldn't understand why he never could beat me.

Well, my arms weren't much bigger than the club shafts, but I could knock a ball out of sight. Hardy Greenwood, who owned the range, watched me hit balls that night, and he never forgot. Every once in a while through the years, Hardy would ask about me and what I was doing, like he had a special interest in me. I sure had a special interest in his driving range. I would have gone there and hit balls in the middle of the night if I could.

My junior golf career began when I was 15 and entered the *Dallas Times Herald* tournament. That's where it ended, too.

I qualified with a 77 at Stevens Park, the municipal course in the Oak Cliff section of Dallas. Strange as it may seem, that was the first complete round of golf I'd ever played. I'd hit nine billion balls by then and played a lot of competitive golf. But that was always as a caddy, sneaking in a few holes out of sight of the clubhouse or on that little layout behind the caddy shed at Glen Lakes. This time I was in official match play, trying to win the championship of the fifteen-year-old division.

In the first round I drew a left-hander, whose name I can't remember, and beat him pretty badly. The second round I drew a player named Frankie Galloway. He had a lot of knowledge about the game. I hit the ball awfully long, but he hit it nine miles. He beat me on the seventh hole.

That was the extent of my

amateur career except for some competition in the Marine Corps a few years later. I only played in the *Times Herald* tournament because Hardy Greenwood entered me in it and furnished me with a complete set of clubs and golf shoes. I was working full-time at Hardy's Driving Range then and I loved golf, but I didn't think I could ever play well enough to have a career. Hardy saw a future for me in golf before I did.

Later I worked at Glen Lakes a few months, and then Hardy sent his handyman, Norman Scott, by my house to ask me to come to see him at the range. Hardy asked me if I wanted to work for him. "Doing what?" I asked. "Picking up golf balls at the range," he said. I guess I didn't act too eager, so Hardy said, "Are you going to mow greens and fairways all your life, or do you want to be a golfer?"

Hardy's encouragement got me moving. For years after that I worked at it. I hit thousands of balls at Hardy's range, played golf while I was a Marine and later spent my time at Tenison Park, a public course in Dallas. In 1965 I moved to El Paso, Texas, to sharpen my skills as the pro and general handyman at little Horizon Hills Country Club. And in 1968, at the age of 28, I won my first U.S. Open championship at Oak Hill in Rochester, N.Y.—a long way from that field in North Dallas.

*Lee Trevino's successful golf career had only begun. He went on to win the British Open in 1971 and 1972 and the U.S. Open once again in 1971. He was the first golfer ever to win the U.S., British, and Canadian Opens in one year. His name ranks among the greatest golfers in the world.*

## CHECK FOR UNDERSTANDING

1. Where did Lee Trevino grow up?
2. How did Lee Trevino get involved with the game of golf?
3. What was the biggest difficulty that Lee Trevino had to overcome?
4. How did he overcome it?
5. How do you think Lee Trevino felt when he compared himself to golfers who were taught by pros?
6. Do you think Lee Trevino would have been as successful if he had not been poor? Explain your answer.

**WRITE ABOUT** *"I Never Had a Lesson"*

Lee Trevino never had a lesson, but there were certain things he did in order to become a great golfer. Pretend that a young golfer wrote to Lee and asked for advice on how to become a successful player. Write the letter that Lee would write to the young golfer.

# STUDY SKILLS

## Choosing an Appropriate Source

In the story we just read, "I Never Had a Lesson," we learned that Lee Trevino, a champion golf player, never had a lesson in golf. He taught himself by watching other people play and then practicing.

Suppose you saw a soccer game one day and got interested in the game. You decided that you wanted to learn to play. You could watch people play. But often, when someone makes a good play or a good kick, it's hard to know exactly how the player was able to do it. There is another way we can learn how to do something, or get facts about something. We can read about it.

One very good place to get all kinds of information is an **encyclopedia**. Your local library or your school library will have an encyclopedia. Because it covers many different subjects, an encyclopedia usually cannot fit into one **volume**. Usually it is made up of many volumes. How do you know which one to use?

The information in an encyclopedia is arranged alphabetically, according to subject. In some encyclopedias,

on the spine of each volume, there are **guide letters**. On others, there are words as a guide.

If you were looking up *animals*, which volume would you check in each set of encyclopedias?

## Key Word

You want to get information on how to play a good game of soccer. Should you look it up under *games* or *soccer*? What is the **key word**? If you look up *games*, you might see an article on games like marbles or hopscotch. That's not what you want. Soccer is an important enough game to have a whole article on it. So you look up *soccer*. *Soccer* is your key word.

## Guide Words

When you open the volume, you will see **guide words** on the top corner of each page. These help you to locate your subject more quickly. Let us say you open the volume and you turn to a page with the following guide words: *Squirrel, Sri Lanka*. These words show that you have to look a bit more to the front of the volume for *soccer*.

Aardvark-Air    Akron-Blowfish    Bluebird-Cat

ENCYCLOPEDIA III

(The articles are arranged alphabetically, and *So* comes before *Sq.*)

When you locate the soccer article, you'll see a lot of information there, covering quite a few pages. It gives you the rules of the game and describes the game step-by-step. There may be a diagram of the field showing each player's position and pictures showing various soccer skills. The text will tell you how to do the various skills: how to kick, pass, fake, and dribble. You will also be able to read about the history of soccer.

At the end of many encyclopedia articles, there will be other key words you could look up in the encyclopedia

that tell even more about the subject. For example, after the soccer article, it might say: "See also *Pelé, the world-famous soccer star from Brazil.*" You might want to read about Pelé. So you will pull out the *P* volume.

A good way to find out more is to read an entire book about soccer. You can look for one in the library. How would you go about finding a soccer book in the library? The thing to do is to look in the **card catalog.** There are three different kinds of cards in the card catalog: **author cards**, **title cards**, and **subject cards**. If you want books on soccer, pull out the *S* drawer of the subject catalog and look for cards that say *soccer* on the first line. The cards in the file are arranged alphabetically. Would *soccer* come before or after *sand*? (*after*) Would *soccer* come before or after *stamps*? (*before*)

You may find that the library has quite a few books on soccer. Each book is listed on a separate card. There is certain information on the card. It gives you the title of the book, the author's name, the number of pages, the publisher, the date the book was published, and a very short description of what is in the book.

The information on the card helps you decide (1) whether the book is one that will interest you and (2) how to find it.

This is what a subject card looks like:

---

796.33-S


SOCCER
Sullivan, George
Better soccer for boys and girls by George Sullivan. New York. Dodd, Mead, and Company, 1978. 64 pp. illustrated with photographs.

Discusses the rules, equipment, and techniques of soccer, the fastest-growing team sport in the United States.

---

An important bit of information on the card is the number you see in the upper-left corner of the card. This is the **call number**. Nonfiction books are arranged on library shelves according to their call number.

Fiction stories are shelved alphabetically, according to the author's name. *Little Women* by Louisa May Alcott would be in the *A*'s. Biography is usually in a different section, and is arranged in a different way. It is arranged alphabetically — but according to the name of the *subject* of the biography. So, the book *Jane Goodall: Living Chimp Style*, a biography of Jane Goodall by Mary V. Fox, would be in the biography section in the *G*'s.

Nonfiction is arranged according to subject. It would be very difficult to find a particular nonfiction book if you did not know its call number.

The call number on a book's card is also on the spine of the book. So, to find *Better Soccer for Boys and Girls*, look first for the 700's section of nonfiction. Then look for the particular book. If you are lucky, it will be there. If not, there may be another soccer book.

Here is a list of books dealing with soccer. Which of them is likely to best suit your purpose, to learn how to become a better soccer player?

1. *Soccer for Young Champions* by Robert J. Antonacci. McGraw-Hill, Inc., 1978.
2. *Heroes of Soccer* by Larry Adler. Julian Messner, Division of Simon and Schuster, Inc., 1980.
3. *Scott and Todd and the Soccer Gang* by Louise K. Lief. Magic Carpet, 1980.
4. *The Best Sports Book in the Whole World* by Mauri Kunnas. Crown Publishers, Inc., 1980.
5. *Better Soccer for Boys and Girls* by George Sullivan. Dodd, Mead & Company, 1978.

*Soccer for Young Champions*. It is nonfiction, and the title seems to show that the book tells you how to become a champion. Good possibility.

*Heroes of Soccer*. The title indicates that it is about star soccer players. It might be interesting, but probably would not be too helpful for your purpose.

*Scott and Todd and the Soccer Gang*. This is listed as fiction. It is probably not what you're looking for.

*The Best Sports Book in the Whole World*. The title doesn't give a clue as to what's in the book, except that it has something to do with sports. Not a good possibility.

*Better Soccer for Boys and Girls*. This seems to be just what you are looking for. It's nonfiction and about playing better soccer.

Using the card catalog will save you time. Knowing how to go about finding the information you need will be a big help to you, not only while you are in school but all through your life.

### Using What You Have Learned
Select an animal you would like to know more about. Look it up in the encyclopedia. Make brief notes on the new facts you have learned.

### Expanding Your Skills
Look up the same animal in the library card catalog. Decide which nonfiction books might be the most helpful.

# The New Teacher

## by ROBERTA WIEGAND

At the beginning of every school year, you get a different teacher. Usually you know something about the teacher from older students. But what happens when the teacher is brand-new to the school, and nobody knows anything about the new teacher? In this story, the fifth-grade class gets a new teacher who surprises everyone.

What trick does the class play on the new teacher? How do they think the new teacher will react to their trick?

Early in October school began as usual. That was when the children who lived around Ponder's Mill were able to leave their work on the farms.

Sarah Lewis and her friend Lilly were beginning the fifth grade. The brick schoolhouse had four grades on each of its three floors. The higher the grades went, the higher up in the schoolhouse the classroom was. So now, for the first time, the girls would be in a room on the second story. Sarah's older brothers, Charlie and Harry, would be down the hall in the sixth and seventh grades. Of the Lewis children, only Georgie and Maryrose would be on the ground level.

"Do you think the new teacher'll be as nice as Miss Benedict?" Lilly asked.

"I really liked Miss Benedict a lot," Sarah answered. Sarah started every year by liking the teacher she was used to better than her new one. This year there was a special mystery because the regular fifth-grade teacher had moved away. No one knew anything about her replacement.

"But it'll be worth having a new teacher to be in one of the rooms with a fire escape."

"You bet," Lilly agreed. "That'll really be fun."

The fire escapes were two big metal tubes. They started in one room on each of the upper floors. They sloped from the school building to the ground outside. Whenever there was a fire drill, Mr. Bostrum, the principal, rang the bell in the tower. Then

347

all the children on the second and third floors hurried into a room with a fire escape in it. One by one they sat down at the top opening of the metal chute and pushed off. They whizzed down the giant slides so fast that the top floors of the school could be emptied quickly. On the second floor, the fire escape began in the fifth-grade room.

All the upstairs pupils in the school learned how to use the tubes and thought they were fun. But Mr. Bostrum only clanged the bell two or three times a year. Everyone agreed it would be a shame to waste such great slides by using them just during fire drills. So sometimes, when the teacher wasn't looking, one of the children disappeared down a chute. If the roll had already been called, he didn't always come back either. When Sarah's older brothers had been in the fifth-grade room, they kept score. Harry got out more times, but Charlie wasn't missed as often. He claimed that made him the winner. Sarah teased, "That just proves your teacher didn't even remember you were in her class."

Now Sarah would have her turn in a fire-escape room.

Sarah and Lilly hung their jackets on hooks in the dark wood-lined hall. The first thing they noticed was the new sign mounted on their classroom door. M. EMERSON, FIFTH GRADE was printed on it.

"She sounds old, don't you think?" Sarah guessed.

"And maybe mean, too." Lilly gave a little shudder. They exchanged worried looks. Then they crossed their fingers for luck and went timidly inside.

But the teacher wasn't there yet. It was still ten minutes early. The other pupils were gathered around the top of the metal tube at the back of the room. They were talking in excited whispers. They motioned to the girls to join them.

Pete Robbins, who was the biggest boy in their class, said, "We've got this plan, see. Whenever the new teacher goes to the blackboard and turns her back, some of us will go down the chute. As many as can before she figures it out. Maybe she doesn't even know about the slide yet."

Sarah wondered if enough of them could get out so it would be hard to punish them all. Even though it was risky, she had to admit it was a great temptation. At least they'd find out right away what the new teacher was like.

Now there was the sound of footsteps in the hall. The pupils all scurried to their seats. They were looking straight ahead when the knob turned. The door opened.

And the new teacher stepped into the room.

He had broad shoulders and narrow hips. He was dressed in a plaid jacket with a tan waistcoat. A heavy gold chain hung across his chest. He walked briskly to the front of the room.

"I am Mr. Maxfield Emerson. I will be your

teacher for the next year." His voice was pleasant, and golden like his watch chain and his hair. His mustache was the same color. It curled up on the ends. Even his eyes glinted gold. He smiled in a dignified way at the children in front of him and brushed his hand over the curl on top of his head. The curl bounced back, as if it were determined for Mr. Emerson to be as handsome as possible.

The class sat perfectly still while he called the roll. There had never been a man teacher except in the very highest grades! Sarah swallowed. She could hear the sound of her own gulp. Mr. Emerson was the handsomest man she had ever seen. She couldn't believe he was going to be her teacher.

Just then Mr. Emerson walked to the blackboard.

at the front of the room. "These are the subjects
we are going to study together during the year,"
he announced.

He picked up the chalk and turned his back to
the class. At the top of the board he wrote *History*.
He had only written *The United States* underneath
it when there was a whispered hiss from the back of
the room.

Sarah and the others looked over their shoulders
just as Pete Robbins disappeared down the slide.
Three of his friends quickly followed him. The last
one went down on his stomach. A few other pupils
slipped into the seats that were now empty closest
to the back corner of the room.

Mr. Maxfield Emerson finished his list under
*History* and turned to face the class. He took the
shiny watch out his vest pocket and glanced at it.
Then he turned his broad shoulders back to the

352

board. Someone in the class giggled. He hadn't noticed a thing!

"Another subject we will study will be *English*."
He started a new column on the blackboard. Five or
six more children seemed to be sucked down the
chute while others shifted to the places they left va-
cant. Their parents would never have believed they
could move so quietly.

The sound of the chalk stopped. Then Mr.
Emerson began another column headed *Arithmetic*.
Sarah was glad it was her turn to leave now. She
didn't want to think about that subject anyway. She
hated arithmetic.

She tiptoed quickly to the tunnel and *swooshed*
down it. Her stomach flipped over on the way
down. Then her heels bumped into the dirt of the
school yard at the bottom. The others were waiting
in a circle around the end of the tube.

"Did he see you?" they snickered.

"No, he doesn't suspect at all."

Someone else chuckled, "Boy, he must be sort
of dumb."

They'd never believed they could be so successful. The rest of their small class followed on each
other's heels. Finally Piggy Hayden, the last one
missing, popped out of the tunnel like an egg pop-
ping out of a hen.

"He wasn't even looking! He'll never guess
where we've gone! Let's get out of here!"

Poor Mr. Emerson. His whole class had disappeared on his very first day. Sarah almost felt sorry for him.

Just then there was another sound. It was a soft swishing noise as if Aladdin's hand was rubbing his magic lamp. Obediently the genie appeared.

Mr. Maxfield Emerson stood up at the bottom of the fire escape. Carefully he smoothed the curl on top of his head. He adjusted the chain across his vest.

The class didn't know what to do—so it did nothing. Mr. Emerson looked around the circle of staring faces.

"Congratulations. You're a very alert class. I confess I didn't even hear the fire-drill bell myself." The smooth golden voice went on. "But soon after this young man left, I started timing you."

His hand dropped casually on top of Pete Robbins's bristly head. Pete groaned.

"From then until the last one was out"—Mr. Emerson looked at Piggy now—"it only took you four and a half minutes. That's excellent. You were so quiet and orderly too. Mr. Bostrum will be pleased. Now, if you'll all march back upstairs, we'll see if you're as smart at your studies."

Without a single word, the fifth grade marched.

## CHECK FOR UNDERSTANDING

1. What was so special about being in the fifth grade in Sarah's school?
2. What was surprising about the new teacher?
3. What trick did the class play on the new teacher?
4. How did they think the new teacher would react to their trick?
5. How did he actually react?
6. How do you think the class felt about Mr. Emerson after the trick?
7. Do you think the students would try to fool Mr. Emerson again? Explain your answer.

## WRITE ABOUT *"The New Teacher"*

Imagine that some members of Sarah's class felt guilty about the trick they had played and want to apologize. Write the class's letter of apology to Mr. Emerson. Explain why the trick was played and how you feel about the way he handled it.

# How Will Computers Affect Our Future?

by NANCY BARTON

**Inventions and discoveries change the way people live. Think about what your life would be like if there were no telephones, no automobiles, no airplanes. Computers have already changed the way people do many things. In the next few years, the effect of computers on our lives will be even greater.**

**How will computers change where people live? How might computers change the way children learn in the future?**

Big changes always seem to follow revolutionary inventions, and the computer is just such an invention. Many people talk about the "Computer Revolution" and try to guess what changes it may make. With credit cards and video games, the computer has already changed many little things in our lives, but like the automobile, it is more than just a tool. It is a force likely to alter the geographic patterns of our cities and the basic nature of society itself.

## APPEARANCE AND FEATURES

Computer hardware and software technology are improving quickly. The computer is becoming smaller, faster, and cheaper, and it has an increasingly larger memory. In less than a decade, it will probably be small and flat — like a book, with a TV screen opening like a book's flyleaf. It will be easy to carry, and it will cost much less, so most families will be able to afford one.

Above all, it will be simple to use. The future computer will respond to voice commands and pointers on the screen, instead of to complicated keyboard languages and codes. It will become as essential to us in the future as the automobile and the telephone seem to us now.

## NEW USES

Some of its more interesting uses will include:

- computerized shopping — from comparing prices to placing orders to paying the bill
- new and more complex games that involve the player in a creative process
- computer-assisted sight for the blind, hearing for the deaf, and motion for the disabled
- intelligent home appliances, traffic lights, robots of all kinds
- vast national data banks for everything, including medical information for diagnosis and for the location of available transplant organs
- computer-based libraries that distribute books electronically to local or home computers
- wrist communicators to provide

constant phone links (people will be at home more often)

## EFFECTS

Apart from these changes, the computer will be responsible for more fundamental changes. In America today, reading, writing, and the use of numbers are basic to almost everything we do. Much "work" focuses on collecting and communicating information — and that is what computers do best. In the future, the computer will play a major part in this communication by substituting "electronic mail" for much of what we presently do with letters, notes, bills, and telephone calls. This means that most people will communicate with each other, full-time, through computers when they are at work.

Consider the effect that computer communication will have on the geography of our cities. Since many people will communicate with each other through computer links, they will no longer have to spend so much time together in one place — "the office." Instead, they can work at home. Children may also be able to spend more of their "school" time working at home. Vast office complexes in the centers of cities will no longer be needed. People will no longer have to live within commuting distance of their offices; they will be able to live wherever they wish. (According to some people, working alone might not be a good thing — people need to be around other people.) Huge population shifts may result as people choose to leave crowded cities and suburbs to settle in more pleasant places. Just as the Industrial Revolution moved masses of people to the cities, the computer may send them back to the country.

The computer is certain to make radical changes in our use of time. Working through computer links, people can schedule their time any way they choose. There will still be work deadlines, but workers will be able to choose exactly how long they will work to meet these deadlines.

Today's 9 A.M. to 5 P.M., Monday through Friday work pattern will change. Some people will choose to work at night or early in the morning. Some might make Tuesday and Wednesday their "weekends." Others may save large blocks of time for vacations. In fact, many may even follow the seasons, carrying their portable computers and "jobs" with them.

Imagine the changes that might occur. Morning and evening rush hours may disappear. Peak hours, days, or seasons at popular recreational sites may level off to more continuous overall use and less waste of facilities.

When most people think of the accomplishments of computers, they think of the dramatic technological breakthroughs. These are, of course, impressive. But the computer's greatest contribution to the future may be the way it changes our use of time, space, and information, which will change the way we live.

## CHECK FOR UNDERSTANDING

1. How will computers change where people live?
2. In what way might computers eliminate rush-hour traffic in big cities?
3. Can you think of one thing that you or someone in your family does differently because of computers? Explain what it is.
4. How might computers change the way children learn in the future?

# THE FUN

by ISAAC ASIMOV

On some days a student might rather be doing something else than going to class. In this story of the future, children *don't* go to school—but their feelings about school are not what you might expect.

How do Margie and Tommy learn? How do they feel about their "school"?

# THEY HAD

Margie even wrote about it that night in her diary. On the page headed May 17, 2157, she wrote "Today Tommy found a real book!"

It was a very old book. Margie's grandfather once said that when he was a little boy *his* grandfather told him that there was a time when all stories were printed on paper.

They turned the pages, which were yellow and crinkly, and it was awfully funny to read words that stood still instead of moving the way they were supposed to—on a screen, you know. And then, when they turned back to the page before, it had the same words on it that it had had when they read it the first time.

"Gee," said Tommy, "what a waste. When you're through with the book, you just throw it away, I guess. Our television screen must have had a million books on it and it's good for plenty more. I wouldn't throw *it* away."

"Same with mine," said Margie. She was eleven and hadn't seen as many telebooks as Tommy had. He was thirteen.

She said, "Where did you find it?"

"In my house." He pointed without looking, because he was busy reading. "In the attic."

"What's it about?"

"School."

Margie was scornful. "School? What's there to write about school? I hate school."

Margie always hated school, but now she hated it more than ever. The mechanical teacher had been giving her test after test in geography and she had been doing worse and worse until her mother had shaken her head sorrowfully and sent for the County Inspector.

He was a round little man with a red face and a whole box of tools with dials and wires. He smiled at Margie and gave her an apple, then took the teacher apart. Margie had hoped he wouldn't know how to put it together again, but he knew how all right. After an hour or so, there it was again, large and black and ugly, with a big screen on which all the lessons were shown and the questions were

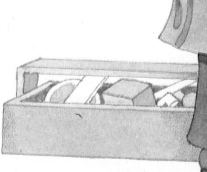

asked. That wasn't so bad. The part Margie hated most was the slot where she had to put homework and test papers. She always had to write them out in a punch code they made her learn when she was six years old, and the mechanical teacher calculated the mark in no time.

The Inspector had smiled after he was finished and patted Margie's head. He said to her mother, "It's not the little girl's fault, Mrs. Jones. I think the geography sector was geared a little too quick.

Those things happen sometimes. I've slowed it up to an average ten-year level. Actually, the over-all pattern of her progress is quite satisfactory." And he patted Margie's head again.

Margie was disappointed. She had been hoping they would take the teacher away altogether. They had once taken Tommy's teacher away for nearly a month because the history sector had blanked out completely.

So she said to Tommy, "Why would anyone write about school?"

Tommy looked at her with very superior eyes. "Because it's not our kind of school. This is the old kind of school that they had hundreds and hundreds of years ago." He added loftily, pronouncing the word carefully, "*Centuries* ago."

Margie was hurt. "Well, I don't know what kind of school they had all that time ago." She read the book over his shoulder for a while, then said, "Anyway, they had a teacher."

"Sure they had a teacher, but it wasn't a *regular* teacher. It was a person."

"A person? How could a person be a teacher?"

"Well, the person just told the boys and girls things and gave them homework and asked them questions."

"People aren't smart enough."

"Sure they are. My father knows as much as my teacher."

"He can't. A person can't know as much as a teacher."

"He knows almost as much, I bet."

Margie wasn't prepared to dispute that. She said, "I wouldn't want a strange person in my house to teach me."

Tommy screamed with laughter. "You don't know much, Margie. The teachers didn't live in the house. They had a special building and all the kids went there."

"And all the kids learned the same thing?"

"Sure, if they were the same age."

"But my mother says a teacher has to be adjusted to fit the mind of each boy and girl it teaches and that each kid has to be taught differently."

"Just the same, they didn't do it that way then. If you don't like it, you don't have to read the book."

"I didn't say I didn't like it," Margie said quickly. She wanted to read about those funny schools.

They weren't even half-finished when Margie's mother called, "Margie! School!"

Margie looked up. "Not yet Mama."

"Now!" said Mrs. Jones. "And it's probably time for Tommy, too."

Margie said to Tommy, "Can I read the book some more with you after school?"

"Maybe," he said nonchalantly. He walked away whistling, the dusty old book tucked beneath his arm.

Margie went into the schoolroom. It was right next to her bedroom, and the mechanical teacher was on and waiting for her. It was always on at the same time every day except Saturday and Sunday, because her mother said little girls learned better if they learned at regular hours.

The screen was lit up, and it said: "Today's arithmetic lesson is on the addition of proper fractions. Please insert yesterday's homework in the proper slot."

Margie did so with a sigh. She was thinking about the old schools they had when her grandfather's grandfather was a little boy. All the kids from the whole neighborhood came, laughing and shouting in the schoolyard, sitting together in the schoolroom, going home together at the end of the day. They learned the same things, so they could help one another on the homework and talk about it.

And the teachers were people. . . .

The mechanical teacher was flashing on the screen: "When we add the fractions ½ and ¼—"

Margie was thinking about how the kids must have loved it in the old days. She was thinking about the fun they had.

## CHECK FOR UNDERSTANDING

1. How did Margie and Tommy usually read books?
2. What was so unusual about Tommy's discovery?
3. How did Margie and Tommy learn?
4. How did they feel about their "school"?
5. Do you think Margie would enjoy school if she were living in the present? Explain your answer.

## WRITE ABOUT *"The Fun They Had"*

Imagine that Margie had a chance to travel back in time to our present. Describe a day at school as she would see it. What would seem strange to her? What would be familiar?

# LITERATURE

## Point of View

If you keep a journal you probably write about how you feel and what happens to you. Someone else reading it would hear your voice in the words. They would learn a lot about your thoughts and observations. When you describe an event they would understand it from your point of view.

Sometimes authors write stories in the same way. They narrate the story from the point of view of one of the characters. A story written in this way is said to be written from a **first-person point of view.**

Authors also use another way to narrate a story. They tell us about all the characters and events from the point of view of an outsider who sees all that happens to the characters. A story narrated in this way is written from a **third-person point of view.**

In the story you just read, "The Fun They Had," Isaac Asimov chooses to narrate the story from the third-person point of view. Read the following passage from the story. Note the use of third-person pronouns such as *she, he* and *her* or the use of a character's name.

Margie always hated school, but now she hated it more than ever. The mechanical teacher had been giving her test after test in geography and she had been doing worse and worse until her mother had shaken her head sorrowfully and sent for the County Inspector.

It is easy to recognize the point of view of a story when you know that the clue is the pronouns. They help you to understand who is telling the story.

Look at "The Fun They Had" again. Is the story about what happened to Margie? The words *she, he,* and *her* are third-person pronouns. They show us that the story is about events that happened to Margie written from a third-person point of view.

Now read this passage from "The Day After Thanksgiving." Watch out for the pronouns *I* and *my.*

I planned my day as I lay listening to the breakfast noise my mother was making in the kitchen. Skating first, I decided, before the sun had time to weaken the ice on the pond, and then a good, long ride.

In the story we hear the voice of a young girl telling us about her plans for the day. Is the story written by the girl? The pronouns *I* and *my* show us that it was written from a first-person point of view. But we know the story was written by the author, Maureen Ash, pretending to be the young girl.

When you read a story look for the pronouns to help you find the point of view. First-person pronouns are *I, me, my, mine, we,* and *ours.* Third-person pronouns are *he, she, it, his, hers, its,* and *theirs.*

The next story you will read is "Fox!" Note how the author's use of first-person point of view helps you to get to know the main character very quickly.

# The
# MIDNIGHT
# FOX

### BY · BETSY · BYARS ·

**⚒ Just·A·Taste ⚒**

**To a city-bred boy, the country can seem terribly slow-moving and dull. But by being quiet and watching carefully, Tom discovers, in this story, that the country can show him things that will change his life.**

**What is Tom's attitude toward the farm at first? Why does he feel that way?**

*To begin with, Tom did not want to spend the summer on his Aunt Millie's farm while his parents bicycled through Europe. To a city-bred boy, a farm meant animals—Tom couldn't stand animals and they couldn't stand him. Being at the farm also meant loneliness—what would he do without his best friend, Petie Burkis?*

The first three days on the farm were the longest, slowest days of my life. It seemed to me in those days that nothing was moving at all, not air, not time. Even the bees, the biggest, fattest bees that I had ever seen, just seemed to hang in the air. The problem, or one of them, was that I was not an enormously adaptable person and I did not fit into new situations well.

I did a lot of just standing around those first days. I would be standing in the kitchen and Aunt Millie would turn around, stirring something, and bump into me and say, "Oh, my goodness! You gave me a scare. I didn't even hear you come in. When *did* you come in?"

"Just a minute ago."

"Well, I didn't hear you. You are so *quiet*."

Or Uncle Fred would come out of the barn wiping his hands on a rag and there I'd be, just standing, and he'd say, "Well, boy, how's it going?"

"Fine, Uncle Fred."

"Good! Good! Don't get in any mischief now."

"I won't."

I spent a lot of time at the pond and walking down the road and back. I spent about an hour one afternoon hitting the end of an old rope swing that was hanging from a tree in the front yard. I made my two models of a race car and a horse. Then I took some of the spare plastic strips and rigged up a harness, so that the horse was pulling the car, and Aunt Millie got very excited over this bit of real nothing and said it was the cleverest thing she had ever seen.

I wrote a long letter to Petie. I went down to the stream and made boats of twigs and leaves and watched them float out of sight. I looked through about a hundred farm magazines. I weeded Aunt Millie's flowers while she stood over me saying, "Not that, not *that,* that's a zinnia. Get the chick-weed—see? Right here."

And she would snatch it up for me. I had none of the difficult chores that I had expected, because the farm was so well run that everything was already planned without me. In all my life I have never spent longer, more miserable days, and I had to keep saying, "I'm fine, just fine," because people were asking how I was all the time.

The one highlight of my day was to go down to the mailbox for the mail. This was the only thing I did all day that was of any use. Then, too, the honking of the mail truck would give me the feeling that there was a letter of great importance waiting for me in the box. I could hardly hurry down the road fast enough. Anyone watching me from behind would probably have seen only a cloud of dust, my feet would pound so fast. So far, the only mail I had received was a postcard from my mom with a picture of the Statue of Liberty on it telling me how excited and happy she was.

This Thursday morning when I went to the mailbox there was a letter to me from Petie Burkis and I was never so glad to see anything in my life. I ripped it open and completely destroyed the envelope I was in such a hurry. And I thought that when I was a hundred years old, sitting in a chair with a rug over my knees, and my mail was brought in on a silver tray, if there was a letter from Petie Burkis on that tray, I would snatch it up and rip it open just like this. I could hardly get it unfolded—Petie folds his letters up small—I was so excited.

*Dear Tom,*

*There is nothing much happening here. I went to the playground Saturday after you left, and you know that steep bank by the swings? Well, I fell all the way down that. Here's the story—*

### BOY FALLS DOWN BANK WHILE GIRL ONLOOKERS CHEER

*Today Petie Burkis fell down the bank at Harley Playground. It was reported that some ill-mannered girls at the park for a picnic cheered and laughed at the sight of the young, demolished boy. The brave youngster left the park unaided.*

*Not much else happened. Do you get Chiller Theater? There was a real good movie on Saturday night about mushroom men.*

*Write me a letter,*
*Petie Burkis*

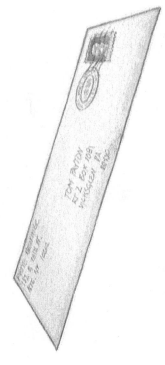

I went in and gave the rest of the mail to Aunt Millie, who said, "Well, let's see what the government's sending us today," and then I got my box of stationery and went outside.

There was a very nice place over the hill by the creek. There were trees so big I couldn't get my arms around them, and soft grass and rocks to sit on. They were planning to let the cows into the field later on, and then it wouldn't be as nice, but now it was the best place on the farm. Incidentally, anyone interested in butterflies would have gone crazy.

There must have been a million in that one field. I thought about there being a contest—a butterfly contest and hundreds of people, with fruit jars under their arms, would come from all over the country to catch butterflies.

Anyway, I sat down and wrote Petie a letter.

*Dear Petie,*

*I do not know whether we get Chiller Theater or not. Since there is no TV set here, it is very difficult to know what we could get if we had one.*

*My farm chores are feeding the pigs, feeding the chickens, weeding the flowers, getting the mail, things like that. I have a lot of time to myself and I am planning a movie about a planet that collides with Earth, and this planet and Earth become fused together, and the people of Earth are terrified of the planet, because it is very weird-looking and they have heard these terrible moanlike cries coming from the depths of it. That's all so far.*

*Write me a letter,*
*Tom*

I had just finished writing this letter and was waiting for a minute to see if I would think of anything to add when I looked up and saw the black fox.

I did not believe it for a minute. It was like my eyes were playing a trick or something, because I was just sort of staring across this field, thinking about my letter, and then in the distance, where the grass was very green, I saw a fox leaping over the crest of the field. The grass moved and the fox sprang toward the movement, and then, seeing that it was just the wind that had caused the grass to move, she ran straight for the grove of trees where I was sitting.

It was so great that I wanted it to start over again, like you can turn movie film back and see yourself repeat some fine thing you have done, and I wanted to see the fox leaping over the grass again. In all my life I have never been so excited.

I did not move at all, but I could hear the paper in my hand shaking, and my heart seemed to have moved up in my body and got stuck in my throat.

The fox came straight toward the grove of trees. She wasn't afraid, and I knew she had not seen me against the tree. I stayed absolutely still even though I felt like jumping up and screaming, "Aunt Millie! Uncle Fred! Come see this. It's a fox, a fox!"

Her steps as she crossed the field were lighter and quicker than a cat's. As she came closer I could see that her black fur was tipped with white. It was as if it were midnight and the moon were shining on her fur, frosting it. The wind parted her fur as it changed directions. Suddenly she stopped. She was ten feet away now, and with the changing of the wind she had got my scent. She looked right at me.

I did not move for a moment and neither did

377

she. Her head was cocked to one side, her tail curled up, her front left foot raised. In all my life I never saw anything like that fox standing with her pale golden eyes on me and this great black fur being blown by the wind.

Suddenly her nose quivered. It was such a slight movement I almost didn't see it, and then her

mouth opened and I could see the pink tip of her tongue. She turned. She still was not afraid, but with a bound that was lighter than the wind—it was as if she was being blown away over the field—she was gone.

Still I didn't move. I couldn't. I couldn't believe that I had really seen the fox.

I had seen foxes before in zoos, but I was always in such a great hurry to get on to the good stuff that I was saying stupid things like, "I want to see the go-rilll-lllas," and not once had I ever really looked at a fox. Still, I could never remember seeing a black fox, not even in a zoo.

Also, there was a great deal of difference between seeing an animal in the zoo in front of painted fake rocks and trees and seeing one natural and free in the woods. It was like seeing a kite on the floor and then, later, seeing one up in the sky where it was supposed to be, pulling at the wind.

I started to pick up my pencil and write as quickly as I could, "P.S. Today I saw a black fox." But I didn't. This was the most exciting thing that had happened to me, and "P.S. Today I saw a black fox" made it nothing. "So what else is happening?" Petie Burkis would probably write back. I folded my letter, put it in an envelope, and sat there. I thought about this old newspaper that my dad had had in his desk drawer for years. It was orange and the headline was just one word, very big, the letters about twelve inches high. WAR! And I mean it was awesome to see that word like that, because you knew it was a word that was going to change your whole life, the whole world even. And every time I would see that newspaper, even though I wasn't even born when it was printed, I couldn't say anything for a minute or two.

Well, this was the way I felt right then about the black fox. I thought about a newspaper with just one word for a headline, very big, very black letters, twelve inches high. FOX! And even that did not show how awesome it had really been to me.

*From that day on, Tom delights in seeing the black fox again. One day he discovers that her life may be in danger. To find out what Tom does, read the rest of the novel* The Midnight Fox *by Betsy Byars.*

## CHECK FOR UNDERSTANDING

1. What was Tom's attitude toward the farm at first?
2. Why did he feel that way?
3. Why did Tom miss Petie so much?
4. How was seeing the black fox different from seeing a fox in the zoo?
5. What do you think the fox thought when she saw Tom?
6. Do you think Tom would feel differently about life in the country after seeing the fox? Explain your answer.

## WRITE ABOUT *"Fox!"*

Imagine that Tom decided he really wanted to tell Petie what seeing the fox had meant to him. Write the letter Tom would write to Petie. Describe the fox and try to explain the effect the experience had on Tom.

# THINK ABOUT IT

Think about the characters in the stories you have read. What was the most important discovery each character made?

- What basic rule about detective work did Paddington learn?
- What important thing did Marshall discover about competition?
- How did Lee Trevino discover that he could play golf well enough to take the game seriously?
- How did Tommy's discovery in "The Fun They Had" make you think differently about your school?
- What do you think Tom discovered about himself after seeing the fox?

After reading and thinking about these different kinds of discoveries, who in the unit do you think made the most important discovery? Why?

# WRITE ABOUT IT

Have you ever made a small discovery that led to a larger discovery about yourself? Maybe, like Tom, you were bored, and discovered something that interested you. And perhaps that discovery led you to understand why you were bored in the first place. Write two paragraphs telling about a personal discovery like this.

# READ ABOUT IT

*Rollo and Tweedy and the Case of the Missing Cheese* by Laura Jean Allen. Harper & Row, Publishers, 1983. In a search that takes them across the Atlantic, mouse detective Tweedy and his assistant Rollo leave no crumb unturned when wealthy J. P. Cadwalader hires them to find his missing five-hundred-year-old cheese.

*All the Money in the World* by Bill Brittain. Harper & Row, Publishers, 1979. The story of a boy who catches a leprechaun and gets three wishes. His third wish—to have all the money in the world—creates problems far beyond anything he could have imagined.

*Miss Pickerell Goes to Mars* by Ellen MacGregor. McGraw-Hill, 1962. Miss Pickerell discovers a mysterious spaceship in her pasture. When she goes on board to investigate, it blasts off. First stop: *Mars!*

*The Hundred Penny Box* by Sharon Bell Mathis. The Viking Press, 1975. A penny for every birthday and the story behind each is the basis for a warm story of love between an aged relative and a young black child.

*Kenny's Window* by Maurice Sendak. Harper & Row, Publishers, 1956. Kenny dreams of a fabulous land where he would like to live always, and in his search for it discovers many things about himself—and about growing up.

# MESSAGES

*What do you think of when you hear the word* messages? *How is a message different from a newspaper article or a phone call? Sometimes messages come from unexpected places. At other times, messages come in the form of codes. A message might be written on a scrap of paper, or even come from a small voice in the night. A message usually has a special purpose, as you will see in this unit.*

*As you read the stories, think about the forms the messages take. Are they sent through the air, written on paper, or spoken? Ask yourself how the form of the message is important to the rest of the selection.*

# THE CODE
## IN THE
# MAILBOX

by KATHY KENNEDY TAPP

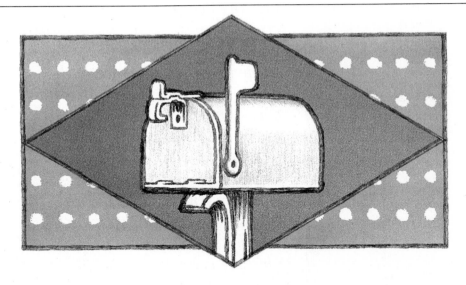

It's fun to send secret messages to a friend. To do that, you need a secret place to leave the messages. Tad and his friend Perry have just such a place, until Mr. James rents the house across the street.

What new "code" does Tad learn? What coded message does he send?

"I don't want to go," Tad said for the third time.

His mother faced him, hands on hips. "Tad Novak, I'm ashamed of you. Mr. James is blind and needs help getting settled. I told him you'd be over."

"Mom, it's Easter vacation. I was going to meet Perry. We made plans."

"More detective stuff, I'll bet." Michelle looked up from the egg she was poking with a pin. She made her voice low and dramatic. "Fingerprints . . . secret codes—"

Tad glared at his sister. "Just stick to your egg blowing, O.K.?"

"Codes are fine," Mom said. "But don't let me catch you using the mailbox across the street for your messages anymore. The place is rented, so it's Mr. James's mailbox now. For *his* mail, Tad."

"I know, I know," Tad muttered.

"And Mr. James needs help unpacking." Mom opened the door and gave Tad a little push. "Now scoot." Then, in a nicer voice, she added, "We'll save the egg decorating until you get back."

Tad slammed the door. So much for his plans to go through the new code book with Perry. Instead he'd be cooped up all afternoon in a stuffy old house with a blind man he didn't even know.

He kicked a rock across the street, hard. It skipped right past the beautiful silver mailbox with the hinged door and the movable signal flag he and Perry always raised when they left secret messages for each other. But it was Mr. James's mailbox now, for his letters and junk mail. They'd have to find a new place to exchange coded notes and detective reports.

A low, gruff voice answered

Tad's knock. "Are you the Novak boy?"

"Yeah."

"Come on in. Careful of the boxes."

The room was dim, with the drapes closed. Boxes lined the walls. Tad stayed by the door, trying to ignore the butterflies in his stomach. Secret agents had to penetrate new territory all the time. Still—being around somebody who couldn't see made him feel nervous.

"We'll start over here," Mr. James said, walking toward the wall, one arm out in front. His foot hit a box, and he reached down into it, frowning. "Pans. They go in the kitchen. Next box should be plates—"

Dishes in the cupboard, shoes in the closet, tapes in the bedroom. The old man sifted through box after box, his face set in a permanent frown. He didn't talk except to give instructions. And Tad made fifty trips down the dark hall, looking longingly at the front door each time. The whole afternoon was slipping away. One more box. Just one more—

"Where do these go?" he muttered.

"Books. Leave them for now. Shelves aren't up yet."

"Books?" Tad stared. He'd never seen books like these before. Big pads of thick pages all covered with bumps.

Braille. Of course. He pulled one out, feeling the dots. Did those bumps really make words? How could anyone read them?

"Hey, Mr. James, did you learn Braille in school?"

"No need then. I learned the regular alphabet, just like you."

Tad set down the book. "You mean . . . you weren't blind when you were a kid?" he stammered.

"I could throw and catch with the best of them. I became blind much later." He turned to Tad. "What about you? You play ball?" The gruffness in his voice didn't sound unfriendly, really. Just low-pitched.

"I play basketball in the winter. Now I'm busy with other stuff. Detective stuff." Tad tried to sound casual, offhand.

"Detective, huh?" The corners of Mr. James's mouth turned up the slightest bit. "Fingerprints, spyglasses—that sort of thing?"

"And codes. I like codes best." Tad was still fingering the Braille bumps. "Can anyone learn Braille?"

"Anyone willing to spend enough time. Don't know why you'd *want* to learn it though, when you don't need to. But wait a minute—" Mr. James started to feel around in the book box, frowning again. That frown almost seemed connected to his fingers—a concentrating frown, not a mad one.

"Here it is." Mr. James held up a little card. "A Braille alphabet card."

"Hey, can I borrow it?"

"I don't need it anymore," Mr.

James said, shaking his head and grinning a little. "Detectives. That's a new one. Spring was baseball time when I was a kid. I was team captain. 'Babe' they called me."

"Babe?" Tad grinned, too, at the thought of the old man standing at the plate with a bat in his hands. "What was your average?"

"Well—" Mr. James chewed his lip a second. The frown relaxed into a thoughtful, remembering look. Then he shook his head. "Too long ago. Let's just say it was a lot better than I could do now." He reached over to a tiny digital clock on the table and pushed a button.

"4:32 P.M.," intoned a flat computer voice.

"A talking clock!" Tad exclaimed.

"Keeps me company." Mr. James got up with a little grunt. "That's enough work for today. It's getting late." He pulled out his wallet, and Tad noticed that

some bills were folded the long way and others the short way. Mr. James fingered them, then held one out to Tad. "Thanks for your help."

A five! Tad stood there, twisting the bill in his hand. A five— just for unloading some boxes. "Thanks. Uh . . . have a happy Easter." That sounded dumb. He tried again. "Do you have family coming or anything?"

"My son will be calling from Texas. If the phone is installed in time."

Tomorrow was Saturday. Crossing the street, Tad wondered if telephone people ever worked on holiday weekends. Somehow he doubted it.

"You're back just in time," Mom greeted him. "The eggs are ready to go. Michelle's done a few already."

"Isn't it professional-looking?" Michelle bragged, holding one up.

Batik egg-dyeing was a family tradition at the Novak house. The designs were drawn on the eggs in pencil first, then traced

with nails or feather quills dipped in hot wax. When the eggs were dyed, the waxed designs remained white.

"Of course *you* wouldn't appreciate it. It's not in code or anything," Michelle said.

Code. Tad fingered the little wax bumps on the egg, remembering the Braille card in his pocket.

"Be back in a minute." He grabbed an egg on his way to the bedroom and shut the door. He'd pencil it in here, in private, then do the wax part in the kitchen. Dots weren't hard at all.

Just dip a nail in hot wax and dab it on the egg. If he'd be very careful and make perfect dots in just the right places . . . if the card showed him how . . .

He studied the alphabet. The card said that six dots make up a Braille cell, and that each letter of the Braille alphabet is formed by a different arrangement of the dots. What a code!

There! He did it on paper first, then on the delicate eggshell, frowning hard, concentrating.

"That's a design?" Michelle cried when he set the finished egg on the rack carefully, each

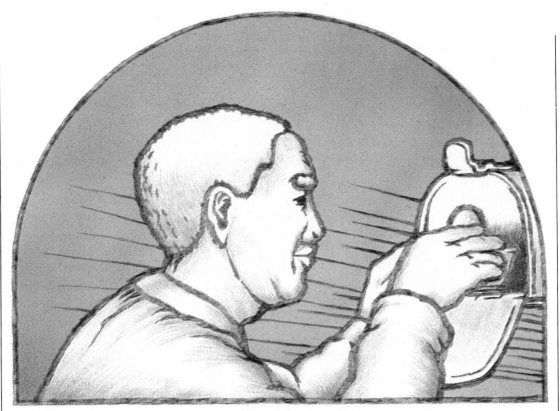

letter dotted in wax. "It's supposed to have decorations, not freckles."

"A lot you know," Tad answered smugly. Old smart-aleck Michelle was staring right at a *genuine* cipher, and she didn't even know it! Tad filled an empty margarine tub with Easter grass and thought about someone who *would* recognize his code.

At 10:15 the next morning, right after the mailcarrier made the Saturday delivery, Tad crouched behind the pine tree in Mr. James's yard, waiting.

Fifteen minutes later, the cane tip-tapped down the walkway. Tad hardly dared breathe as Mr. James pulled the margarine tub out of the mailbox and picked up the egg.

Did it make sense? Were the wax dots close enough? Were they in the right position for

B-A-B-E? Tad felt ready to explode, watching, waiting.

Mr. James's face wrinkled into that concentrating frown as his fingers turned the egg over and over in his hand. Suddenly he smiled, and his face softened into that thoughtful, remembering look. He leaned back against the mailbox, still fingering the egg.

Finally Mr. James put the egg carefully into his shirt pocket and picked up his cane. Not like a cane, but like a baseball bat! With both hands gripping below the curve, he pulled back in a mock swing.

Tad crept away, feeling a bit embarrassed, but proud, too.

Case of the code in the mailbox—closed.

## CHECK FOR UNDERSTANDING

1. What time of year was it?
2. What are three reasons for Tad's attitude about going over to Mr. James's house?
3. Why do you think Mr. James's house was dim, with the drapes closed?
4. Why did Mr. James frown so much?
5. What new "code" did Tad learn?
6. What coded message did Tad send?

**WRITE ABOUT** *"The Code in the Mailbox"*

Make up a code of your own using numbers for letters. In your secret code, write the note you think Mr. James might have left in the mailbox for Tad after Mr. James received the Easter egg.

# VOCABULARY · LANGUAGE

## Prefixes

In the story "The Code in the Mailbox," Tad was *unwilling* to help Mr. James move in at first. Tad was *unhappy* that Mr. James had rented the house next door. It meant that Tad would be *unable* to use the mailbox for sending and receiving messages.

Look at the words *unwilling*, *unhappy*, and *unable* in the paragraph above. Each word begins with the letters *un-*. These letters are known as a **prefix.**

A prefix is a group of letters added to the beginning of a word. A prefix has its own meaning that changes the meaning of the word. For example, the prefix *un-* means "not." Therefore, the meaning of *unwilling* is "not willing." When the prefix *un-* is added to *happy*, the new word, *unhappy*, means "not happy." What is the meaning of *unable*? Explain how you figured out the answer.

In the story Mr. James asked Tad if he played ball. When Mr. James spoke, "The gruffness in his voice didn't sound *unfriendly*." You know that the prefix *un-* means "not." What is the meaning of *unfriendly*?

Listed below are some words that contain the prefix *un-*. Figure out the meaning of each word. Then explain how you arrived at your answers.

| | |
|---|---|
| unwise | unsafe |
| unlucky | unafraid |
| unaware | unchanged |

Sometimes, difficult or unfamiliar words contain a prefix. If you know the meaning of the prefix, you may be able to figure out the word's meaning. Look at the word *extraordinary,* for example. The prefix *extra* has been added to the word *ordinary.* The prefix *extra* means "beyond." Therefore, *extraordinary* means "beyond the ordinary," or "unusual."

Here are some common prefixes with their meanings. After you learn them, you will be able to figure out the meanings of many difficult or unfamiliar words.

| | |
|---|---|
| **un-** = "not" | **pre-** = "before" |
| **extra-** = "beyond" | **in-** = "not" |
| **re-** = "again" or "back" | **mis-** = "wrong" or "bad" |

In the story, Tad was a detective. He enjoyed working with codes. You should be able to use your knowledge of prefixes to "break the code," or figure out, the meaning of the word *rewrite.* You learned that *re-* means "again" or "back." Therefore, *rewrite* means "to write again."

Below are some words that contain prefixes. Break the code. Figure out the meaning of each word. Then explain how you arrived at your answers.

| | |
|---|---|
| unskilled | misdeed |
| redo | return |
| inexpensive | prejudge |

Look for prefixes as you read the next story, "The Southpaw."

# The Southpaw

by

JUDITH VIORST

Have you ever been *so* angry at someone you didn't want to talk to that person? If so, you could still get your message across by writing an angry letter. That's what Janet does when her "former friend" Richard doesn't have the sense to use the best southpaw pitcher in town.

How can you tell that Richard and Janet were good friends before? What "unbroken record" probably helps Richard change his mind?

Dear Richard,
Don't invite me to your birthday party because I'm not coming. And give back the Disneyland sweatshirt I said you could wear. If I'm not good enough to play on your team, I'm not good enough to be friends with.

Your former friend,
Janet

P.S. I hope when you go to the dentist he finds 20 cavities.

Dear Janet,
Here is your stupid Disneyland sweatshirt, if that's how you're going to be. I want my comic books now—finished or not. No girl has ever played on the Mapes Street baseball team, and as long as I'm captain, no girl ever will.

Your former friend,
Richard

P.S. I hope when you go for your checkup you need a tetanus shot.

Dear Richard,
I'm changing my goldfish's name from Richard to Stanley. Don't count on my vote for class president next year. Just because I'm a member of the ballet club doesn't mean I'm not a terrific ballplayer.

Your former friend,
Janet

P.S. I see you lost your first game 28-0.

Dear Janet,
I'm not saving any more seats for you on the bus. For all I care you can stand the whole way to school. Why don't you just forget about baseball and learn something nice like knitting!

Your former friend,
Richard

P.S. Wait until Wednesday.

Dear Richard,
My father said I could call someone to go with us for a ride and hot-fudge sundaes. In case you didn't notice, I didn't call you.

Your former friend,
Janet

P.S. I see you lost your second game, 34-0.

Dear Janet,
Remember when I took the laces out of my blue-and-white sneakers and gave them to you? I want them back,

Your former friend,
Richard

P.S. Wait until Friday.

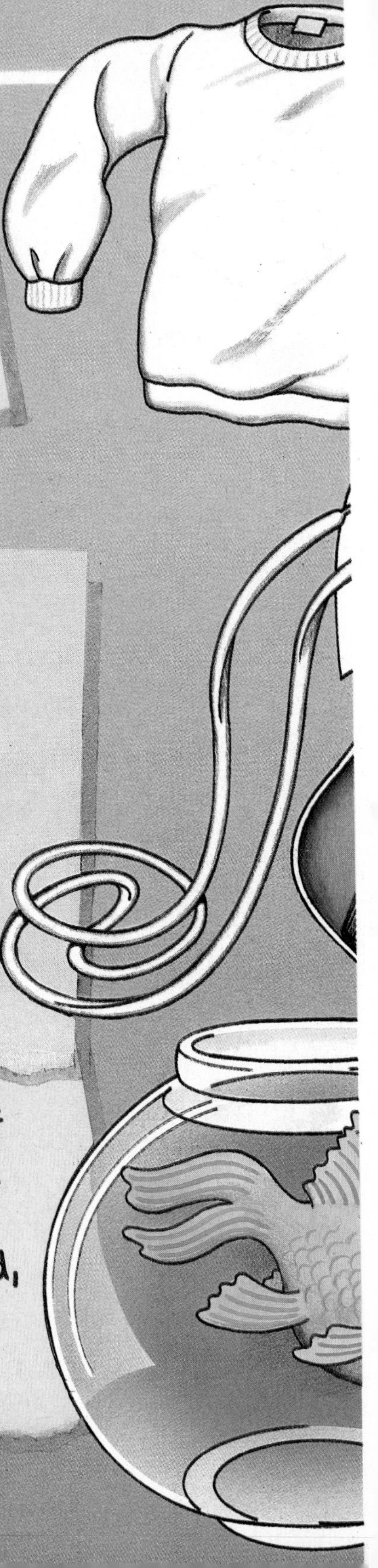

Dear Richard,
Congratulations on your unbroken record. Eight straight losses — wow! I understand you're the laughing-stock of New Jersey.

Your former friend,
Janet

P.S. Why don't you and your team forget about baseball and learn something nice like knitting maybe?

Dear Janet,
Here's the silver horseback riding trophy that you gave me. I don't think I want to keep it anymore.

Your former friend,
Richard

P.S. I didn't think you'd be the kind who'd kick a man when he's down.

Dear Richard,
I wasn't kicking exactly. I was kicking <u>back</u>.

Your former friend,
Janet

P.S. In case you were wondering, my batting average is .345.

Dear Janet,
Alfie is having his tonsils out tomorrow. We might be able to let you catch next week.
Richard

401

Dear Richard,
I pitch.
                    Janet

Dear Janet,
Joel is moving to Kansas and Danny sprained
his wrist. How about a permanent place in
the outfield?
                    Richard

Dear Richard,
I pitch.            Janet

Dear Janet,
Ronnie caught the chicken pox and Leo broke
his toe and Elwood has these stupid violin lessons.
I'll give you first base, and that's my final offer.
                    Richard

Dear Richard,
Susan Reilly plays first base, Marilyn
Jackson catches, Ethel Kahn plays center
field, I pitch. It's a package deal.
                    Janet
P.S. Sorry about your 12-game losing streak.

Dear Janet,
Please! Not Marilyn Jackson.
                    Richard

Dear Richard,
Nobody ever said I was unreasonable.
How about Lizzie Martindale instead?
                        Janet

Dear Janet,
At least could you call your goldfish
Richard again?
                        Your friend,
                        Richard

## CHECK FOR UNDERSTANDING

1. Why did Janet want her Disneyland sweatshirt back?
2. Who had never played on Richard's baseball team? How did Richard feel about it?
3. How can you tell that Richard and Janet were good friends before?
4. What "unbroken record" probably helped Richard change his mind?
5. What was Janet's reason for turning down Richard's first offers to play on the team?
6. After Richard gave in, how did Janet show that she was willing to give in, too?

## WRITE ABOUT *"The Southpaw"*

For the first time in its history, the Mapes Street baseball team will have some female players. Write a short article for the local newspaper describing this event. Mention the names of the four female players and the positions they will play. You can make up the details about their next game: the name of their opponent, the date, time, and place.

# COMPREHENSION

## Drawing Conclusions

The enjoyment you get from reading a story comes as much from what the author *does not* say as from what he or she *does* say. A good story leaves you with some things to figure out on your own. In this way, a story is like a puzzle.

As you read a story, look for the parts the author is purposely leaving out. Look for other parts of the story that tell enough for you to **draw conclusions.**

Read the following passages from the story you just read, "The Southpaw." Think about what the author has left out of each passage that you can draw conclusions about. Then ask yourself the questions that follow each passage.

Dear Richard,
Don't invite me to your birthday party because I'm not coming. And give back the Disneyland sweatshirt I said you could wear. If I'm not good enough to play on your team I'm not good enough to be friends with.
                Your former friend,
                Janet

1. Are Richard and Janet good friends or just acquaintances?
2. What are two things Janet and Richard do as part of their friendship?

Here is another passage.

> Dear Janet,
> I'm not saving any more seats for you on the bus. For all I care you can stand the whole way to school. Why don't you just forget about baseball and learn something nice like knitting!
>> Your former friend,
>> Richard

**3.** What conclusion can you draw about the school bus Janet and Richard travel on?

**4.** What conclusion can you draw about where Richard lives in relation to Janet?

Here is a third passage from the story. One of the conclusions that follows can be drawn from reading the passage. The other conclusion cannot be drawn from the passage. See if you can't figure out which is which.

> Dear Janet,
> Ronnie caught the chicken pox and Leo broke his toe and Elwood has these stupid violin lessons. I'll give you first base, and that's my final offer.
>> Richard

**5.** Ronnie and Leo do not take music lessons.

**6.** Ronnie, Leo, and Elwood are members of the team.

You probably figured out that you can't draw the conclusion that Ronnie and Leo don't take music lessons. But you can draw the conclusion that Ronnie, Leo, and Elwood are members of the team. You know that Richard is mentioning their absence from the team as the reason Janet can now play on the team.

# Questions and Answers

by PATRICIA MACLACHLAN

If you were shy and very curious, you might "talk" to people through messages. Instead of asking people questions in person, you might write the questions. If you wanted people to answer your written questions, where would be the best place to put them?

Why does Cassie want a space of her own? Who do you think Cassie expects to answer the question she tapes to the wall?

*Cassie Binegar (whose name rhymes with* vinegar) *hates her new home. The house is big, it is right by the ocean, it is surrounded by guest cottages, but in all this space there is no place that Cassie can call her own. Trying to find her own private space, Cassie gets into the habit of sitting under the dining room table. Hidden by the long tablecloth, she listens in secret to family conversations. It is from this secret place that Cassie gets her first glimpse of the writer, who will be staying in one of the guest cottages while he works on his new book. Cassie sees the writer again a few days later when he moves into the cottage.*

The first thing the writer did when he arrived was to put up a small bird feeder. He hung it from the porch hook and filled it with sunflower seeds. Cassie saw this from her perch up a small tree nearby. She had not meant to be up the tree when he arrived. It had just happened. And now there was no coming down until he left.

Cassie's mother walked up the path and into the hidden yard where the small cottage stood.

"Is everything all right?" she called to him.

"Fine." He turned and smiled at her. "First things first. I'm feeding the birds."

"Come for dinner tonight," said Cassie's mother. "You can meet everyone. Then we'll leave you on your own."

Cassie's mother went off again, humming to

herself. When she had disappeared, the writer
walked over to the tree and looked up.

"You can come down now, little bird."

Cassie sighed and climbed down the tree.

"I didn't mean it. This time," she added, red-
faced.

The writer smiled at her and held out his hand.

"I'm Jason."

"I know. The writer. I'm Cassie." Cassie took
his hand.

"Ah, of course you know. You were under the
table when I spoke with your mother. I'd almost
forgotten."

"It was nice of you not to say anything," said Cassie.

"You're welcome," said the writer. "You know, hiding is not always a good thing."

"You sound like Margaret Mary," said Cassie.

"And who's Margaret Mary?"

"My friend," explained Cassie. "She's from England and she has plastic plants that her mother sprays with disinfectant and her favorite word is hair ball."

The writer laughed for a long time.

"Anyway," said Cassie, "she thinks my hiding is not good. But I'm doing it because I want to be a writer, like you. And hiding is the best way to find out what you want to know."

"Not so," said the writer, sitting on the porch steps. "Being a part of it all is the best way."

"But aren't you hiding?" asked Cassie. She waved her arm. "Here?"

"I don't think so," said the writer. "No," he said more positively, "I don't think so at all."

"Margaret Mary says asking questions is the best way to find out," said Cassie.

"True," said the writer.

"Well, sometimes I can't ask questions. Not the right ones."

The writer thought a moment.

"Well, then, since you are going to be a writer, do the next best thing."

"What's that?"

"Write the questions," said the writer. *Write them.*

"But who will write back?"

"I'll bet the most important person will," said the writer.

"Who's that?"

"The person who knows the answers," said the writer. He looked closely at Cassie. Finally, he got up and stretched.

"I'm going," said Cassie, knowing that her time was up. "But before I go, could I ask you one very important and personal question?"

The writer paused, midstretch. "Starting right off? All right." He finished the stretch. "What?"

Cassie wanted to ask if he was married, with a sharp-chinned wife and horrid children; if he loved the color blue; if he liked sunrises or sunsets.

She took a deep breath.

"Do you write with an outline?" she asked in a hurry.

"An outline, an outline!" mimicked the writer, laughing. "Get off with you while I think about it." He picked up some sand and tossed it after her legs as she ran down the path.

Very quietly, without a fuss, Cassie taped up a large sheet of paper on the bathroom wall. It was the place most likely, she thought, for the person who had the answers to take the time to think about them. And write them down.

QUESTIONS          ANSWERS

Cassie stood back and looked at the neat lettering, the tip of her pencil in her mouth. Finally, she leaned over and wrote under "Questions":

*Why don't I have a space of my own?*

Then the sounds of the dinner guests below intruded. Cassie stood for a moment on the stairway, watching hidden from above before she went downstairs to become a character in the scene below.

Everyone had brought something for dinner. Gran had baked all day and the kitchen still smelled of homemade bread and cookies. Cassie was overjoyed to see that her mother had roasted a turkey instead of fish. The writer had brought cheese.

"What are the sticks and weeds in the salad?" asked Cassie.

"Sticks and weeds?" Cousin Coralinda, flushed from the kitchen, laughed. "Those are herbs and bean sprouts, Cassie."

"Whatever is that in the bathroom?" asked James, coming into the kitchen.

"What do you mean? What's there?" asked Cassie's mother.

"It looks to me," said Gran, "like a sheet for questions and answers. Put there, I suppose, by someone who wishes to know more. A good idea,

I might say."

Cassie grinned at Gran.

"You know I put it there," she said.

"It did look like your handwriting," said James, smiling.

The writer said nothing, but smiled at Cassie from across the table. He turned to Cassie's father.

"Your boat is beautiful," he said.

Cassie saw that her father was pleased.

"You've seen her? Yes, she is beautiful. You like boats?"

The writer nodded. "Never had much of a chance to use them. I grew up in the west, where there is not much water."

Beautiful? Cassie thought about her father's boat, solid and gray with painted decks, the smell of fish never washed away, the windows of the wheelhouse blurred and sticky with salt spray.

Cassie's father sat back. He looked past everyone there, as if reaching for something far away. "I've loved boats forever," he said softly. "When I was seven, I built a raft out of building boards and old nails. Launched it on the river."

Cassie studied him. She had hardly ever thought of him as a boy of seven. What did he look like then? Was he tall or short, curly haired, fair, sad, happy? Was he the same person as now?

After dinner, everyone gone to bed, the writer gone home to his very own sheets and towels, Cassie walked quietly into the upstairs bathroom and turned on the light. There, on the sheet of paper, was something that had not been there before. The writing was new, tall and straight. Cassie smiled. She knew who had written it. She came closer to read:

*Each of us has a space of his own. We carry it around as close as skin, as private as our dreams. What makes you think you don't have your own, too?*

Cassie's smiled faded. What did that mean? It was just like the writer to answer a question with another question, thought Cassie.

"He must have been a teacher once," she announced right out loud in the bathroom. No quick answers after all, thought Cassie unhappily. And she turned off the light, leaving herself and the questions in the dark.

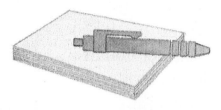

## CHECK FOR UNDERSTANDING

1. What did Cassie mean when she said from the tree, "I didn't mean it. This time"?
2. Do you think the writer is a nice person? Explain your answer.
3. What advice did the writer give Cassie about being a writer?
4. Who do you think Cassie expected to answer the question she taped to the wall?
5. Who wrote the answer to the question? What do you think the answer meant?

## WRITE ABOUT *"Questions and Answers"*

Think of three places that would be good places to leave questions so that you got answers from different kinds of people. For each place, write three questions you would like to have answered.

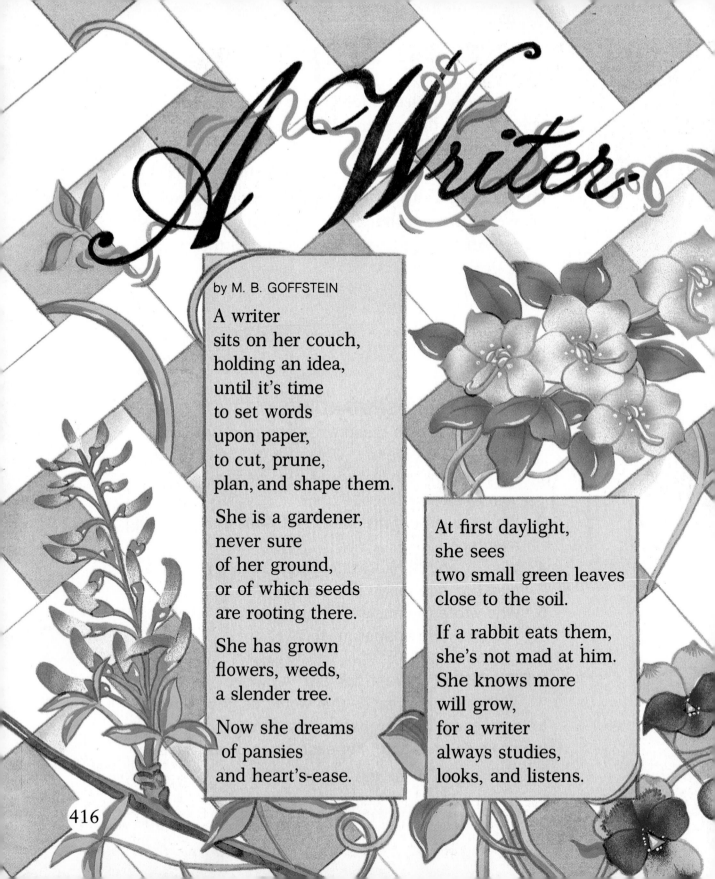

# A Writer

by M. B. GOFFSTEIN

A writer
sits on her couch,
holding an idea,
until it's time
to set words
upon paper,
to cut, prune,
plan, and shape them.

She is a gardener,
never sure
of her ground,
or of which seeds
are rooting there.

She has grown
flowers, weeds,
a slender tree.

Now she dreams
of pansies
and heart's-ease.

At first daylight,
she sees
two small green leaves
close to the soil.

If a rabbit eats them,
she's not mad at him.
She knows more
will grow,
for a writer
always studies,
looks, and listens.

Thoughts that open
in her heart,
and weather every mood
and change of mind,
she will care for.

She's only one
of many writers,
working alone
at her desk,
hoping her books
will spread the seeds
of ideas.

417

## Making an Outline

In the story we have just read, "Questions and Answers," Cassie asks the writer whether he makes an **outline** when he writes.

Why does she ask him this? There are good reasons why a writer would make an outline. An outline helps you to organize your facts. It helps you understand relationships between one fact and another. If you outline it helps you to remember to include the important facts.

Making an outline can help a reader as well as a writer. Outlining is a way to make notes in an organized fashion. It will help you to study. An outline will help you understand the material. It will help you to *make connections* between the facts. When you write things down in an organized way, it helps you to remember them.

There is a certain way of making an outline. First we ask ourselves: What is this passage about? To answer this we must **preview** it. Look at it quickly. What is it about? Look at the article on page 419. The title answers this. It's about prehistoric cave paintings. We ask another question: What are the **main topics**? (A long passage will usually have more than one.) We will find the main topics when we read the passage. For main topics in an outline we use Roman numerals, *I, II, III,* and so on.

Then we ask ourselves: What are the **subtopics**? A subtopic is a particular point the article makes *about* the main topic. To find the subtopics, we must study the material. For subtopics, we use capital letters. These we indent like a paragraph, and list, one below the other.

Now we ask ourselves: Are there any particular **facts**

about these subtopics? Under each subtopic, these will be listed. For these we use numbers.

This is the form of an outline:

I Main topic
   A. Subtopic
      1. Fact
      2. "
      3. "
   B. Subtopic
      1. Fact

II Second main topic
   A. Subtopic
      1. Fact
      2. "
      3. "
   B. Subtopic

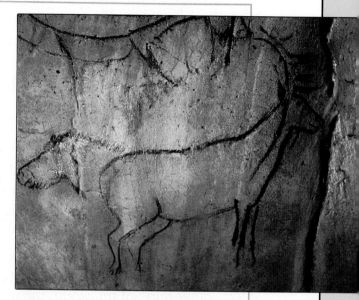

The number of main topics, subtopics, and particular facts will vary. You put in as many as you need. It depends on what is in the material you are outlining. But the *form* of the outline is always the same.

Now we are going to read "Prehistoric Cave Paintings." Then, following these steps, we will make an outline of its contents.

### Prehistoric Cave Paintings

Twenty thousand years ago, even before people wrote, they painted pictures. They did not use canvas or paper. They did their painting on big rocks and cave walls. The first discovery of this kind of art was made in Altamira, Spain, in 1875. Paintings of horses, reindeer, and people were found deep in caves. Some were paintings of animals that no longer exist, such as woolly rhinos and mammoths.

They were wonderful, lively paintings, many in color. These early artists often used hard pieces of earth, which gave them rich yellows, reds, and browns.

Mixing dishes were also found in the caves. Prehistoric artists probably mixed colors with melted fat, to make the paints go on more easily. Sometimes they used their fingers to paint. Sometimes they drew with sharpened charcoal sticks. Some used a tool still used by artists — a brush made of animal hairs.

Though prehistoric paintings have been found in other parts of the world, most of them — more than 100 — have been found in the Pyrenees Mountains in northern Spain and southern France. In Parpallo, Spain, and Niaux, France, the artists worked deep in the dark using oil lamps to see by. In 1940, more cave paintings were discovered in Lascaux, France. To get special effects, the artists dabbed colors on with fur pads. To make wispy manes and tails, they painted with feathers and twigs.

The title of your outline can be "Prehistoric Cave Paintings."

Read the article again carefully. What are the **main topics**? The article tells us *what* was shown in the paintings: the subjects. *Subjects* are a main topic. It says the subjects were animals and human figures. These are **subtopics**. The article mentions different animals. These are particular **facts** and are listed under the subtopic: *Animals*.

But the article tells us more. There is more than one main topic. It tells what tools or equipment were used to make the paintings. So, *Equipment* is the second main topic. The different tools can be listed as subtopics.

The article tells something else. Where were the paintings found? That is the third main topic.

This is what our outline would look like:

**Prehistoric Cave Paintings**

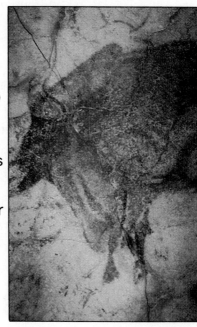

I  Subjects
   A. Animals
      1. Bison
      2. Mammoth
      3. Woolly rhino
      4. Horse
      5. Reindeer
   B. Human Figures

II  Equipment
   A. Brushes of hair
   B. Fingers
   C. Feathers
   D. Twigs
   E. Fur pads
   F. Mixing dishes
   G. Fat
   H. Pieces of colored earth
   I. Charcoal sticks

III Where Found (Pyrenees area in Europe)
- A. France
  1. Lascaux, discovered 1940
  2. Niaux
- B. Spain
  1. Altamira, discovered 1875
  2. Parpallo

How does an outline help you to learn? Why isn't it just as good to read the article very carefully?

When you make an outline, you pull out the most important facts and organize them so that related facts are together. They are not grouped that way in the article. When facts are organized in an outline they make more sense. And it is easier to remember them.

## Using What You Have Learned

Read the following passage. Then make an outline of it.

### Temporary Houses

Houses are different in different parts of the world. But no matter how different they all have two functions. Houses protect people from danger and they give shelter from cold, rain and sun.

But some people need something else from a house. It has to be easily movable, or it has to be replaced very quickly.

An Inuit's igloo is built quickly of blocks of snow. Skins pegged to the inside wall give insulation. When the Inuit move on, they leave the igloo behind. They can build another one quickly.

Pygmies living in the tropical forests also move from place to place in search of food. They stay in an area awhile. Then move on in search of food elsewhere. The Pygmies make small huts out of broad leaves. New huts can be built in less than a day.

The Plains Indians in the West also moved around, according to the season. They lived in tepees made of skins which they could easily take down and carry with them. The tepees were quickly put up at the next stopping place.

### Expanding Your Skills

Read an article in the encyclopedia. Then make an outline of it.

# KEPLIK, THE MATCH MAN

by MYRON LEVOY

Sometimes one person's private message spreads further than might be expected. If the message is important enough, even strangers pay attention to it. Mr. Keplik has one message for the train that passes by his house, but he can't believe anyone will listen.

How does Mr. Keplik treat the objects he repairs and builds? What is Mr. Keplik's masterpiece, and why is it difficult to finish?

There once was a little old man who lived in a big old tenement on Second Avenue. His name was Mr. Keplik and he had once been a watchmaker. In the window of his tiny watch-repair shop he had put up a sign that read: WHEN YOUR WRISTWATCH WON'T TICK, IT'S TIME FOR KEPLIK. Keplik loved watches and clocks and had loved repairing them. If a clock he was repairing stopped ticking he would say to himself, "Eh, eh, eh, it's dying." And when it started ticking again he would say, "I am *gebentsht.* I am blessed. It's alive."

Whenever an elevated train rumbled by overhead, Keplik would have to put down his delicate work, for his workbench and the entire shop would shake and vibrate. But Keplik would close his eyes and say, "Never mind. There are worse things. How many

people back in Lithuania wouldn't give their right eye to have a watch-repair shop under an el train in America."

While he worked Keplik never felt lonely, for there were always customers coming in with clocks and watches and complaints.

"My watch was supposed to be ready last week," a customer would say. "I need my watch! Will you have it ready by tonight, Keplik?"

And Keplik would answer, "Maybe yes, maybe no. It depends on how many el trains pass by during the rush hour." And he would point his finger up toward the el structure above.

But when Keplik grew very old, he had to give up watch repairing, for he could no longer climb up and down the three flights of stairs to his apartment. He became very lonely, for there were no longer any customers to visit him and complain. And his hands felt empty and useless, for there were no longer any gears or pivots or hairsprings or mainsprings to repair. "Terrible," said Keplik to himself. "I'm too young to be old. I will take up a hobby. Perhaps I should build a clock out of walnut shells. Or make a rose garden out of red crepe paper and green silk. Or make a windmill out of wooden matchsticks. I'll see what I have in the house."

There were no walnuts and no crepe paper, but there were lots and lots of burned matchsticks, for, in those days, the gas stoves had to be lit with a match every time you wanted a scrambled egg or a cup of hot cocoa. So Keplik started to build a little windmill out of matches.

Within a month's time, the windmill was finished. Keplik put it on his kitchen table and started to blow like the east wind. The arms turned slowly, then faster, just like a real windmill. "I'm gebentsht," said Keplik. "It's alive."

Next, Keplik decided to make a castle, complete with a drawbridge. But the matches were expensive; he would need hundreds and hundreds for a castle. So he put a little sign outside his apartment door, and another in his window: USED MATCHSTICKS BOUGHT HERE. A PENNY FOR FIFTY. IF YOU HAVE A MATCHSTICK, SELL IT TO KEPLIK.

The word spread up and down the block very quickly, and soon there were children at Keplik's door with bags and boxes of used matches. Keplik showed them the windmill on the kitchen table and invited them to blow like the east wind. And Keplik was happy, because he had visitors again and lots of work for his hands.

Day after day, week after week, Keplik glued and fitted the matches together. And finally the castle stood completed, with red and blue flags flying from every turret. The children brought toy soldiers and laid siege to the castle, while Keplik pulled up the drawbridge.

Next, Keplik made a big birdcage out of matches, and put a real canary in it. The bird sang and flew back and forth while the delicate cage swung on its hook. "Ah ha," said Keplik. "The cage is alive. And so is the canary. I am double gebentsht."

Then he made little airplanes and jewelry boxes from matchsticks and gave them to the boys and girls who visited him. And the children began calling him "the Match Man."

One day, Keplik decided that

it was time for a masterpiece. "I am at my heights as an artist," Keplik said to himself. "No more windmills. No more birdcages. I am going to make the Woolworth Building. Or the Eiffel Tower. Or the Brooklyn Bridge. Eh . . . eh . . . but which?"

And after much thought, he decided that a bridge would be better than a tower or a skyscraper, because if he built a bridge he wouldn't have to cut a hole in the ceiling. The Brooklyn Bridge would be his masterpiece. It would run across the living room from the kitchen to the bedroom, and the two towers would stand as high as his head. "For this I need matches!" Keplik said aloud. "Matches! I must have matches."

And he posted a new sign: MATCH FOR MATCH, YOU CANNOT MATCH KEPLIK'S PRICE FOR USED MATCHES.

ONE CENT FOR FIFTY. HURRY! HURRY! HURRY!

Vincent DeMarco, who lived around the corner, brought fifty matches that very afternoon, and Cathy Dunn and Noreen Callahan brought a hundred matches each the next morning. Day after day, the matches kept coming, and day after day, Keplik the Match Man glued and fixed and bent and pressed the matches into place.

The bridge was so complicated that Keplik had decided to build it in separate sections, and then join all the sections afterward. The bridge's support towers, the end spans, and the center span slowly took shape in different parts of the room. The room seemed to grow smaller as the bridge grew larger. A masterpiece, thought Keplik. There is no longer room for me to sit in my favorite chair. But I must have more matches! It's time to build the cables!

429

Even the long support cables were made from matchsticks, split and glued and twisted together. Keplik would twist the sticks until his fingers grew numb. Then he would go into the kitchen to make a cup of soup for himself, not so much for the soup, but for the fact that lighting the stove would provide him with yet another matchstick. And sometimes, as he was having his soup, he would get up and take a quick look at his bridge, because it always looked different when he was away from it for a while. "It's beginning to be alive," he would say.

And then one night, it was time for the great final step. The towers and spans and

cables all had to be joined together to give the finished structure. A most difficult job. For everything was supported from the cables above, as in a real bridge, and all the final connections had to be glued and tied almost at the same moment. Nothing must shift or slip for a full half hour, until the glue dried thoroughly.

Keplik worked carefully, his watchmaker's hands steadily gluing and pressing strut after strut, cable after cable. The end spans were in place. The center span was ready. Glue, press, glue, press. Then suddenly, an el train rumbled by outside. The ground trembled, the old tenement shivered as it always did, the windows rattled

431

slightly, and the center span slid from its glued moorings. Then one of the end cables vibrated loose, then another, and the bridge slipped slowly apart into separate spans and towers. "Eh, eh, eh," said Keplik. "It's dying."

Keplik tried again, but another train hurtled past from the other direction. And again the bridge slowly slipped apart. I am too tired, thought Keplik. I'll try again tomorrow.

Keplik decided to wait until late the next night, when there would be fewer trains. But again, as the bridge was almost completed, a train roared past, the house shook, and everything slipped apart. Again and again, Keplik tried, using extra supports and tying parts together. But the bridge seemed to enjoy waiting for the next train to shake it apart again.

Ah me, thought Keplik. All my life those el trains shook the watches in my hands, down below in my shop. All my life I said things could be worse; how many people back in Lithuania wouldn't give their left foot to have a watch-repair shop under an el train in America.

But why do the el trains have to follow me three flights up? Why can't they leave me alone in my old age? When I die, will there be an el train over my grave? Will I be shaken and rattled around while I'm trying to take a little well-deserved snooze? And when I reach heaven, will there be an el train there, too, so I can't even play a nice, soothing tune on a harp without all this *tummel,* this noise? It's much too much for me. This is it. The end. The bridge will be a masterpiece in parts. The Brooklyn Bridge after an earthquake.

At that moment, another el train roared by and Keplik the

Match Man called toward the train, "One thing I'll *never* do! I'll never make an el train out of matches! Never! How do you like *that!*"

When the children came the next afternoon, to see if the bridge was finished at last, Keplik told them of his troubles with the el trains. "The bridge, my children, is *farpotshket*. You know what that means? A mess!" The children made all sorts of suggestions: hold it this way, fix it that way, glue it here, tie it

there. But to all of them, Keplik the Match Man shook his head. "Impossible. I've tried that. Nothing works."

Then Vincent DeMarco said, "My father works at an el station uptown. He knows all the drivers, he says. Maybe he can get them to stop the trains."

Keplik laughed. "Ah, such a nice idea. But no one can stop the Second Avenue el."

"I'll bet my father can," said Vincent.

"Bet he can't," said Joey

433

Basuto. And just then, a train sped by: *raketa, raketa, raketa, raketa.* "The trains never stop for anything," said Joey.

And the children went home for dinner, disappointed that the bridge made from all their matchsticks was farpoot . . . farbot . . . *whatever* that word was. A mess.

Vincent told his father, but Mr. DeMarco shrugged. "No. Impossible. Impossible," he said. "I'm not important enough."

"But couldn't you *try?*" pleaded Vincent.

"I know *one* driver. So what good's that, huh? One driver. All I do is make change in the booth."

"Maybe that driver will tell everybody else."

"*Assurdita.* Nonsense. They have more to worry about than Mr. Keplik's bridge. Eat your soup!"

But Mr. DeMarco thought to himself that if he did happen to see his friend, the driver, maybe, just for a laugh, he'd mention it. . . .

Two days later, Vincent ran upstairs to Keplik's door and knocked. *Tonight* his father had said! Tonight at 1 A.M.! Keplik couldn't believe his ears. The trains would stop for his bridge? It couldn't be. Someone was playing a joke on Vincent's father.

But that night, Keplik prepared, just in case it was true. Everything was ready: glue, thread, supports, towers, spans, cables.

A train clattered by at five minutes to one. Then silence. Rapidly, rapidly, Keplik worked. Press, glue, press, glue. One cable connected. Two cables. Three. Four. First tower finished. Fifth cable connected. Sixth. Seventh. Eighth. Other tower in place. Now gently, gently. Center span in position.

Glue, press, glue, press. Tie threads. Tie more threads. Easy. Easy. Everything balanced. Everything supported. Now please. No trains till it dries.

The minutes ticked by. Keplik was sweating. Still no train. The bridge was holding. The bridge was finished. And then, outside the window, he saw an el train creeping along, slowly, carefully: *cla . . . keta . . . cla . . . keta . . . cla . . . keta . . . cla . . . keta. . . .* Then another, moving slowly from the other direction: *cla . . . keta . . . cla . . . keta . . .*

And Keplik shouted toward the trains, "Thank you, Driver!

Tomorrow, I am going to start a great new masterpiece! The Second Avenue el from Fourteenth Street to Delancey Street! Thank you for slowing up your trains!"

And first one driver, then the other, blew the train whistle as the trains moved on, into the night beyond. "Ah, how I am gebentsht," said Keplik to himself. "In America there are kind people everywhere. All my life, the el train has shaken my hands. But tonight,

435

it has shaken my heart."

Keplik worked for the rest of the night on a little project. And the next morning, Keplik hung his sign made from matches outside his window, where every passing el train driver could see it:

## CHECK FOR UNDERSTANDING

1. What was Mr. Keplik's profession? What interfered with his work?
2. How did Mr. Keplik treat the objects he repaired and built?
3. What did Mr. Keplik miss when he stopped repairing watches?
4. In what two ways did Mr. Keplik's hobby make him happier?
5. What was Mr. Keplik's masterpiece? Why was it difficult for him to finish?
6. What does *gebentsht* mean? Why did Mr. Keplik say, "I am gebentsht" at the end of the story?

## WRITE ABOUT *"Keplik, the Match Man"*

Suppose you were a newspaper reporter who found out about Mr. Keplik and the el trains. Write a three-paragraph news story about it. Remember to answer the questions Who, What, Where, When, and Why in your story.

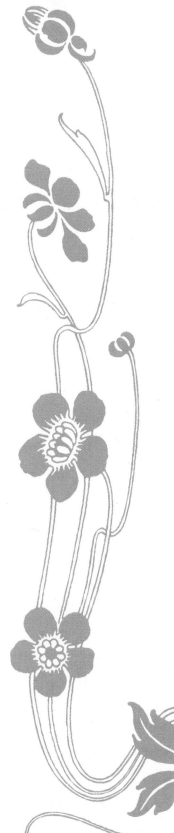

# 馬日木

# *Chinese Writing*

**by DIANE WOLFF**

**Messages can be sent in many ways: in letters, on signs, in codes, and in spoken words. But did you know that some messages are a form of art? In this selection, you will learn about Chinese writing.**

**Why was the language of *putong hua* so important to China? Besides their meaning, what else is important about Chinese words?**

China is a country about the same size as the United States. One-fourth of all the people in the world live there. With a five-thousand-year history, the Chinese are credited with the invention of paper, printing, silk, porcelain, spaghetti, and other things. They have beautiful sculpture, painting, architecture, furniture, costumes, and gardens.

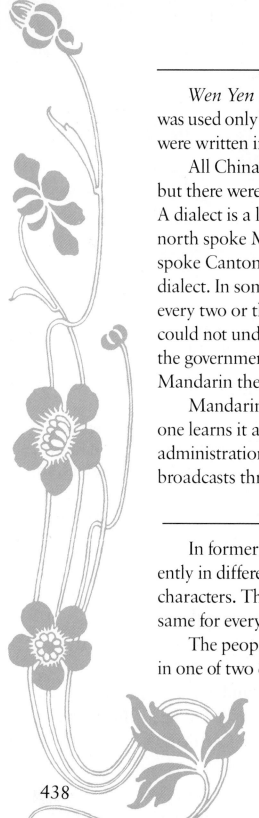

## CHINA'S LANGUAGES

*Wen Yen* is the ancient classical language of China. It was used only for writing and was never spoken. All books were written in classical Chinese.

All China had the same written language, *wen yen,* but there were hundreds of different spoken **dialects.** A dialect is a local language. Most of the people in the north spoke Mandarin, while the people in the south spoke Cantonese. People from Shanghai spoke Shanghai dialect. In some places in the south, the dialect changed every two or three miles. People in neighboring villages could not understand each other. To solve this problem, the government of the People's Republic of China made Mandarin the national language.

Mandarin or *putong hua* is now widely used. Everyone learns it at school. It is the standard language of the administration and can be heard on radio and television broadcasts throughout China.

## THE CHARACTER

In former times, even though the people spoke differently in different parts of China, they all read the same characters. The written word, the **character,** was the same for everyone.

The peoples of the world write their languages down in one of two different ways: alphabets or pictures. English is an **alphabet language.** Alphabets are used to write the sound of a word. They usually have one symbol for every sound. An alphabet word makes sense to your ear. A **picture language** makes sense to your eye. Chinese is a picture language. There is one picture for every word. Sometimes, this one picture will be made up of a number of smaller pictures put together.

Picture-words can be made in several ways. The simplest way is to draw the animal, plant, person, or object. Notice the pictures in ancient Chinese:

SUN ☉   MOON ☾   WATER 川   GATE 門

Words were combined to make new words:

SUN 日 AND MOON 月 TOGETHER MEAN "BRIGHT." 明

WOMAN 女 AND CHILD 子 TOGETHER MEAN "LOVE." 好

BRAIN 田 AND HEART 心 TOGETHER MEAN "THINK." 思

The basic idea of Chinese picture-words has stayed the same for thousands of years. But when the writing-brush came into use, the words got a new appearance. The ancient style of writing was rounder and had more detail. With the brush, the writing became squarer and had very little detail. The examples on the next page show this change.

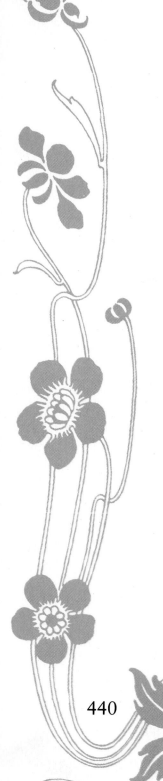

|  | ANCIENT | MODERN |
|---|---|---|
| SUN | ⊖ | 日 |
| MOON | Ɖ | 月 |

## THE ART OF CALLIGRAPHY

In China beautiful handwriting, or **calligraphy,** is considered a great art. Although the Chinese were the first people to invent printing, they find the written word more beautiful than the printed word.

Calligraphy is the art of writing characters. Because the Chinese love beauty, they make each character pleasing to the eye. By putting many characters together, the whole piece becomes a piece of art.

Chinese words make sense to the eye. The keys to the art of calligraphy are movement, balance, flow, and energy. Not only the *meaning* of the character, but the *way* it is written is important.

To write characters, the Chinese use many different kinds of lines. The lines of Chinese writing are called **strokes,** and they must appear alive — sitting, walking, or standing firmly.

## WRITING CHINESE WORDS

Here are some words for you to practice. The character is given, along with its meaning and its pronunciation. The ancient character is given when it will help you understand how the modern word came to be. The characters are simple

440

everyday words which are easy to understand and easy to write. The order for putting the strokes together to form a character is called stroke order. Correct stroke order is essential for calligraphy. It is included here to show you how to write the word, step by step. Just follow along, until you have the whole character.

MAN
*(ren)*

This word is a drawing of a man walking.

Stroke Order: 丿 人

BIG
*(da)*

Man with an additional stroke, indicating out-stretched arms, suggests bigness.

Stroke Order: 一 ナ 大

WOMAN
*(nyu)*

The above word is the modern version of 内.

Stroke Order: く 夂 女

441

**RAIN**
*(yu)*

The ancient word for rain is a cloud with drops of water falling. 雨

Stroke Order: 一 厂 冂 雨 雨 雨 雨 雨

**TREE**
*(mu)*

In this drawing of a tree, the vertical stroke represents the trunk. The horizontal stroke represents branches, and the sweeping strokes stand for roots.

林 Two trees together is the word for forest.

森 Three trees together means thicket.

Stroke Order: 一 十 才 木

**SUN**
*(r)*

The old drawing was 日 , a good example of how Chinese was round in the ancient writing and became square.

442

Stroke Order: 丨 冂 日 日

HORSE
*(ma)*

A very good drawing of a horse. Broken down, 耳 is the neck with the mane flying, ㄱ is the back and tail, ꞏꞏꞏꞏ are the four legs.

Stroke Order: 一 厂 厂 厍 厍
馬 馬 馬 馬 馬

## CHECK FOR UNDERSTANDING

1. Why was the language of *putong hua* so important to China?
2. What is the main difference between the English and Chinese languages?
3. When did Chinese writing begin to get a new appearance?
4. What were some of the differences between the ancient and modern characters?
5. Besides their meaning, what else is important about Chinese words?

## WRITE ABOUT *"Chinese Writing"*

Use the information in this selection to write a short article about the art of Chinese calligraphy for the school newspaper.

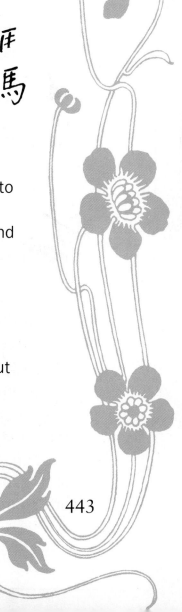

443

# LITERATURE

## Identifying Characters

If a story is well-written, it is easy to forget that everything in it was put in there for a purpose. A good story seems to flow from one event to another as naturally as real life. The author deliberately tries to get you to forget that what you are reading is the result of hard work.

The hard work of writing is choosing what to say. After all, if you set out to write about characters, there is no limit to what you might say about them. It might be said that the hardest work in writing a story is deciding what to *leave out.*

Because every author thinks so hard about what to put into a story, you can bet that very little gets into a story by accident. That means in turn that every detail in the story has a purpose. This is especially true of what the author tells you (and *does not* tell you) about the characters.

The author doesn't want to interrupt the natural feeling of the story by listing a lot of details about a character. At the same time, you can't understand or enjoy a story without a good grasp of the characters. To solve this problem, authors reveal what characters are like in other ways. This means that almost every detail you learn about a character has some importance.

The way a character behaves is important. If a character's reaction to something is a *shrug* instead of a *smile,* that reveals something. What a character *says* is important, as well as *how* the character says it. In a particular situation, the character speaking in a clear, loud voice means something different from the same words in a soft, stammering voice.

444

As you read a story, pay special attention to the adjectives and adverbs the author chooses when referring to a character. These words often give you a good idea of what the author wants you to think of the character. But most of all, remember that the author has included details about characters on purpose. Every time a character does or says something, ask yourself why the author had the character do or say this. Consider this as you read the passage from "Questions and Answers." The details that reveal character are in dark type.

Cassie's mother walked up the path and into the hidden yard where the small cottage stood.

"Is everything all right?" she **called** to him.

"Fine." He **turned and smiled at her.** "First things first. **I'm feeding the birds.**"

"Come for dinner tonight," said Cassie's mother. "You can meet everyone. Then we'll leave you on your own."

Cassie's mother went off again, **humming to herself. When she had disappeared, the writer walked over to the tree and looked up.**

"You can come down now, **little bird.**"

Cassie **sighed** and climbed down the tree.

"I didn't mean it. **This time,**" she added, **red-faced.**

As you read other stories in this book, think carefully about what the author reveals about the characters. The more you understand *why* they do and say what they do, the more you will enjoy the story.

Can you think of a worse feeling in the world
than loneliness? Maybe the only thing that is worse
is being lonely on a rainy day. Perhaps what's even
worse is being lonely on a rainy day and getting medicine instead of friendship. For Wilbur, the only friendly
message he gets on his lonely, rainy day comes from
a small voice whose owner he cannot see.

What part of Wilbur's plans does the rain ruin?
Why isn't Wilbur eating?

BY E. B. WHITE

**Just·A·Taste**

# Loneliness

The next day was rainy and dark. Rain fell on
the roof of the barn and dripped steadily from the
eaves. Rain fell in the barnyard and ran in crooked
courses down into the lane where thistles and pig-
weed grew. Rain spattered against Mrs. Zuckerman's kitchen windows and came gushing out of the
downspouts. Rain fell on the backs of the sheep as
they grazed in the meadow. When the sheep tired of
standing in the rain, they walked slowly up the lane
and into the fold.

Rain upset Wilbur's plans. Wilbur had planned
to go out, this day, and dig a new hole in his yard.
He had other plans, too. His plans for the day went
something like this:

Breakfast at six-thirty. Skim milk, crusts, middlings, bits of doughnuts, wheat cakes with drops of
maple syrup sticking to them, potato skins, leftover
custard pudding with raisins, and bits of Shredded
Wheat.

Breakfast would be finished at seven.

From seven to eight, Wilbur planned to have a
talk with Templeton, the rat that lived under his
trough. Talking with Templeton was not the most

interesting occupation in the world but it was better than nothing.

From eight to nine, Wilbur planned to take a nap outdoors in the sun.

From nine to eleven he planned to dig a hole, or trench, and possibly find something good to eat buried in the dirt.

From eleven to twelve he planned to stand still and watch flies on the boards, watch bees in the clover, and watch swallows in the air.

Twelve o'clock—lunchtime. Middlings, warm water, apple parings, meat gravy, carrot scrapings, meat scraps, stale hominy, and the wrapper off a package of cheese. Lunch would be over at one.

From one to two, Wilbur planned to sleep.

From two to three, he planned to scratch itchy places by rubbing against the fence.

From three to four, he planned to stand perfectly still and think of what it was like to be alive, and to wait for Fern.

At four would come supper. Skim milk, provender, leftover sandwich from Lurvy's lunchbox, prune skins, a morsel of this, a bit of that, fried potatoes, marmalade drippings, a little more of this, a little more of that, a piece of baked apple, a scrap of up-sidedown cake.

Wilbur had gone to sleep thinking about these plans. He awoke at six and saw the rain, and it seemed as though he couldn't bear it.

"I get everything all beautifully planned out and it has to go and rain," he said.

For a while he stood gloomily indoors. Then he walked to the door and looked out. Drops of rain struck his face. His yard was cold and wet. His

trough had an inch of rainwater in it. Templeton was nowhere to be seen.

"Are you out there, Templeton?" called Wilbur. There was no answer. Suddenly Wilbur felt lonely and friendless.

"One day just like another," he groaned. "I'm very young, I have no real friend here in the barn, it's going to rain all morning and all afternoon, and Fern won't come in such bad weather. Oh, *honestly!*" And Wilbur was crying again, for the second time in two days.

At six-thirty Wilbur heard the banging of a pail. Lurvy was standing outside in the rain, stirring up breakfast.

"C'mon, pig!" said Lurvy.

Wilbur did not budge. Lurvy dumped the slops, scraped the pail, and walked away. He noticed that something was wrong with the pig.

Wilbur didn't want food, he wanted love. He wanted a friend—someone who would play with him. He mentioned this to the goose, who was sitting quietly in a corner of the sheepfold.

"Will you come over and play with me?" he asked.

"Sorry, sonny, sorry," said the goose. "I'm sitting-sitting on my eggs. Eight of them. Got to keep them toasty-oasty-oasty warm. I have to stay right here, I'm no flibberty-ibberty-gibbet. I do not play when there are eggs to hatch. I'm expecting goslings."

"Well, I didn't think you were expecting woodpeckers," said Wilbur, bitterly.

Wilbur next tried one of the lambs.

"Will you please play with me?" he asked.

"Certainly not," said the lamb. "In the first place, I cannot get into your pen, as I am not old enough to jump over the fence. In the second place, I am not interested in pigs. Pigs mean less than nothing to me."

"What do you mean, *less* than nothing?" replied Wilbur. "I don't think there is any such thing as *less* than nothing. Nothing is absolutely the limit of nothingness. It's the lowest you can go. It's the end

of the line. How can something be less than nothing? If there were something that was less than nothing, then nothing would not be nothing, it would be something—even though it's just a very little bit of something. But if nothing is *nothing*, then nothing has nothing that is less than *it* is."

"Oh, be quiet!" said the lamb. "Go play by yourself! I don't play with pigs."

Sadly, Wilbur lay down and listened to the rain. Soon he saw the rat climbing down a slanting board that he used as a stairway.

"Will you play with me, Templeton?" asked Wilbur.

"Play?" said Templeton, twirling his whiskers. "Play? I hardly know the meaning of the word."

"Well," said Wilbur, "it means to have fun, to frolic, to run and skip and make merry."

"I never do those things if I can avoid them," replied the rat, sourly. "I prefer to spend my time eating, gnawing, spying, and hiding. I am a glutton but not a merrymaker. Right now I am on my way to your trough to eat your breakfast, since you haven't got sense enough to eat it yourself." And Templeton, the rat, crept stealthily along the wall and disappeared into a private tunnel that he had dug between the door and the trough in Wilbur's yard. Templeton was a crafty rat, and he had things pretty much his own way. The tunnel was an example of his skill and cunning. The tunnel enabled him to get from the barn to his hiding place under the pig trough without coming out into the open. He had tunnels and runways all over Mr. Zuckerman's farm and could get from one place to another without being seen. Usually he slept during the daytime and was abroad only after dark.

Wilbur watched him disappear into his tunnel. In a moment he saw the rat's sharp nose poke out from underneath the wooden trough. Curiously Templeton pulled himself up over the edge of the trough. This was almost more than Wilbur could stand: on this dreary, rainy day to see his breakfast being eaten by somebody else. He knew Templeton was getting soaked, out there in the pouring rain, but even that didn't comfort him. Friendless, dejected, and hungry, he threw himself down in the manure and sobbed.

Late that afternoon, Lurvy went to Mr. Zuckerman. "I think there's something wrong with that pig of yours. He hasn't touched his food."

"Give him two spoonfuls of sulphur and a little molasses," said Mr. Zuckerman.

Wilbur couldn't believe what was happening to him when Lurvy caught him and forced the medicine down his throat. This certainly was the worst day of his life. He didn't know whether he could endure the awful loneliness any more.

Darkness settled over everything. Soon there were only shadows and the noises of the sheep chewing their cuds, and occasionally the rattle of a cow-chain up overhead. You can imagine Wilbur's surprise when, out of the darkness, came a small voice he had never heard before. It sounded rather thin, but pleasant. "Do you want a friend, Wilbur?"

it said. "I'll be a friend to you. I've watched you all day and I like you."

"But I can't see you," said Wilbur, jumping to his feet. "Where are you? And *who* are you?"

"I'm right up here," said the voice. "Go to sleep. You'll see me in the morning."

The night seemed long. Wilbur's stomach was empty and his mind was full. And when your stomach is empty and your mind is full, it's always hard to sleep.

A dozen times during the night Wilbur woke and stared into the blackness, listening to the sounds and trying to figure out what time it was. A barn is never perfectly quiet. Even at midnight there is usually something stirring.

The first time he woke, he heard Templeton gnawing a hole in the grain bin. Templeton's teeth scraped loudly against the wood and made quite a racket. "That crazy rat!" thought Wilbur. "Why does he have to stay up all night, grinding his clashers and destroying people's property? Why can't he go to sleep, like any decent animal?"

The second time Wilbur woke, he heard the goose turning on her nest and chuckling to herself.

"What time is it?" whispered Wilbur to the goose.

"Probably-obably-obably about half-past eleven," said the goose. "Why aren't you asleep, Wilbur?"

"Too many things on my mind," said Wilbur.

"Well," said the goose, "that's not *my* trouble. I have nothing at all on my mind, but I've too many things under my behind. Have you ever tried to sleep while sitting on eight eggs?"

"No," replied Wilbur. "I suppose it *is* uncomfortable. How long does it take a goose egg to hatch?"

"Approximately-oximately thirty days, all told," answered the goose. "But I cheat a little. On warm afternoons, I just pull a little straw over the eggs and go out for a walk."

Wilbur yawned and went back to sleep. In his dreams he heard again the voice saying, "I'll be a friend to you. Go to sleep—you'll see me in the morning."

About half an hour before dawn, Wilbur woke and listened. The barn was still dark. The sheep lay motionless. Even the goose was quiet. Overhead, on the main floor, nothing stirred: the cows were resting, the horses dozed. Templeton had quit work and gone off somewhere on an errand. The only sound was a slight scraping noise from the rooftop, where the weather vane swung back and forth. Wilbur loved the barn when it was like this—calm and quiet, waiting for light.

"Day is almost here," he thought.

Through a small window, a faint gleam appeared. One by one the stars went out. Wilbur could see the goose a few feet away. She sat with head tucked under a wing. Then he could see the sheep and the lambs. The sky lightened.

"Oh, beautiful day, it is here at last! Today I shall find my friend."

Wilbur looked everywhere. He searched his pen thoroughly. He examined the window ledge, stared up at the ceiling. But he saw nothing new. Finally he decided he would have to speak up. He hated to break the lovely stillness of dawn by using his voice, but he couldn't think of any other way to locate the mysterious new friend who was nowhere to be seen. So Wilbur cleared his throat.

"Attention, please!" he said in a loud, firm voice. "Will the party who addressed me at bedtime last night kindly make himself or herself known by giving an appropriate sign or signal!"

Wilbur paused and listened. All the other animals lifted their heads and stared at him. Wilbur blushed. But he was determined to get in touch with his unknown friend.

"Attention, please!" he said. "I will repeat the message. Will the party who addressed me at bedtime last night kindly speak up. Please tell me where you are, if you are my friend!"

The sheep looked at each other in disgust.

"Stop your nonsense, Wilbur!" said the oldest sheep. "If you have a new friend here, you are probably disturbing his rest; and the quickest way to spoil a friendship is to wake somebody up in the morning before he is ready. How can you be sure your friend is an early riser?"

"I beg everyone's pardon," whispered Wilbur. "I didn't mean to be objectionable."

He lay down meekly in the manure, facing the door. He did not know it, but his friend was very near. And the old sheep was right—the friend was still asleep.

Soon Lurvy appeared with slops for breakfast. Wilbur rushed out, ate everything in a hurry, and licked the trough. The sheep moved off down the lane, the gander waddled along behind them, pulling grass. And then, just as Wilbur was settling down for his morning nap, he heard again the thin voice that had addressed him the night before.

"Salutations!" said the voice.

Wilbur jumped to his feet. "Salu-*what?*" he cried.

"Salutations!" repeated the voice.

"What are *they,* and where are *you?*" screamed Wilbur. "Please, *please,* tell me where you are. And what are salutations?"

"Salutations are greetings," said the voice. "When I say 'salutations,' it's just my fancy way of saying hello or good morning. Actually, it's a silly expression, and I am surprised that I used it at all. As for my whereabouts, that's easy. Look up here in the corner of the doorway! Here I am. Look, I'm waving!"

At last Wilbur saw the creature that had spoken
to him in such a kindly way. Stretched across the
upper part of the doorway was a big spiderweb.
And hanging from the top of the web, head down,
was a large gray spider. She was about the size of a
gumdrop. She had eight legs, and she was waving
one of them at Wilbur in friendly greeting. "See me
now?" she asked.

"Oh, yes indeed," said Wilbur. "Yes indeed!
How are you? Good morning! Salutations! Very

pleased to meet you. What is your name, please? May I have your name?"

"My name," said the spider, "is Charlotte."

"Charlotte what?" asked Wilbur, eagerly.

"Charlotte A. Cavatica. But just call me Charlotte."

"I think you're beautiful," said Wilbur.

"Well, I *am* pretty," replied Charlotte. "There's no denying that. Almost all spiders are rather nice-looking. I'm not as flashy as some, but I'll do. I wish I could see you, Wilbur, as clearly as you can see me."

"Why can't you?" asked the pig. "I'm right here."

"Yes, but I'm nearsighted," replied Charlotte. "I've always been dreadfully nearsighted. It's good in some ways, not so good in others. Watch me wrap up this fly."

A fly that had been crawling along Wilbur's trough had flown up and blundered into the lower part of Charlotte's web and was tangled in the sticky threads. The fly was beating its wings furiously, trying to break loose and free itself.

"First," said Charlotte, "I dive at him." She plunged headfirst toward the fly. As she dropped, a tiny silken thread unwound from her rear end.

"Next, I wrap him up." She grabbed the fly, threw a few jets of silk around it, and rolled it over and over, wrapping it so that it couldn't move. Wilbur watched in horror. He could hardly believe what he was seeing, and although he detested flies, he was sorry for this one.

"There!" said Charlotte. "Now I knock him out, so he'll be more comfortable." She bit the fly. "He can't feel a thing now," she remarked. "He'll make a perfect breakfast for me."

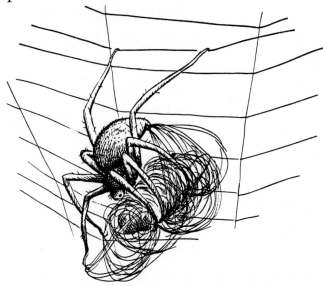

"You mean you *eat* flies?" gasped Wilbur.

"Certainly. Flies, bugs, grasshoppers, choice beetles, moths, butterflies, tasty cockroaches, gnats, midges, daddy-longlegs, centipedes, mosquitoes, crickets—anything that is careless enough to get caught in my web. I have to live, don't I?"

"Why, yes, of course," said Wilbur. "Do they taste good?"

"Delicious. Of course, I don't really eat them. I drink them—drink their blood. I love blood," said Charlotte, and her pleasant, thin voice grew even thinner and more pleasant.

"Don't say that!" groaned Wilbur. "Please don't say things like that!"

"Why not? It's true, and I have to say what is true. I am not entirely happy about my diet of flies and bugs, but it's the way I'm made. A spider has to pick up a living somehow or other, and I happen to be a trapper. I just naturally build a web and trap flies and other insects. My mother was a trapper before me. Her mother was a trapper before her. All our family have been trappers. Way back for thousands and thousands of years we spiders have been laying for flies and bugs."

"It's a miserable inheritance," said Wilbur, gloomily. He was sad because his new friend was so bloodthirsty.

"Yes, it is," agreed Charlotte. "But I can't help it. I don't know how the first spider in the early days of the world happened to think up this fancy idea of spinning a web, but she did, and it was clever of her, too. And since then, all of us spiders have had to work the same trick. It's not a bad pitch, on the whole."

"It's cruel," replied Wilbur, who did not intend to be argued out of his position.

"Well, *you* can't talk," said Charlotte. "*You* have your meals brought to you in a pail. Nobody feeds me. I have to get my own living. I live by my wits. I have to be sharp and clever, lest I go hungry.

I have to think things out, catch what I can, take what comes. And it just so happens, my friend, that what comes is flies and insects and bugs. And *fur-ther*more," said Charlotte, shaking one of her legs, "do you realize that if I didn't catch bugs and eat them, bugs would increase and multiply and get so numerous that they'd destroy the earth, wipe out everything?"

"Really?" said Wilbur. "I wouldn't want *that* to happen. Perhaps your web is a good thing after all."

The goose had been listening to this conversation and chuckling to herself. "There are a lot of things Wilbur doesn't know about life," she thought. "He's really a very innocent little pig. He doesn't even know what's going to happen to him around Christmastime. He has no idea that Mr. Zuckerman and Lurvy are plotting to kill him." And the goose raised herself a bit and poked her eggs a little further under her so that they would receive the full heat from her warm body and soft feathers.

Charlotte stood quietly over the fly, preparing to eat it. Wilbur lay down and closed his eyes. He was tired from his wakeful night and from the excitement of meeting someone for the first time. A breeze brought him the smell of clover—the sweet-smelling world beyond his fence. "Well," he thought, "I've got a new friend, all right. But what a gamble friendship is! Charlotte is fierce, brutal, scheming, bloodthirsty—everything I don't like. How can I learn to like her, even though she is pretty and, of course, clever?"

Wilbur was merely suffering the doubts and fears that often go with finding a new friend. In good time he was to discover that he was mistaken about Charlotte. Underneath her rather bold and cruel exterior, she had a kind heart, and she was to prove loyal and true to the very end.

*Before long, Wilbur learns of his owner's plan to kill him. Read the rest of the novel* Charlotte's Web *by E.B. White, to find out how his new friend tries to save his life.*

## CHECK FOR UNDERSTANDING

1. Where did the story take place?
2. What part of Wilbur's plans did the rain ruin?
3. Why wasn't Wilbur eating?
4. Why didn't the goose or the lamb play with Wilbur?
5. How does Charlotte get her meals? Explain your answer.
6. How might the goose have found out about Mr. Zuckerman's plans for Wilbur?
7. What did Wilbur mean when he said that friendship was "a gamble"?

## WRITE ABOUT *"Loneliness"*

Have you ever had a lonely day like Wilbur's? Write a letter to Wilbur. List ten things that he could do the next time he feels lonely.

# THINK ABOUT IT

Think about the characters in the stories you have read. What important role did a message play in what happened to each character?

- What *unspoken* message did Tad Novak give Mr. James by writing *BABE* in Braille?
- How were the messages Richard and Janet sent each other about playing baseball probably more useful than their talking in person?
- How will the message Cassie received help her to be a writer?
- What made the people running the trains pay special attention to Mr. Keplik's message?
- What message did Wilbur want most to hear, and how did he finally hear it?

After reading and thinking about these different kinds of messages, how would you say a message is different from other ways of sending information?

# WRITE ABOUT IT

Imagine that you want to send a message to someone, but you want your message to be a secret. You also don't want the person receiving the message to guess that you sent it. Describe in a paragraph how you would send the message.

# READ ABOUT IT

*Communication* by Ruth and Irving Adler. The John Day Company, 1967. This book tells the story of communication from earliest times. Included are sections on how communication helps the growth of knowledge, and the different methods of communication.

*Communications Satellites: Message Centers in Space* by Bernice Kohn. Four Winds Press, 1975. The author discusses the work of early science-fiction writers, the investigations of space flight pioneers such as Goddard, and the development of the liquid fuel rocket. She notes the improvements that have been made in communication satellites and anticipates the ways in which they will serve humanity.

*Secret Language* by Ursula Nordstrom. Harper & Row, Publishers, 1960. Victoria dislikes the idea of boarding school, but she changes her mind after meeting Martha. Martha teaches her the secret language and gradually Victoria begins to like school, and especially her new friend Martha.

*Sending Messages* by John Warren Stewig. Houghton Mifflin Company, 1978. Various means of communication are presented in pictures and words. Personal and professional message systems are explored.

*Words: A Book About the Origins of Everyday Words and Phrases* by Jane Sarnoff and Reynold Ruffins. Charles Scribner's Sons, 1981. This book traces the origins of common American-English words and phrases, and explains how the English language developed and words are formed.

# 6

# DARE TO TRY

What do you think of as a daring adventure? Is it doing something that is exciting, or doing something that you have never done before? As you will see in this unit, danger often goes hand in hand with daring adventures.

As you read the stories, ask yourself whether the characters could choose not to face the danger they do. Think about what makes each character face danger rather than give up.

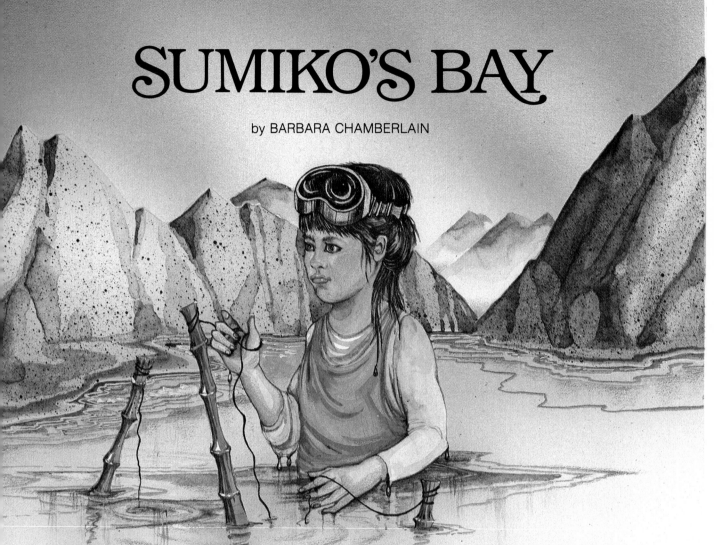

# SUMIKO'S BAY

by BARBARA CHAMBERLAIN

There are many different and interesting ways to earn a living. Sumiko and her grandmother raise oysters and then sell the pearls. But now thieves are stealing Sumiko's treasured pearls, and she is determined to catch them.

What makes Sumiko believe that thieves, and not shellfish, are destroying the oyster beds? Why do Sumiko and her grandmother have to take matters into their own hands?

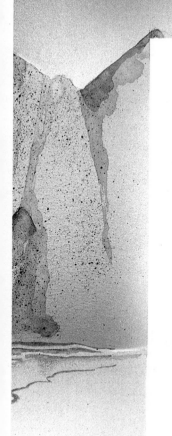

Sumiko found the broken threads on her first dive into the warm water of the bay. For the last two months, the girl had found that a few valuable oysters were missing each week from their home on the rocky floor of the bay. Yesterday she tied thread between the bamboo poles that marked the oyster beds.

Sumiko came to the surface for air. She clung onto the raft between the poles. "They came last night!" The girl knew every shell in the oyster beds. She checked them in their home every day to keep them safe from hungry shellfish. "It couldn't be anyone from my village," she told herself. "A thief must come in from the ocean, through the small opening in the mountains."

There was no other entrance to the bay. It was ringed on all sides by high mountains, the highest on the island of Okinawa. The mountains sloped directly into the water, except for one small beach below Sumiko's northern village.

The twelve-year-old girl swam to shore. She did not stop at the beach to say hello to anyone. She ran right to the home of the mayor of their small village. His house, with its gray-tiled roof, stood out among the sixteen other thatched-roof houses.

"A broken thread is not enough, Sumiko," Mayor Yamada told her. "A large fish may have done it, and taken the oysters as well. A strong pull from the tide could also have broken the threads."

*He didn't understand.* She knew every oyster growing in the beds. Some were missing. "If I were older,"

Sumiko thought, "or if Father were alive, the mayor would pay more attention." *It was up to her to do something, but what?*

At Sumiko's one-room home, her grandmother had a meal of sweet potatoes with rice on the table. It was good for a change from their usual meal of rice and cabbage.

"The oysters are ours, Grandmother. I work hard to keep them safe. I can't let someone steal our years of work."

Her grandmother poured tea. "Could you be imagining the loss?" said Grandmother.

"No! I've been diving and caring for the beds since I was small."

"You learned everything so well when you were small. Your father taught you when he realized he had the same sickness that took your mother." Grandmother opened her sleeping mat. "If you are right, they must come in by boat from one of the villages on the China Sea. But what can an old woman and a twelve-year-old girl do?"

"Grandmother, the oysters are our living. Other people farm the rice fields, but we have no land. We must keep the oysters safe until we sell the pearls and the shells."

Two weeks later, Sumiko slipped leather coverings over her hands for protection. She dived into the warm water for her first inspection of the morning. It took seven years for the pearls to become large enough to sell. Each bed held oysters planted in a different year. "By now the thieves know which are the large pearl beds," she thought.

A white spot stood out on the waving moss that stuck to the gray oysters. Reaching into the bed, she found three white shellfish eating three of the oysters. She surfaced for breath. Then she put the shellfish in a bag that hung around her neck. These shells were a danger.

The oysters rested on their sides on the bay floor. They would never leave that spot. It would be easy for any hungry fish to eat them. Spiral shell snails would drill through the oyster shell and suck out the meat. Even if they were allowed to destroy only a few, soon they would multiply. If left alone, they would destroy the beds.

Sumiko dived again and again that morning, examining the beds carefully. She collected a dozen spiral shells, more than she had seen in a year.

She and her grandmother could sell the shells to a shopkeeper down the coast. The shop was in a large village where they sold their pearls each month.

The girl swam to shore. She sat on the beach to dry out her white blouse and her black cotton skirt.

She lifted a spiral shell from her bag. Sumiko held the animal in her hand. "I'm sorry. You don't have an evil plan. You take only for your own food, but I must protect the oysters. Whoever is stealing our oysters is throwing away the animals and selling the pearls. I must catch them! If only they couldn't get into the bay . . ."

*There was a chance to do something!* She raced home to tell her plan to Grandmother.

After their plans were made, Sumiko and her grandmother spent five nights on the beach. They tried to sleep when they could. During the day, Sumiko practiced ways of swimming through the water without making a splash or a sound. She knew that she could swim better than anyone in the village. *That* made her feel less afraid of being caught when the thieves *did* come.

"I may have to give up tomorrow, Sumiko. My old bones like to sleep in our home," her grandmother said. "Now that the moon has left, we can't see very well."

Sumiko had been sleeping for only a short time when a sound from the bay woke her. She heard splashing from the direction of the oyster rafts. "Of course! They waited for a dark night!" She woke her grandmother, who went to awaken the people of the village. Then Sumiko went into the water.

Her feet kicked strongly. She used her arms in an underwater breast stroke, with her nose just out of the water.

Yes, she could see the shadows of two men by a canoe. Her heart seemed to pound through the water so loudly that she thought the men would hear. But they were too busy diving with some kind of lights they wore attached to their face masks.

Closing the new gate to the bay was the first part of her plan. She and her grandmother had tied some of the bamboo poles together during the week they had waited. They tied them to the rocks on one side of the sea opening, where they would not be seen at night.

474

Sumiko swung them around. She tied them to the rocks above and under the water. Then she swam straight for the canoe.

*Splash!* One of the men surfaced by the boat. Sumiko immediately slipped under the water. When the man dived again, Sumiko quickly cut the canoe's anchor rope and raced to shore with the boat.

Grandmother put her arm around the girl's shaking shoulders. "The two men are trapped in the bay. They can't swim forever."

Finally the thieves swam to the small shore where the village people waited with lanterns. The thieves tried to run, but the people surrounded them. There was no escape.

"We will take you to the island police in the morning," Mayor Yamada said. "Nothing like this has ever happened in our village. We want to be certain that it won't happen again. To think a young girl showed us how to catch these men."

"You mean that girl trapped us?" said one of the men, frowning.

"Sumiko and her grandmother. We have the proof against you in the boat." The mayor turned to Sumiko and said, "I'm sorry you have lost more of your oysters."

"The ones in the boat are dead, but we can still sell the pearls," Grandmother told him.

Sumiko took one of the oysters from the boat. She opened it with her knife. She felt for the hard, round lump. Even in the dark night the white gleam from the pearl flashed between her fingers as she lifted it from the shell.

"You have saved our treasure, Sumiko," Grandmother said. "Now let's go home. We have had enough excitement to last for a long time!"

## CHECK FOR UNDERSTANDING

1. Why did Sumiko tie threads across the bamboo poles that marked the oyster beds?
2. Why was the loss of a few oysters a week so important? Explain your answer.
3. What made Sumiko believe that thieves, and not shellfish, were destroying the oyster beds?
4. Why did Sumiko and her grandmother have to take matters into their own hands?
5. How did Sumiko plan to catch the thieves? How did her plan work?
6. Because of Sumiko's clever actions, what proof would the mayor have against the thieves?

## WRITE ABOUT *"Sumiko's Bay"*

The story contains a lot of facts about oysters, their natural enemies, and how oysters are used to make pearls. Use these facts to write a two-paragraph report on oysters.

# VOCABULARY · LANGUAGE

## Synonyms and Antonyms

What do the words *discovered*, *found*, and *learned* have in common? They are all verbs, of course. Each word shows action. But they are also **synonyms.**

*Synonyms* are words that have the same or almost the same meaning. The words *fast* and *swift* are synonyms. *Throw* and *toss* are synonyms. *Calm* and *peaceful* are synonyms, too.

In "Sumiko's Bay," Sumiko "knew that she could swim better than anyone in the village. That made her feel less *afraid* of being caught." *Frightened* and *fearful* are synonyms for *afraid*. Can you think of another?

Authors use synonyms to make their writing more interesting. And by using synonyms, authors can pick just the shade of meaning they want. For example, the words *tall*, *high*, and *lofty* are all synonyms. Yet each has a slightly different shade of meaning. You might read about a *tall* basketball player, a *high* mountain, and a *lofty* aim or goal.

Below are some sentences from "Sumiko's Bay." See how many synonyms you can think of for the words that are underlined. Notice how each synonym you chose

Sumiko <u>discovered</u> that the oysters were missing.

Then she and her grandmother <u>found</u> the thieves.

They <u>learned</u> that it was not a fish that had broken the threads.

changes the flavor of the sentence. Explain why you think the author selected the synonyms she used.

> She <u>clung</u> onto the raft between the poles.
>
> When the man dived again, Sumiko quickly cut the canoe's anchor rope and <u>raced</u> to the shore with the boat.
>
> Even in the dark night the white gleam from the pearl <u>flashed</u> between her fingers as she lifted it from the shell.

**Antonyms** are words with *opposite* meanings. Some examples of antonyms are *near—far, happy—sad,* and *after—before.*

Below are some words found in "Sumiko's Bay." Think of an antonym for each.

| | |
|---|---|
| warm | good |
| entrance | strongly |
| large | under |

The following passage is from "If You Dare," the next story you are going to read. Find a synonym and an antonym for each word that is underlined.

> There in the mist, only a few feet from our cabin, was a <u>huge</u> elephant munching the bark off a tree. I swallowed hard, remembering that our cabin was made of logs. It was <u>hard</u> to sleep that night, wondering when the elephant would <u>start</u> eating our cabin.

# IF YOU DARE

by ROXIE and ANDY SHIRK

**What if the sound you heard at night were not an elevated train but a trumpeting elephant? What if the car you were riding in had to stop not because there was a dog in the road, but a hippopotamus? If you were living in Africa, these could be your adventures.**

**What do the words *safari* and *hatari* mean? What animal does the family especially want to find in the trees?**

Have you ever been lulled to sleep at night by the distant trumpeting of an elephant or the raucous roar of a lion? Neither had I—until my family and I moved to Tanzania, East Africa, when I was eleven. Soon after our arrival in the capital city of Dar es Salaam, we packed our jeep, grabbed our binoculars and cameras, and were off on our first safari.

In Swahili, the spoken language of Tanzania, *safari* means trip. *Hatari* means danger, and the game parks of Tanzania are not without their hatari. Our safari began in the Arusha National Park.

It was a clear day, and we were lucky to have a good view of the snowy peak of Mt. Kilimanjaro, at 19,340 feet the highest mountain in Africa. We spent the day sightseeing, and near dusk we headed for the exit gate. Tall trees lined the curving dirt trail, and it was spooky not knowing what would pop out at us around the next bend. At one point a hyena came bounding straight for our car. He must have been blinded for a moment by our lights, because he was only a few feet away when he suddenly turned and ran off into the bush.

Although the Arusha Park has no lions, we found the king of beasts on our next stop, Mikumi National Park. As we were driving through the park we happened on a large pride of lions with many small cubs. They let the jeep get very close to them, and we watched their playful antics for quite some time. We were so close, I could have reached out and patted one on the head. But my dad said that was hatari. He said although they seemed peaceful and friendly from the car, any move made toward them outside the vehicle would result in an immediate attack.

The elephant, on the other hand, isn't quite as patient with vehicles. My mom still trembles when she watches the movies we took of a bull elephant

the next day. He put up with this for only a few minutes. Then he flared his floppy ears, curled up his trunk as he blasted his trumpet, and swung his head violently from side to side as if to say, "No more!" Translating this to mean hatari, my dad quickly put the jeep into gear and hit the accelerator. The dust flew as we made our getaway.

Our next stop was Lake Manyara National Park. The lodge is situated high up on a cliff, overlooking the lake and the game park. As baboons munched on the flowers below our balcony, we got out our binoculars to watch the other animals in the park below. That's how we discovered our first rhino. We marked his location on our map, jumped into the jeep, and drove quickly down to the park,

483

hoping he would stay put until we arrived. He was still there all right, standing very close to the trail. As Dad stopped the jeep, the rhino lifted his head, his ears pricked high. Although rhinos have poor eyesight, it hadn't taken him long to get wind of us. He turned and ran a few yards in the opposite direction, then turned again and stopped suddenly. He looked as if he were trying to decide whether or not to charge. We didn't stick around for his decision.

A couple of miles farther on, we found a pleasant spot by the lake to have our lunch. As we peeled oranges and munched on sandwiches, a large herd of elephants emerged from the forest and went straight to a nearby water hole. They splashed and squirted playfully. They rolled and wallowed in the water as we watched them curiously from a comfortable distance. Then, refreshed from their baths and their drinks, they lumbered back into the forest again.

Soon after that we came upon another jeep stopped under an acacia tree. The people in the jeep had their cameras trained on something in the branches. Tree lions? We hoped so, for we had not yet been able to find them. Luck was with us. Sprawled lazily on the big limbs of the tree were a male and a female lion. The male was sound asleep, but the female opened one eye to check us out and then closed it again as if to say, "Oh, it's only you."

During the half hour that we watched them,

they changed position, yawned and stretched. At one point they completely straddled the limb with all four paws hanging. We were amazed at their good balance. Other than opening their eyes when they heard our cameras, they didn't seem to mind that we watched their afternoon siesta. They were still snoozing peacefully when my dad turned the jeep around to make the steep climb back up to the lodge.

Early the next day we were on the road to the Ngorongoro Crater. The crater is an extinct volcano that now resembles a huge basin. On its floor roam many animals. It was cold and misty at the top of the crater, and we all appreciated the warm fire blazing in the fireplace of the lodge as we ate dinner.

The electric power at the Crater Lodge is turned off after a certain hour, and as I lay in bed that night in total blackness, I heard a strange noise outside the window. There in the mist, only a few feet from our cabin, was a huge elephant munching the bark off a tree. I swallowed hard, remembering that our cabin was made of logs. It was hard to sleep that night, wondering when the elephant would start eating our cabin. But when I awoke the next morning, the elephant, apparently full from his tree-bark dinner, had left. I couldn't find a single bite taken from our cabin.

It had been an exciting trip, but I was looking forward to being back in my own cozy bed in Dar es Salaam that night. It would be nice to fall asleep knowing that no hatari was lurking outside. I found, however, that this was not exactly the case.

That evening, as we were sitting down to eat, a long green snake slithered in the back door to join us for dinner. His or ours? Again we didn't wait to find out. We all jumped at his entrance, and he slithered quickly into the kitchen. My dad spent fifteen minutes chasing him around with a butcher knife. We all waited with bated breath to see which one would emerge the victor. Then we heaved sighs of relief as Dad finally appeared, the snake dangling limply from one hand. We cheered as he put the snake on the back porch. He would take it to his office the next day to see if anyone could identify it, since there are many poisonous snakes in Tanzania. But in the morning the snake had mysteriously disappeared from the porch.

As you can see, Dar es Salaam has its hatari, too. Come visit me sometime—if you dare.

## CHECK FOR UNDERSTANDING

1. What do the words *safari* and *hatari* mean?
2. What did the author want to do in Mikumi National Park that would be *hatari*?
3. What made the lodge at Lake Manyara National Park a good place from which to watch animals?
4. What kind of activities do the different animals seem to be engaged in most often?
5. What animal did the family especially want to find in the trees?
6. Why was it hard for the author to sleep at the Crater Lodge?

## WRITE ABOUT *"If You Dare"*

Think about an adventure you have had during a trip outdoors or on a trip with your family. Write two paragraphs about your adventures. Include the Swahili words *safari* and *hatari* in what you write.

# COMPREHENSION

## Fact and Fictionalized Detail

There aren't many people who wouldn't like to travel to some time in the past. There aren't even many people who haven't daydreamed about it. Just imagine: there you are standing on the beach at Kitty Hawk watching the Wright brothers fly their plane. Or you are on a Spanish dock watching three little ships sail away under the command of a man named Christopher Columbus.

The idea of actually being present for events in history is exciting. But of course, no one can really go back in time. However, it is possible to get a sense of what daily life in the past was like. You can read stories and books about the past that are part fiction, and part fact. These books are fun to read because they give you that "time machine" feeling of being personally involved in the past. Books of this kind are called **historical fiction**.

It is important to remember that these books are always based on real facts. For example, the next selection, "Toliver's Journey," is based on real events during the American Revolution. The facts about places, troop movements, and the names of leaders are all true. But to make the events seem more alive, the author has *invented* details. These are details no one can really be sure happened the way the author writes about them.

Because historical fiction is based on facts, it is an interesting way to learn history. But you have to be careful to know which parts of the story are true, and which are made up. Generally, statements about major events are true in historical fiction.

Authors of historical fiction do a lot of research before they begin their stories. They look at books written in and about a certain period. They read diaries of people who lived then. Old records from the period give an idea of what things cost at the time.

If you are unsure of what part of a story is real history, ask yourself whether a fact can be *proven* by research. Look up in an encyclopedia any statements that may or may not be historically true.

Usually, though, your own common sense will tell you whether a detail is fact or fiction. Read this passage from the next selection. Decide for yourself which parts of the passage are made up by the author. Think about which parts of the passage you feel sure are historically true. Finally, decide which parts of the passage you would look up to make sure they are real history.

---

Ellen nodded her head. She craned her neck to look at the ships in the harbor. They were sailing past seven great warships anchored there — the seven British warships that she and Grandfather had seen from the Battery. He said the British had brought seven hundred ships all told, last summer. And thirty thousand soldiers. That was almost twice as many men as there were people in New York.

---

As you read the rest of the next selection, ask yourself these same questions. Make sure you know which parts of the selection are fact, and which are fiction.

# Toliver's Journey

## by ESTHER WOOD BRADY

How could the actions of one girl affect the future of a country? In the days of the Revolutionary War, the American Patriots were struggling for freedom. In these troubled times one person's success or failure in an important task could make a serious difference.

What does Ellen have to do? Why does she disguise herself as a boy?

*In November of 1776, the Patriots, led by General George Washington, were fighting the British soldiers in and around New York City.*

*Ellen Toliver's grandfather had important information that had to reach General Washington. Grandfather could not deliver the message himself because he had sprained his ankle. So ten-year-old Ellen disguised herself as a boy and set off for Elizabeth-town, New Jersey. She carried the message hidden in a small metal box baked inside a loaf of bread. The owner of the Jolly Fox Tavern in Elizabeth-town was expecting the bread and the important message it contained. But to get to Elizabeth-town, Ellen had to find a boat that would take her across New York Harbor.*

## FINDING A BOAT

Long before Ellen Toliver reached Front Street she heard the beat of army drums and the shrill piping of the fifes. Trim lines of redcoats marched up and down the streets and formed in squads and companies on all the wharves.

The East River bristled with the masts of small sloops and riverboats. But Ellen could not see the fat broad-beamed boats of the farmers or the oyster boats from Jersey.

Near the Market-house she stopped a spindly little man pushing a wheelbarrow with only two small pumpkins in it.

"Where are the oyster boats," she asked anxiously, "or the farmers' boats from Elizabeth-town?"

"Oh," he said, "not many of them came over today. Food is scarce and the oyster catch was poor. Those who came started back a few moments ago."

"Back!" cried Ellen. "Why, they can't have gone yet. It's

491

too early for them to leave."

"Well, they have!" he said. "Only British boats are here now."

"You must be mistaken," Ellen said. "They must be at another dock." She'd have to hurry to find them.

"Look for yourself, boy," the man called after her. "They say twenty boats are taking troops over to Elizabeth today."

With her heart pounding wildly, Ellen ran from one dock to another all up and down Front Street. She raced among the chests and barrels and great coils of rope as she looked at every boat tied up there. She darted among the soldiers and the sailors, but no one stopped her or noticed her.

The man was right. There were only British boats filling up with soldiers, all along the waterfront. The men sat on planks and were crowded together as closely as kernels of corn on a cob.

"What can I do now?" she thought desperately. "There isn't a fisher to ask for a ride." She jingled the coins in her pocket. "If I dared to ask."

It was plain to see that nothing could be done. Surely Grandfather would understand. . . .

Perhaps she could get to Elizabeth-town on one of the redcoats' boats. She could slip on board quietly and hide herself under a seat. No one would find her there.

"You could do it," she said to herself. "You could make yourself do it." As she stood there staring at the boats, trying to get up enough courage to start, she was surprised to see one of the redcoats lean across the side of the boat and grin at her.

He was a husky man with a dirty fringe of scraggly hair beneath his black hat. She couldn't take her eyes from his large nose. It was as big and red as a sweet potato.

493

"What are you huggin' so tight?" he asked her. "It smells right good."

"Oh, don't pester the boy, Dow," said the sad-faced soldier who sat slumped over beside him. His mouth drooped at the corners and looked as tired and woebegone as his eyes. Then he leaned across Dow and said, "I've got a boy back home in London who looks like you. What's your name?"

"Ellen Toliver, sir," she answered.

"How's that?"

Ellen gasped. She had forgotten how she was dressed, but with all the noise he apparently had not heard her. Raising her voice she said, "I said my name is Toliver, sir."

"My boy's name is Tom. But he looks like you. Same pale face. Same big eyes. It makes me homesick to see a boy who favors Tom," he said forlornly.

Ellen could see by his sad face that he really was homesick. But he also looked kind. Perhaps she dared ask him if she could just ride across the bay with them.

But these were British soldiers. How could she trust an enemy?

Before she could decide what to do, she felt a tug at her blue bundle. "Smells like fresh bread there," she heard the big man say. Quickly Ellen snatched the bundle away. Then suddenly she, herself, was seized around the waist by two big red hands and whisked across the side of the boat. She was too surprised and frozen with fear to make a sound.

The man with the sweet potato nose laughed as he squashed her down on the bench beside him. "No noise from you," he muttered.

What was happening to her? This wasn't what she had meant to do. She felt as if a humming-bird were caught inside her chest, her heart was beating so

fast. She stared at the wet brown planks of the deck and the row of black boots and white leggings that stretched to the other side of the boat.

The man bent down and grinned at her. Under his bushy eyebrows his blue eyes were laughing at her. "Surprised, be ye?" he asked.

Ellen could hear the home-sick soldier on her other side say impatiently, "What are you doing that for, Dow?"

"Because I'm hungry as a bear in spring. That's why. Nothing but salt biscuits and dried herring, day after day."

Hungry! Ellen gasped at the thought of it.

It was too late to get back to the dock. She could tell the sloop was casting off, for she could hear the sails being hoisted, and flapping loudly in the breeze, then smoothing out as the boat came about in the river and turned into the wind. She felt it rock as it headed into the waves.

As she sat up cautiously and looked around, the thin man with the sad face peered at her sharply. "Are you all right, boy?" he asked with concern. "My friend is a joker."

"A joker!" snorted the other. "I'm hungry." Then he turned to Ellen. "Dow's my name. And this here is Higgins—him who's homesick for his boy in London. And you're Toliver, you say."

Ellen nodded her head. She craned her neck to look at the ships in the harbor. They were sailing past seven great warships anchored there—the seven British warships that she and Grandfather had seen from the Battery. He said the British had brought seven hundred ships all told, last summer. And thirty thousand soldiers who had camped on Staten Island. Thirty thousand soldiers. That was almost twice as many soldiers as there were people in New York.

"Are we going to Elizabethtown?" she asked the homesick Mr. Higgins.

He shrugged. "That's what our orders are," he said. "You are the picture of my boy Tom, I swear."

Dow smiled at her as he took a knife from his belt and pulled it from its case. "Now that we are friends"—he coughed politely—"now that we are friends, I'll just share your fresh bread with us."

He leaned down and quickly snatched Ellen's blue bundle from her mittened hands.

"Oh sir!" she cried as she clung to the blue kerchief, "I can't share it. It's for an old man's birthday present!"

His thick red tongue ran around his lips. "I could smell that good fresh bread when you stood there on the dock," said Dow as he slapped her hands away. "I said to myself, 'That boy will be happy to share his bread with a soldier of the King.'"

"But it's for my grandfather's friend!" cried Ellen. "Please give it back to me."

497

"Too bad for your grandfather's friend," Dow grunted as he fumbled awkwardly with the knot in the kerchief.

Ellen stared at his knife. The bright gleaming blade in Dow's rough hands seemed more awful than a sword at her throat. In a moment he would cut into the bread and find the little metal box. Then he'd open the box and find Grandfather's message to General Washington. Soon he'd know that she was a spy's messenger. Grandfather had told her to say she didn't know anything about it. But they'd find out where she lived and Grandfather would be caught! She knew well enough what would happen then.

Suddenly, without thinking what she did, she snatched the blue bundle from Dow's hands so quickly he lost his grip. In an instant she tucked it under her jacket, doubled up, and locked her arms beneath her legs.

The sad-faced Higgins laughed so hard his tall black hat almost fell from his head. "You're a quick one, Toliver."

Dow's fat jowls shook with anger. "Why you little rascal," he snarled as he tried to pry her arms loose. "Give me back that bread!"

"No!" said Ellen stubbornly. Her arms were locked in fear so tightly she could not have moved them if she'd tried.

"Give me that bread!" Dow grunted as he pulled at her pigtail.

"No," said Ellen.

"I haven't had fresh bread for weeks," Dow complained, tugging at her arm with his fat red hands, "and so I mean to have it!" He pulled harder on her arm.

Ellen's arms felt like an iron clamp. "You won't have my bread. I won't give it to you," she muttered. And then she remembered the corncakes her mother had given her. "There

are some good corncakes in my pocket, sir. Take both of them."

The redcoats sitting on the bench in front of them turned around and started to laugh at the sight of a small boy defying big old Dow.

"Hang on, boy!" they shouted.

Ellen hung on. "Take the corncakes, sir. They are just as good. Right in my pocket beside you."

She could hear Higgins laughing until he began to hiccup and gasp for air. "He's like an oyster shell!" Higgins could hardly catch his breath. "You'll have to pry him open."

From the stern of the boat a voice roared at them. "Stop that ruckus amidship! You'll send us all into the waves!"

Everyone became quiet at once. In the silence Ellen heard only the waves banging along the sides of the sloop. And Higgins's muffled hiccups.

She held her breath as she sat doubled up over the bread. If the officer had seen her that would have been the end of her. She was grateful the broad shoulders of the soldiers covered her.

At last Dow shrugged and said from the side of his mouth, "You little scamp. I'll take those corncakes."

"They're in my pocket. Take them all. And welcome."

Dow cut a piece of corncake and put it in his mouth on the end of his knife. "That bread is squashed flat by now. So keep it! I hope the old fellow likes squashed bread."

Higgins nudged her with his sharp elbow. "Not bad, Toliver! You're a spunky one—just like my Tom back home."

Ellen glanced up at Higgins. He seemed to mean what he said. No one had ever called her spunky. She eased the blue bundle up under her jacket, and kept her arms tightly locked across the bulge as she cautiously sat up.

## Journey to Elizabeth-Town

Grandfather had said that the trip across the Bay to Elizabeth-town would take about two hours of good sailing. But with a cold blustery wind in her face it seemed longer to Ellen. High above the white sails she could see that the sun had come out among ragged patches of clouds. But it had no warmth.

Higgins patted her arm. "I'm right sorry we got you on this boat," he said. "But you'll get yourself home all right. All you Yankees are plucky."

"Plucky!" scoffed Dow. "Just plain fools. Foolish enough to fight the King. And in winter yet," he growled. "Back home no army fights in winter!" He put up his hands and rubbed his red ears.

"This war will be over in no time," said Higgins. A smile spread over his gloomy face. "And we'll be going home! Why, it's bound to be over soon. They can't hold out much longer. We took three thousand prisoners when we took Fort Washington up there on the Hudson's River."

"And a hundred and fifty cannons," Dow reminded him, "when we took Fort Lee on the Jersey side. Sent them running like rabbits over to Pennsylvania! Ragtag army!" Dow laughed. "Some have hunting jackets with fringe. Some have farmers' smocks—any old thing—all marching together. I never saw an army look like that."

"They're sharpshooters, though," Higgins said seriously.

"Oh, they can shoot all right," said Dow, "when they're not running away. Like at Kip's Bay."

Ellen remembered hearing talk about Kip's Bay. The Patriot soldiers had turned tail and run away. No one could believe it.

Dow gave her a nudge. "We never saw nothing but their backs. They are all a bunch of cowards!"

"No!" Ellen protested. "They are not cowards!"

"Oh, ho! A rebel we have!" said Dow as he looked at her from under his heavy eyebrows. "A hot little rebel boy."

A burly soldier turned around and snorted. "Throw the rebel overboard. There'll be one less rebel to fight."

Ellen tightened her arms around the bundle inside her jacket and ducked her head to make herself as small as possible. She felt as cold as an icicle and yet her face was damp with sweat. If they threw her overboard she'd take the loaf of bread down with her. They'd never, never get the box away from her.

Higgins threw back his head and started to sing in a loud twangy voice, "Come all you soldiers bold, lend an ear, lend an ear." Immediately the others around him sang out a loud refrain, "Lend an ear, lend an ear."

Higgins sang verse after verse and the men joined in the refrain. Ellen was glad because it took their minds off her. By the time they had sung "Hearts of Oak" and "Old King Cole," she felt more relaxed. As the soldiers sang "The British Grenadiers," Ellen began humming along too, very softly.

"What's amiss with you?" Dow growled at her.

Ellen shrank back. She didn't want any trouble with Dow.

"You scare the boy," Higgins spoke up sharply. "He didn't ask to come along, did he?"

"What's he afraid of?" Dow asked. "Me? Are you afraid of me, boy?"

"No," said Ellen quickly. It wasn't true. She really was scared of him, and she wished he would leave her alone. But Dow kept staring at her, and she had to drop her eyes. "Well, maybe—a little," she confessed.

"A big chap like you shouldn't be afraid of anything," sneered Dow.

"Talk right back to him, Toliver." Higgins's face was red and his black stubble of beard looked dark across his chin.

"I can't," said Ellen without looking up.

"Why"—Dow made his eyes look round and innocent—"I'm as gentle as a morn in May."

Higgins snorted. For a long time he sat staring off at the clouds in the sky. At last he said to Ellen, "When I was a boy I had a brother who pestered me like that. I had to learn to talk back to him. Funny thing was—when he saw I wasn't afraid of him, he didn't bother me any more." He turned and smiled. "Bullies are like that."

After a long silence she said, "Are you ever afraid of anything now, Mr. Higgins?"

Higgins did not answer her question right away. At last he leaned down and said in a low voice that only she could hear, "Well, son, I'll answer you true as I would answer my own son back home. Sometimes."

He nodded his head. "Sometimes I am afraid—as many men are. Being afraid is nothing to be ashamed of." He threw a sidelong glance at her. "But when something has to be done," he said firmly, "don't wonder and wonder about being afraid. If it's important to you—do the best you can."

Ellen stared up at the white sails. This trip was important.

At first it had been important to her because it was very important to Grandfather. But now she had seen the British soldiers with their guns and bayonets—hundreds of them— going to fight the Patriots' army. Now she was eager to help General Washington. She was impatient to get to the Jolly Fox Tavern and deliver the loaf of bread.

At last she could see on the right the church spires and the frosty roofs of a town white against the pine trees. Everywhere the lines of marching soldiers looked like busy ants on an anthill. As the boat came closer she strained her eyes to see a sign of the Jolly Fox Tavern.

"I hope the Shannons have a crackling fire and a hot meat pie," Ellen thought.

With sails flapping noisily, their boat headed toward a dock and glided in for a landing.

Ropes were tossed to the dockhands who waited to pull them in.

"All ashore!" shouted the officer in the stern. "And step smartly."

The soldiers stood up and stretched. Ellen was glad the officer could not see her. She quickly scrambled up on the dock, and when she was well out of Dow's reach, she turned and grinned at him. "Good-by, Mr. Dow!" she cried happily.

"Hold your tongue," growled Dow.

"Good-by, Mr. Higgins," she called to him. "I'll remember the things you told me."

"I'll remember you, Toliver."

Ellen's brown eyes were sparkling and her cheeks were red as winter apples. She slipped the blue bundle out of her jacket and swung it jauntily around her head as she turned to run.

Dow grunted. "Pert little beggar," he said to Higgins.

But Ellen didn't hear that. She was racing to the Jolly Fox Tavern.

## CHECK FOR UNDERSTANDING

1. What did Ellen have to do?
2. Why did she disguise herself as a boy?
3. Why were there no boats going to Elizabeth-town?
4. How did Ellen's reason for delivering the message change by the end of the story?
5. What did Ellen learn from Higgins?
6. Do you think Ellen would be willing to deliver more messages for the Patriots? Explain your answer.

**WRITE ABOUT** *"Toliver's Journey"*

Imagine that Ellen decides to gather her friends together to help the Patriot cause. Write a speech for her to give to the group. In the speech, have her tell about the journey she took and what it meant to her.

## Following Directions

In the story "Toliver's Journey," Ellen had to deliver an important message to General Washington. Her grandfather gave her precise directions. *Dress as a boy. Take a boat to Elizabeth-town. Take the message to the owner of the Jolly Fox Tavern.*

Suppose she had not followed these directions? Suppose she had not dressed as a boy? She would not have been allowed on the boat. She could not have delivered the message.

If she had been caught, her grandfather might have been arrested. It was vital that Ellen follow her grandfather's directions exactly.

Sometimes directions may seem so simple that you don't really pay attention to small details. This is a mistake. Remember—if something is included in directions, there is a reason for its being there. Read this story.

On a brisk winter morning Fred and Joe decided to make some oatmeal. They took the oatmeal out and read the recipe on the box.

1. Pour two cups of water into a saucepan.
2. Add 1 cup of oatmeal.
3. Add a pinch of salt.
4. Bring mixture to a boil, stirring rapidly all the time.

**5.** Still stirring, boil for five minutes.

**6.** Lower heat, cover, and leave to cook slowly for five more minutes.

"That's simple," said Fred. He put the water into a pot, added the oatmeal and salt, heated it up and stirred. When the mixture started to boil, he lowered the heat and let it simmer for five minutes while he got out the bowls.

"It's all lumpy," said Joe. He was right. The oatmeal had stuck together in big lumps.

"What happened?" said Fred, "I don't understand it."

What was wrong? Do you know?

Fred did not follow the directions exactly. He did not stir the oatmeal when it was boiling.

Most of us never get involved in delivering secret messages. Still, directions are a part of everyday life. To follow a recipe, do a science experiment, or just find your way somewhere, you must be able to follow directions.

There are important things to remember when following directions.

Directions are often given step by step. With written directions, it is a good idea to read through *all* the steps first.

Directions must be read carefully. You must pay attention to details.

You must also make sure you do the steps in correct order. And you must be sure not to skip over any steps by mistake.

Even with simple directions, you must follow them exactly.

Sometimes we have to follow directions that are not written down, as in the following story.

---

Jack and his family were on vacation.

They stopped at a general store, where a woman gave them directions to Willow Lake. "Go exactly three miles down Route 87—that's the road you're on," she said. "Then take a left. In a few minutes, you'll see a Girl Scout camp. Turn right at the camp, and you'll be at the lake in half a minute. You can't miss it," she said.

---

They got back in the car. They checked the mileage and set off. But they got into a conversation, and when they checked the mileage again they saw that they had already gone four miles.

Should they go back? "Oh," said Jack, "why waste time? Left is left. Why don't we just take the *next* road going left?" They did this. They never found the lake.

"She said we couldn't miss it," said Jack.

Why do you think they missed the lake? This map shows you why.

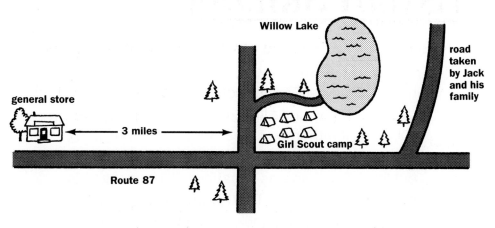

They did not follow the directions exactly. They had gone more than three miles before they turned.

Here is another example of what can happen when directions aren't followed carefully.

Fran, Bill, Mack, and Jessie went on a hike. It was winter, and quite cold, but they didn't care. They loved the snowy woods.

They carried their gear in their knapsacks. They had sandwiches for lunch, apples, and a thermos jug of water. Mack also had a book on first aid. "First aid?" said Fran. "What for?"

"We might have an emergency," said Mack.

They *did* have an emergency. Bill dropped one of his mittens over a ledge. They couldn't get it. "It's okay," he said. "I'll keep my hand in my pocket." But he had to take his hand out occasionally. After a while, it got numb.

"It's tingling," he said. "And boy, does it hurt."

"Wow," said Jessie. "Maybe it's frostbite. Let's rub it with snow. I've heard that's what you do."

509

"Wait a sec," said Mack. "I'll check out my first aid book. Here it is: Frostbite."

He read, frowning a little. "Wait," he said to Jessie. "Don't rub it with snow. That's exactly the wrong thing to do." He began to read the emergency directions out loud. But Fran was impatient. "I'll massage his hand with my hands. That'll warm it up."

"Wait a sec," said Mack. "Let me read it all."

This is what the book said:

Symptoms: tingling, numbness, pain. The area becomes extremely white. DO NOT RUB WITH SNOW. It can remove skin and damage tissue. DO NOT MASSAGE. This can also cause damage. Use heat of a hand to warm it, or cover with a cloth. Do not use very hot water. Do not use heating pads. See a doctor as soon as possible.

"No massage either," said Jessie. "Here's my scarf. We'll wrap it around your hand."

They headed back and went immediately to a doctor.

"It's a good thing you didn't put snow on this," the doctor said. "Doing the wrong thing is worse than doing nothing."

Bill smiled. "Your book was a lifesaver, Mack."

The book *was* a lifesaver. But something else was important. Mack insisted on reading *all* the directions before doing anything. Mack's care in reading the directions possibly saved his friend's hand from permanent damage.

As we have seen, being able to follow directions can be vital. Just remember these important rules:

**1.** Read, or listen to, the directions carefully.
**2.** Read, or listen to, every step before beginning to *do* things.
**3.** Be sure not to leave out any steps.
**4.** Do the steps in the proper order.

## Using What You Have Learned
Follow these directions:

**1.** *Write down the number 880.*
**2.** *Cross out the last figure.*
**3.** *Divide by 2.*
**4.** *Add 60.*

What is your answer? If it is 104, you followed the directions carefully.

## Expanding Your Skills

**1.** Think of a certain place located in your school.
**2.** Write clear, step-by-step directions on how to reach that place from your classroom.
**3.** Then, when you have a chance, follow the directions exactly. Did you get there? Or were there steps you left out?

Being able to *give* good directions is often as important as being able to *follow* directions.

# Snowshoe Trek to OTTER RIVER

adapted from a story by DAVID BUDBILL

For some people, the wilderness is an opponent to be overcome. For others, it is a friend to live with peacefully. In this story Daniel survives a dangerous winter hike because of his knowledge and respect for the wilderness.

How does the hike become dangerous? How does Daniel's reaction to danger save his life?

512

## A PERFECT DAY FOR A HIKE

Early in the morning after Daniel finished breakfast, he took his backpack off the wall and un-
packed it. He had packed everything carefully last
night, but now that it was time to go, he had to be
sure everything was there, ready, in case he needed
it. Daniel could see his mother moving about the
kitchen, watching him out of the corner of her eye.
He knew she was laughing to herself about the way
he fussed over his equipment. But the gear was important. If he got caught out there in a blizzard, or
if something happened to him and he couldn't get
back, his life might depend on the few things he carried on his back.

He spread the backpack's contents on the
kitchen floor. Nested cookpots, one 8-inch skillet
with folding handle, one 6-inch plate. One quart
pail with lid, a metal cup, a fork and spoon. His
pocketknife would do the cutting. A bunch of
waterproof matches wrapped in tinfoil. Two fire
starters he had made by rolling paper tightly, tying
it with string, and soaking it in hot paraffin. A compass, a hatchet, and a sleeping bag. Daniel cut three
thick slices of his mother's homemade bread, but-
tered them, then took two chunks of bacon and
three eggs from the refrigerator. He wrapped everything carefully and put it in the backpack with a
bag of nuts and raisins. As far as Daniel was concerned, bacon and eggs, bread, and water was the

perfect campfire lunch for a winter's day of snow-shoeing.

Daniel was only twelve, but he knew a lot about getting along in the woods. His parents were dairy farmers. Although they lived surrounded by the wilderness, they never really were part of it. But down the road from Daniel's house there was an old man, a Frenchman by the name of Mr. Bateau, who had come down from Canada years ago. Mr. Bateau was Daniel's favorite person. He was a man of the woods—a logger, a hunter, a fisherman, and a trapper. Mr. Bateau had taught Daniel all he knew about the wild world. He had shown him how to fish, build wilderness camps, and identify wildflowers and animal tracks. He had taught him how to talk to birds, call foxes, and make coyotes howl. But most of all Mr. Bateau had given Daniel a love of the wilderness that drew Daniel out now into the white, cold world beyond his house.

Daniel's plan was to strike out across the high swamp behind his farm and continue down the mountain to Otter River in the valley below. Last summer he and his best friend, Seth, had built a lean-to on the far side of Otter River. Daniel planned to have his lunch at the camp, check the supplies they had stashed there, and return home before dark.

When the backpack was packed again, Daniel put on two pairs of heavy wool socks and pulled his rubber-bottom, leather-top winter boots over them. He wore long underwear and wool pants. Over a long-sleeved undershirt he wore a cotton shirt and over that a wool shirt and over that another, heavier wool shirt. If he got hot, he could peel off a layer or two, but he doubted he'd get hot. He looked out the window at the thermometer. It said ten degrees below zero. By noon it might be ten above.

He was ready. He slipped his backpack on, kissed his mother good-by, and went onto the porch. He pulled his wool cap down over his ears, put on his mittens, picked up his snowshoes, and stepped out into the snow. He slipped his boots into the snowshoe harnesses and adjusted the bindings carefully.

It was a clear, bright, still day. The spruce and fir trees on the horizon made a deep green band that separated the bright blue sky from the white, pure white earth. As Daniel struck out across the pasture behind the house, the cold air stung his face. It felt good. It was the perfect day for a hike.

Last night's snow had added six inches to the three feet already on the ground. Daniel knew the new snow meant animal tracks would be fresh. He'd do some tracking along the way.

Soon he was beyond the open fields and deep into the swamp. It was a different world, darker, quieter. The big spruce and fir trees covered up the sky. There was no sound. It was as if this swamp were a noiseless chamber. All Daniel could hear were his snowshoes, whispering, hissing as he moved along. He stopped. Listened. Now there was no sound at all. None. It was as if everything in the world were dead except for one boy who stood silent and alone, deep in a snowy evergreen swamp.

Suddenly, out of nowhere, the sound of galloping broke the silence. Daniel's heart jumped. He crouched down and waited. Then, in a crash of twigs, a shower of snow, three deer burst into a clearing right in front of him—a buck, a doe, and last year's fawn. The three deer stopped. They stood silent in their tracks. Slowly the buck raised his head and sniffed the wind. He caught Daniel's scent. The buck gave a terrible snorting roar, stomped his

foot, and away the three went in a muffled thunder
of hooves, their sleek, brown bodies plowing
through the snow. Daniel stood up and watched the
three deer disappear into the dark trees. His heart
was still pounding.

He came to a broad open place in the middle of
the swamp. Beavers had dammed the swamp brook
and made a pond. Daniel could see a large hump in
the level snow near the dam. It was a beaver house.
As Daniel crossed the pond, he thought about the
beavers under all that snow and ice, lazing away the
winter, safe in their underwater home. At this very
moment there could be a beaver swimming only a
few feet below his snowshoes.

On the other side of the beaver pond, Daniel
pushed on. He was out of the evergreen swamp now

and starting down the mountain toward the river. Here the trees were all hardwoods, and the sun shone brightly through the bare branches. A chickadee scolded Daniel from a nearby tree.

Daniel saw tiny ruffed grouse tracks everywhere. The grouse had come to the hardwoods to eat the buds off birch trees. Suddenly there was a thundering rush, a wild flutter of wings. Daniel stopped. Grouse were flying everywhere, weaving crazily between the trees. One bird flew right at him. He threw his hands up in front of his face. Then the bird was gone.

Soon Daniel was down the mountain. Otter River was before him. He could see the snow-covered camp on the other side.

## THE FAR SIDE OF OTTER RIVER

Daniel walked up and down the riverbank looking for a place to cross. He knew that where the river ran still and deep the ice would be the thickest. There was a place like that about a hundred yards upstream, but the river looked safe here, too, and it wasn't quite so wide. Daniel took off his snowshoes. If he fell through with them on, his feet would be trapped under the ice. He stepped out onto the river and jumped up and down a couple of times. The ice was solid. He started across.

When he was almost to the far shore, he heard a loud, thundering crack begin near him and shoot up the river. Slowly, he began to sink. Then more and louder cracks. Then a deep, rumbling roar. He was going down! The whole river was opening up!

Daniel heaved his snowshoes onto the shore and grabbed for solid ice. His boots were full of water, his legs numbed by the cold. Again and again he reached for the edge of solid ice. Each time the ice broke away and bobbed uselessly in front of him. Then his feet struck bottom. He stood waist deep in icy water. He could wade to shore. But there were great slabs of loose ice floating between him and the bank. When he tried to climb on top of them, they sank. When he tried to push them out of his way, they bumped into each other and blocked the way. He was trapped.

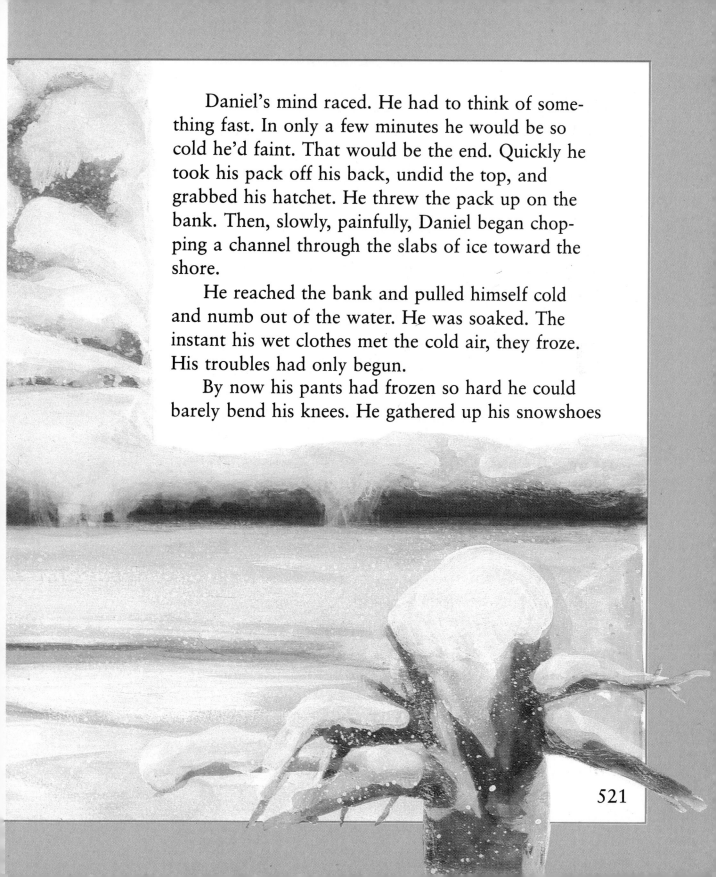

Daniel's mind raced. He had to think of something fast. In only a few minutes he would be so cold he'd faint. That would be the end. Quickly he took his pack off his back, undid the top, and grabbed his hatchet. He threw the pack up on the bank. Then, slowly, painfully, Daniel began chopping a channel through the slabs of ice toward the shore.

He reached the bank and pulled himself cold and numb out of the water. He was soaked. The instant his wet clothes met the cold air, they froze. His troubles had only begun.

By now his pants had frozen so hard he could barely bend his knees. He gathered up his snowshoes and pack and limped, stiff-legged, to his camp. Daniel was freezing, not just freezing cold, but actually freezing, freezing to death.

He took the small shovel he and Seth had stashed in the lean-to and cleaned the snow away from the fire pit. He broke an armful of dead branches off a hemlock tree for kindling, took one of the fire starters out of his pack, and lit a fire. He was glad now that last summer he and Seth had stacked dry wood next to the camp.

Soon the fire was burning. Daniel was sleepy and cold, so cold. All he wanted to do was lie down, but he knew he couldn't. Not yet.

He stuck two forked sticks in the snow, one on each side of the fire. Then he laid a long pole between the two sticks above the fire. He propped his snowshoes near the fire, crawled inside the lean-to, and spread his sleeping bag on the bare, dry ground inside the shelter. Then he put more wood on the fire.

When all this was done, he was ready to do the only thing left to do. He couldn't go home. It was too far away. He'd freeze before he got there. He couldn't call for help. There was no one for miles. He'd have to thaw and dry out before he could go any farther.

Although it was below zero, Daniel took off his clothes. He draped his pants and long underwear, socks, and mittens over the long pole. He hung a wool shirt on each snowshoe. He put his boots on a rock near the fire. The snow was so cold on his bare feet that it felt hot. When all his clothes were hung over the fire, he limped into the lean-to and climbed inside his sleeping bag. He shivered violently. He wanted to cry, but he was too cold. Slowly, very slowly, his body heat began to fill the sleeping bag. He began to warm up. He took the bag of nuts and raisins from his pack and ate. He could see his clothes dripping and steaming over the fire. Daniel was relaxed now. His eyes grew heavy. He fell asleep.

When Daniel woke up, the fire was down to coals. It was warm inside the bag. He had no idea

how long he had slept. It may have been an hour or two. He got up and put more wood on the fire. He felt his clothes. They were dry, except for his boots. He got dressed. His clothes smelled like wood smoke. He hung his boots from the pole by their laces and began to fix lunch.

Daniel set the bacon to frying in the skillet and put some snow to melt in the quart pail. He reached into his backpack for the eggs. They were smashed. They must have broken when he threw the pack up on the bank. He dumped the slimy mixture into his metal plate and separated shell from egg as best he could. He took the cooked bacon out of the skillet and put the eggs in, scrambling them with his fork.

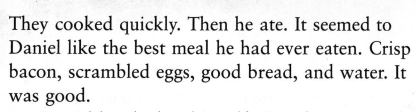

They cooked quickly. Then he ate. It seemed to Daniel like the best meal he had ever eaten. Crisp bacon, scrambled eggs, good bread, and water. It was good.

Daniel laughed to himself. Here he was, in the middle of winter, sitting by a fire, by a river he had just fallen into, thinking how good the lunch was! It was hard to believe. A couple of hours ago he was almost dead. Now he sat comfortably, his feet warmed by the fire, almost as if nothing had happened.

When the last of the water was gone, he put his boots on and cleaned and packed his gear. He shoveled snow on the fire, rolled the sleeping bag, and started home. This time he headed upstream to where the river moved slowly and the ice was thick. Nobody ever crossed a frozen river more carefully than Daniel did that afternoon.

When he reached the other side, he noticed that the sun was low in the southern sky. It got dark early this time of year, and home was a long way off. He'd have to travel to get there before dark.

He followed his own trail up through the hardwoods, over the brow of the mountain, and down
into the swamp.

By the time he reached the other side of the beaver pond, the sun was almost down. It was dark in
the thick trees of the swamp. Daniel had trouble
finding his trail. It got darker and darker. He was
hurrying now, and although it was growing colder,
he was sweating. Then out of the darkening sky fear
dropped down and seized him. He had gotten off
the trail. He was lost.

Daniel was running. He had to find his old trail
and fast. But the faster he moved, the more confused he got. Then he stopped. He found a log
sticking up above the snow, brushed the snow off its
top, and sat down. He knew that to get panicky
when lost was the worst thing that could happen.
He took the bag of nuts and raisins from his pack
and ate a handful. He would sit here until he

quieted down and decided what to do. But it was hard. He had to force himself to sit on that log. Something inside urged him to get up and run. It didn't matter where, just run! He fought the urge with all the strength he had.

Then he heard the soft rustle of wings. A large white bird floated silently into a tree above him. It was a snowy owl. Its fierce yellow eyes shot through him like needles. Why did that bird sit there, staring? What did it want? Daniel couldn't stand it. He jumped up, made a snowball, and threw it at the owl. The snowball almost hit the owl, but the owl didn't move. He sat there, staring, as if to say, "I'm not the one who is afraid." Then, as if nothing had happened, the snowy owl rolled backward off the branch and disappeared without a sound into the dark trees.

The owl, the noiseless chamber of a forest, and the darkness frightened Daniel more than falling in the river. When he had gone down in the river, he knew what he had to do to save himself. The only question was whether he could do it. But here, in this wild place, there was something unknown, something strange. He felt out of place, alone, deserted. It seemed as if even the trees around him were about to grab him, take him off somewhere, deeper into the swamp, where he would be lost forever.

He decided what to do. He would get up,

calmly, and follow his tracks back to where he lost the trail. He'd get back on the trail and go home. It was hard to go back, but he had to do it.

When he found the trail again, he moved along it slowly. It was so dark now he couldn't afford to get lost again. At last, after what seemed like hours, he found himself standing at the edge of a broad, open field. At the far end of the field he could see his house. The kitchen window glowed warm and orange in the dusky evening light. He struck off across the meadow toward the lighted window.

## CHECK FOR UNDERSTANDING

1. The author says that Daniel's parents were never really part of the wilderness. What does this mean?
2. How did the hike become dangerous?
3. How did Daniel's reactions to danger save his life?
4. Why did getting lost scare Daniel more than falling into the river?
5. Had Daniel expected danger on his hike? Explain your answer.
6. Do you think Daniel would go on a hike alone to Otter River again? Explain your answer.

## WRITE ABOUT "Snowshoe Trek to Otter River"

Imagine that you were there when Daniel saw the three deer. Describe the scene in a poem. Use descriptive adjectives in your poem. Include at least one metaphor and one simile. The poem does not have to rhyme.

# The Deer, the Deer

by COCHITI

The deer, the deer, here he went,
Here are his tracks over mother earth...
Tramping, tramping, through the deep forest.

# WHO IS THIS?

by CHIPPEWA

Who is this?
Who is this?
Giving light
On the top of my lodge.

It is I—the little owl,
    coming,
It is I—the little owl,
    coming,
Down! Down!

529

# THE GIRL WHO SAVED A TRAIN

by JOHN LOVELAND

What ingredients make up a recipe for adventure? A dark, stormy night? A river flooding its banks? A railroad bridge washed out by the flood, and a train due to pass over it any second? Add one brave girl, and you have the true life adventure of Kate Shelley.

What gives Kate a special feeling for the danger of the river and the railroad bridge even before the storm? During what part of her adventure was Kate's own life in danger?

As if drawn by some strange magnet, fifteen-year-old Kate Shelley kept near her window on that stormy July night in 1881. Her mother sat nearby mending a stocking for one of the younger children asleep in the next room.

"Sit down and relax," Mrs. Shelley begged for the dozenth time. But there was to be no rest for either Kate or her mother that night.

Kate pressed her nose against the cold, wet windowpane. She peered into the night at the Chicago and North Western Railroad tracks that lay between Moingona and Boone, Iowa. Blinding lightning danced about the sky and seemed to strike the railroad bridge that crossed the wildly rushing Des Moines River.

It was near this bridge that her father, a railroad man, was killed just three years ago. And it was in this river that her older brother had drowned while swimming a few months later. Now the weight of providing for the family rested on Kate.

Nervously, Kate pushed her blonde hair from her face. She paced to the window on the opposite side of the room. From here she could see another bridge. This one crossed Honey Creek, a stream that emptied into the Des Moines River. The non-stop sheets of rain that had fallen during the past week had already swollen the creek beyond its capacity. The rain tonight was sending the angry water higher up the hillside. The family horse and cows, in a stable near the creek, were in danger of being trapped.

"I'm going to let the livestock out," Kate said. She grabbed her mother's old raincoat from behind the door, threw it over her head, and bolted out into the storm. Kate made her way to the stable and opened the door. The water was knee deep. The animals galloped up the hill to safer ground. On her way back to the house, Kate rescued a group of baby pigs that had sought refuge on a pile of hay.

Kate was about to throw her wet coat off when she heard something that made her stop short. She dashed to the window and saw a steam engine pulling slowly onto the Des Moines River Bridge. As flashes of lightning lit the countryside, she could see it was engine No. 12. She knew it was sent ahead of

the Midnight Express passenger train to check for washouts. Kate remembered hearing her father tell of the ruin storms such as this could cause to railroad bridges and roadbeds.

Slowly, the engine pushed across that bridge and moved toward the one that crossed Honey Creek. Kate's heart was pounding almost as hard as the rain. She ran to the other window. The engine inched its way onto the swaying Honey Creek Bridge.

When the engine was almost halfway across, the bridge buckled. The hot engine pitched forward into twenty-five feet of swirling water. Kate heard a hissing scream. Then she saw a billowy cloud of steam as the engine went down.

"They've gone down, Mother!" Kate cried. This time she put the raincoat on and tied it. Then, she headed for the door once again.

"There's nothing you can do, child!" her mother pleaded.

"I'm going to Moingona to stop the passenger train," Kate said firmly. Unwillingly, her mother agreed to let her go.

With her father's railroad lantern in her hand, Kate whispered a prayer and walked into the angry night.

At the wrecked Honey Creek Bridge she spotted two of the four crewmen clinging to tree branches in the frothy waves. The other men were nowhere in sight. Realizing that she could be of no help here, she headed in the opposite direction.

Moingona Station lay one mile west. To get there Kate knew she would have to cross the Des Moines River Bridge. Most people avoided that bridge even at high noon on a calm day.

Meant only for trains, the bridge was little more than two steel rails, strung across widely spaced crossties. Some of the ties were far enough apart that a girl like Kate could easily slip through. There were no handrails for her to hold. There was no place for her to go should a train come along. She prayed that tonight the train would be late.

Frightened as she had never been before, Kate made her way onto the shaky bridge. The roar of the

water was deafening, and the gusty wind whipped angrily. Suddenly, the gale blew out the flame in her lantern. She was forced to continue in the blackness and blinding flashes of lightning. Dropping to her knees and holding onto the cold railroad track, she felt her way, foot by foot. She shivered as the wind-driven rain almost took her breath away. Her legs burned from being scraped on the spike-studded ties.

About mid-stream, a flash of lightning revealed an enormous tree in the water. It was headed like a battering ram toward the bridge support right below the spot where Katie was clinging. Holding her breath, she watched the thing heave up and down in the water like an angry sea monster. Suddenly, Kate was showered with muddy water. The tree slipped between the supports and was out of sight as quickly as it had appeared.

On she crept. After what seemed to be a long time, Kate cried with joy. Cold mud squished between her fingers. She had crossed the bridge and was on solid ground!

Rising to her feet and still clutching the unlighted lantern, she dashed down the track.

A few minutes later, soaked and exhausted, she pulled open the station door.

"Honey Creek Bridge is out!" Kate blurted. And she collapsed on the floor. She had done all a fifteen-year-old could do. The rest was up to the agent.

The express passenger train was not scheduled to stop at Moingona. It had to be flagged. The agent rushed desperately to the front of the station just in time. The train was stopped. Men were sent off to the washed-out bridge to rescue the men who had been in the engine.

Kate regained consciousness. To her it all seemed like a bad dream, a nightmare she wanted to forget.

But the world did not let her forget. The passengers on the train collected money to help further her education. A gold watch was given to her by the Order of Railway Conductors. The Chicago and North Western Railroad gave her a cash gift, a half-barrel of flour, a load of coal, and a lifetime pass to ride the trains. From across the nation, letters of praise poured into the Shelley home. Children from a nearby school presented her with a medal.

The Honey Creek Bridge was rebuilt, of course, immediately after the flood. Later, in 1900, the Des Moines River Bridge was replaced by a magnificent steel structure.

Kate went to school and earned a teaching degree. For a time, she taught at a school not far from her home. Then, in 1903, she accepted a job still

537

closer to the Shelley cottage—that of station agent at Moingona, Iowa. And twice each day, going to and from her new job, Kate crossed the new Kate Shelley Bridge, the bridge named for a girl who saved a train.

## CHECK FOR UNDERSTANDING

1. What is the setting of the story?
2. What gave Kate a special feeling for the danger of the river and the railroad bridge even before the storm?
3. What tragedy was Kate unable to prevent? Why was Kate the only person who could stop a second tragedy from occurring?
4. During what part of her adventure was Kate's own life in danger? Explain your answer.
5. Of all her rewards for her bravery, which do you think probably meant the most to Kate? Explain your answer.

**WRITE ABOUT** *"The Girl Who Saved a Train"*
    Imagine that the railroad wanted to put a plaque on the Kate Shelley Bridge, explaining how the bridge got its name. The plaque has space for only fifty words, and you have been given the job of writing its message. Write what you would put on the plaque.

# A Song of Greatness

A Chippewa Indian Song
by MARY AUSTIN

When I hear the old men
Telling of heroes,
Telling of great deeds
Of ancient days,
When I hear that telling
Then I think within me
I too am one of these.

When I hear the people
Praising great ones,
Then I know that I too
Shall be esteemed,
I too when my time comes
Shall do mightily.

# LITERATURE

## Setting

The **setting** of a story is simply the *time and place* in which the story occurs. The time of the story may be pinpointed exactly, or it may be indicated in a very general way. The same is true of the place in which the story occurs. The place where events in the story take place could be as small as a room, or as broad as a region.

There is no rule either that the setting can't change within a story. It is possible to have a story begin on a summer day, and end on a winter day four years later. And it is just as easy for a story to begin in a room in Texas and end in a Tokyo traffic jam. Generally, though, stories of short length don't have these kind of drastic changes in setting.

The importance of the setting to your understanding of the story can vary, too. Usually, the less exactly the setting is defined, the less important it is to the story. For example, a story might be about a boy in a modern city. All the author might do is let you see the boy surrounded by tall buildings and waiting for a bus. The tall buildings tell you he is in a city. The bus tells you he is in modern times. If it isn't particularly important to the story, the author may not name the city or mention a particular date.

In other stories, the setting is so important that the story wouldn't make sense without its being clearly stated. In this case, the time and place are both described early in the story, and fairly exactly.

A good example is the story you just read, "The Girl Who Saved the Train." What does this first sentence of the

540

story tell you about the importance of the setting to the story?

---

> As if drawn by some strange magnet, fifteen-year-old Kate Shelley kept near her window on that stormy July night in 1881.

---

Two things tell you that the time of this story is important for you to know. The first is the fact that the author has been exact about when the story takes place. The second is that the author has included this information in the first sentence of the story.

And of course the date on which this story takes place is vital to understanding the actions of the girl. For example, think of what reading the story might be like if the date were left out. Then you might assume that the events in the story were taking place recently. If you assumed that, you might say to yourself throughout the story, "Why doesn't Kate Shelley just pick up the telephone and call the police, or the fire department, or someone at the train station?" Knowing the date gives you the understanding you need for the story to make sense. You know that telephones were not in use at that time.

When you read the last story in this book, note the way the author treats the setting. Pay particular attention to how *exactly*, and how *early* in the story, the author describes the setting.

by NATALIE BABBITT

One of the most interesting things about people is that each one is different. This can also be a very troublesome fact, as Gaylen and his guardian discover in this story.

How do differences among the people of the kingdom cause trouble in the story? What does the Prime Minister suggest to solve the problem?

# DEFINING DELICIOUS

In his workroom at the top of the tower, DeCree, the Prime Minister, was pacing up and down. Occasionally he would pause, throw up his arms in a gesture of helplessness, and then resume his pacing. From her perch, his cockatoo watched with beady interest, turning her head this way and that as he crossed and recrossed before her.

"There will be civil war!" he burst out at last. "Splits, up-heavals, and people taking sides! Smiles will be forgotten and spring will escape notice! Little flowers will push up, only to be trodden down, and birds will sing unheeded."

From a pile of cushions in a corner of the room, his Special Assistant, a skinny, pleasant boy of twelve named Gaylen, put down the book he had been reading and frowned. "Civil war?" he said. "But why? What happened?"

543

"It was like this," said the Prime Minister, climbing onto the stool at his desk. "I went down, you see, to show the King how far I'd gone on my dictionary. He was pleased with the first part. He liked 'Affectionate is your dog' and 'Annoying is a loose boot in a muddy place' and so on, and he smiled at 'Bulky is a big bag of boxes.' As a matter of fact, there was no trouble with any of the *A*'s or *B*'s, and the C's were fine, too, especially 'Calamitous is saying no to the King.'

"But then we got to 'Delicious is fried fish' and he said no, I'd have to change that. He doesn't care for fried fish. The Queen said, 'Delicious is a plum pudding,' and then the King said nonsense, everyone knew the most delicious thing is an apple, and they began quarreling. Not just the two of them—the whole court. When

544

I left, they were all yelling and shouting and shaking their fists. The King and the General were glaring at each other, and the Queen was trying to get everyone to listen to the recipe for plum pudding."

"That doesn't sound like civil war to me," said Gaylen, turning back to his book with a smile. "It only sounds silly."

"Of course it's silly," said the Prime Minister impatiently.

"But a lot of serious things start silly."

Gaylen put his book down again and sighed. "Why don't you just leave *Delicious* out of the dictionary?"

"I can't do that," said the Prime Minister. "If this is going to be a proper dictionary, I can't leave anything out."

At that moment there was a great racket in the courtyard below. Gaylen ran to the window and looked down. People

545

were pouring out of the castle door to form a noisy ring around two men shoving each other about on the grass. After a moment, one knocked the other flat, shouted "Plums!" and strode triumphantly back inside, followed by the cheering crowd. The man who had been flattened swayed to his feet and went off muttering.

The Prime Minister shook his head sadly. "Now here's a pretty kettle of fish," he said.

"Or apples," said Gaylen.

Gaylen had lived in the castle ever since he'd been left, a tiny baby, gurgling in a basket at the main gate. The basket had been carried in to the King, who was very annoyed to see its contents.

"Now, by Harry," the King had said with a frown, "I suppose some silly mother thinks I'll adopt this baby and leave the kingdom to him when I die. Well, I won't do it. I ex-pect to have a son of my own some day. Take this baby away and see if one of the kitchen maids will have it."

But the Prime Minister was hovering nearby and sprang forward when he heard what the King was saying. "Please, your Majesty, let *me* have the baby," he said. "I'll take good care of him, and I promise he'll never be a bother to you."

"Humph!" said the King. "What on earth do *you* want a baby for? Well, go ahead. Take it. Why not?" So the Prime Minister went joyfully off with the basket and the King promptly forgot all about it.

Now the truth is that De-Cree was a very lonely man. He had never had a wife, and he lived all by himself in the castle tower. But it wasn't a wife he was lonely for; it was a child. He wanted a child so badly that it kept him awake thinking about it. And when he couldn't sleep, he got over-tired and caught colds and went about sniffling, with his beard wrapped around his throat to keep it warm. It made him feel achy and wretched, and when he went to advise the King on important matters, he would say things like "Dow thed" for "Now then" and "Dot eddy bore" for "Not any more." When he did this, the King would get cross, and that made the Prime Minister feel worse than ever.

But after the baby came to live with him in the tower, the Prime Minister slept nine hours every night without even snoring, and he was never lonely again. So he named the baby Vaungaylen, which means "little healer." It was a very long name, so the baby was mostly called Gaylen for short, which suited him very well, and as soon as he was old enough, the Prime Minister taught him to read and write and made him Special Assistant.

And if Gaylen came to believe that the world was a bright and flawless garden where no weeds grew, a garden in the center of which the castle tower rose high and watchful and serene, it was not to be wondered at. After all, he was cared for very tenderly, with never a wish ungratified, and he and the Prime Minister loved each other as much as any real father and son since time began.

That night the conversation around the King's dinner table was strained. Nobody was letting anybody forget the arguments of the afternoon.

"What's for dinner tonight?" said the King to the Queen with a broad smile. "Apples, I hope?"

"Dear me, no," said the Queen in a bored tone. "Not apples again. One gets so very tired of them."

"Well, at least, seeing as it's nearly spring," said the King through his teeth, "I don't suppose we'll have to sit through plum pudding."

The Queen turned away with a toss of her head.

Just then the royal dinner was carried in, a huge roast of venison with carrots and potatoes and a variety of fruits in bowls. The guests began muttering to each other about the meal. Everyone was dissatisfied with it in one way or another, but the Prime Minister rose and bowed to the Queen. "An excellent dinner, your Majesty," he said politely. "I'm sure we'll all enjoy it enormously."

"Even without fried fish?" asked the Queen, glaring at him.

"Well, of course," answered the Prime Minister in an effort to be generous, "one can't eat fried fish every night."

"One can't eat fried fish any night *at all,* unless one is a troublemaking old fool," said the King flatly.

The Prime Minister sat down abruptly and closed his eyes.

"Very well, then," came a deep voice from the end of the table, "where are the nuts? The walnuts, the chestnuts, the pecans?" It was the voice of Hemlock, a brother to the Queen, who stood at his place scowling. "Where, I say, are the nuts? We always have nuts for dinner."

"We never have nuts for dinner," said the King, "starting now."

Hemlock smiled dangerously. He was a tall, unpleasant man and a friend to no one, not even his sister the Queen. He reached into his pockets and pulled out two large handfuls of nuts, which he threw high into the air. Then he turned and left the

room. The nuts came raining down on the tabletop, and bounced off the heads of the guests, who rose in a body, with a great deal of noise and confusion.

When the King had restored order at last and everyone was sitting down again, he thumped on the table with his fist. "See here," he said, "this cannot continue! Now, where has Hemlock gone?" He looked around, frowning. "Well, let him go. Things always seem more peaceful without him. And anyway, DeCree started all this and he'll have to find a way to settle it." He looked at the Prime Minister. "Well?" he said.

"Well," said the Prime Minister hopefully, "we could just forget all about it."

"No," said the King, "we couldn't."

"Then," said the Prime Minister, "we'll have to find out what everybody thinks and write it all down and then whatever gets the most votes for *Delicious* will be the thing I use in the dictionary."

"That's a very good idea, DeCree," said the King. "Go all around the kingdom and ask everybody. It'll turn out to be apples, anyway."

"Pudding," murmured the Queen.

The King looked as if he were going to lose his temper, but he gritted his teeth and managed to pull himself together. "Start right away on this journey, DeCree," he said. "There's no time to lose."

"But I can't go myself," protested the Prime Minister. "I'm too old for a long trip like that."

"Then who shall go?" asked the King in some alarm. "Whom can we trust?"

"I'll send my assistant, Vaungaylen," said the Prime Minister.

"Well, all right," said the King, "as long as he's trustworthy."

"He's an upright and honest boy," said the Prime Minister firmly, "and the apple of my eye."

"The *pudding*," murmured the Queen.

"Now, by Harry," the King began angrily, and then paused. Someone was galloping across the courtyard below and on over the drawbridge. The King went to the window and peered out. "There goes Hemlock," he announced. "He's riding that big gray horse of his, Ballywrack. Well, maybe he'll stay away. I wish he would, by Harry. He's always trying to take over and run things." He went back to his place at the table and looked severely at the assembled guests. "Too many cooks spoil the soup, you know," he said.

"Too many cooks spoil the *pudding*," murmured the Queen.

The next morning everyone gathered in the courtyard to see Gaylen start off. He had been well equipped and instructed by the Prime Minister and knew exactly what to do. There was a large notebook in his saddlebag, pens and ink, the proclamation he was to read to the people, and a map of the kingdom. It was not very large, as kingdoms go, perhaps thirty miles square, and there were four towns. It was on the basis of this number that DeCree and the King had decided to allow four weeks to complete the poll.

"Four weeks if he's trustworthy, that is," said the King to the Prime Minister, whom he had drawn to one side.

"I raised him myself," said DeCree, "and he's true to the core."

"I hope so," said the King. "There's something about this whole business that makes me nervous."

551

"You don't need to worry about Vaungaylen," said the Prime Minister.

"Well maybe," said the King suspiciously. "Maybe. What's his choice for *Delicious*?"

"He hasn't said," replied the Prime Minister.

"Just as well," said the King. He turned back to where Gaylen sat high on a fine horse, waiting to start off. The horse, whose name was Marrow, was one of the King's best and was draped in the royal colors.

"Here, boy," said the King to Gaylen. "Here's a little something to munch along the way." And he handed up a sack of apples. Gaylen said thank you and stowed the apples away in his saddlebag, alongside the packet of cold fried fish and the sheaf of recipes for plum pudding.

"And now," said the King to the assembled company, "before this boy starts out to poll the people, I want to make

552

one thing quite clear. All of you here at the castle are going to stay here at the castle. There'll be no running ahead to buy up votes for this or that. We'll all stay here quietly for the four weeks, and we'll talk of other things."

"That's right," said the Prime Minister. "That's the

only way to handle it. Good luck, Gaylen, and I'll send my cockatoo after you with the news each Wednesday and Saturday."

"You're off then," said the King, and he gave Marrow a slap. The horse went booming over the drawbridge and everybody cheered. They went on cheering until horse and rider had disappeared over a grassy hill and down through a stand of hornbeams, where the first road led to the first town.

🍎

*During Gaylen's journey, new problems plague the kingdom. To find out what the most popular definition of* delicious *is and how Gaylen saves the kingdom, read the rest of the novel* The Search for Delicious *by Natalie Babbitt.*

## CHECK FOR UNDERSTANDING

1. How did differences among people cause trouble?
2. What plan did the Prime Minister suggest to solve the problem?
3. Why wasn't Hemlock chosen to make the journey?
4. Why was it decided that a person would need four weeks for the journey?
5. Why was Gaylen given apples, fish, and recipes for plum pudding right before he left?
6. What do you think Gaylen will discover on his journey?

## WRITE ABOUT *"Defining Delicious"*

Write your own definitions, in DeCree's style, of the words listed below. When you are done, compare them with classmates' definitions. Do you agree on any?

| | | |
|---|---|---|
| delicious | frightening | happy |
| delightful | gruesome | irritating |

# THINK ABOUT IT

Think about the characters in the stories you have read. What choice did each of them make that turned out to be dangerous? Why did each of them make that choice?

- What happened when Sumiko went to the mayor about the thieves stealing the oysters?
- What would have been the effects to Ellen Toliver if Dow had cut the bread?
- What choice did Daniel make that endangered his life, and what choice did he make that probably saved it?
- In what two ways might Kate Shelley have lost her life in her attempt to save the passenger train?
- What dangers do you think Gaylen might run into as he sets out to find a definition for *delicious?*

After reading and thinking about these different kinds of daring adventures, which character from the stories do you admire the most and why?

# WRITE ABOUT IT

Imagine that you are the brother or sister of one of the characters in the unit. Write a paragraph telling what you would say to try to convince the person not to take the risk. Write a second paragraph telling what the person would probably reply.

554

# READ ABOUT IT

*The Princess and the Lion* by Elizabeth Coatsworth.
Pantheon Books, 1963. Adventure and suspense await
a young princess in ancient Abyssinia as she strives to
reach her imprisoned brother who is to be king.

*Antarctica, the Great White Continent* by Miriam Schlein.
Hastings House Publishers, 1980. Stories of adventure
and discovery in the frozen land once thought impossible to explore. Included are 70 photos of Antarctic
wildlife and unusual geographical features plus up-to-date science discoveries.

*The Knight of the Golden Plain* by Mollie Hunter. Harper &
Row, Publishers, 1983. A boy's dream becomes an
exciting fantasy-adventure when he sets forth on his
great horse to vanquish a magician and restore the
voice of beautiful Dorabella.

*The Secret Soldier: The Story of Deborah Sampson* by
Ann McGovern. Four Winds Press, 1975. The story of
Deborah Sampson and her successful plan to pose as
a man and join the Continental Army.

*Long Meg* by Rosemary Minard. Pantheon Books, 1982.
Dressed as a boy in her father's old clothes, the
innkeeper's daughter Margaret defeats the most
famous swordsman in England.

# GLOSSARY

## A

**a·blaze** (ə blāz′) *adj.* in flames; on fire.

**a·breast** (ə brest′) *adv.* side by side and facing in the same direction.

**a·brupt** (ə brupt′) *adj.* sudden; unexpected.

**ac·cel·er·a·tor** (ak sel′ ə rā′ tər) *n.* a device for increasing the speed of a machine, especially the foot pedal that controls the speed of an automobile engine.

**ac·com·pa·ny** (ə kum′ pə nē) *v.* to go with.

**ac·com·plish·ment** (ə kom′ plish mənt) *n.* something finished; achievement; ability to do something.

**a·dapt·a·ble** (ə dap′ tə bəl) *adj.* capable of being changed to fit new uses or places.

**ad·di·tion·al** (ə dish′ ən əl) *adj.* added; further.

**ad·just** (ə just′) *v.*, **ad·just·ed, ad·just·ing.** 1. to change or arrange to fit a need; make suitable. 2. to move or arrange parts so as to put in working order.

**ad·mi·ral** (ad′ mər əl) *n.* an officer in the navy of the highest rank.

**ad·mir·er** (ad mīr′ ər) *n.* a person who admires, or who feels high regard or appreciation of someone.

**af·fec·tion·ate** (ə fek′ shə nit) *adj.* full of love; tender.

**a·lert** (ə lurt′) *adj.* keenly watchful.

**al·ly** (ə lī′) *v.* to unite or associate with.

**al·ter** (ôl′tər) *v.* to make different; change.

**am·a·teur** (am′ə chər) *n.* a person who does something for pleasure, rather than as a career or for money; a person who does something without experience.

**am·ble** (am′ bəl) *v.*, **am·bled, am·bling.** 1. to walk at a relaxed pace. 2. for a horse, to move at a slow pace by lifting both legs on the same side together.

**a·mid** (ə mid′) *prep.* in the middle of; among.

**a·miss** (ə mis′) *adj.* wrong; improper.

**an·ces·tor** (an′ ses′ tər) *n.* a person or thing from which another is developed or descended.

**an·nu·al** (an′ yoo əl) *adj.* yearly.

**an·tic** (an′ tik) *n.* a silly or comical action; caper; prank.

**ap·par·ent** (ə par′ ənt) *adj.* easily seen or understood; evident. —**ap·par·ent·ly,** *adv.*

**ap·pro·pri·ate** (ə prō′ prē it) *adj.* suitable; fitting; proper.

**arc** (ärk) 1. *n.* a curved line; part of a circle. 2. *v.* to move in a curved line.

**arched** (ärcht) *adj.* having the form of an arch; curved.

**ar·chi·tec·ture** (är′ kə tek′ chər) *n.* the art of designing, planning, and constructing buildings or other structures in a particular style.

**ar·ti·fi·cial** (är′ tə fish′ əl) *adj.* not natural; man-made.

**as·sault** (ə sôlt′) *n.* a violent or vigorous attack.

**as·sem·ble** (ə sem′ bəl) *v.*, **as·sem·bled, as·sem·bling.** to meet or come together.

**as·sem·bly** (ə sem′ blē) *n.* a group of people gathered together for a common purpose.

**at·tempt** (ə tempt′) *v.* to make an effort to do something; try.

**awe·some** (ô′ səm) *adj.* inspiring wonder, combined with fear or respect.

# B

**back·lands** (bak' lands) *n.* a rural and thinly settled area.

**back·woods** (bak' woodz') *n., pl.* heavily wooded or thinly settled areas that are far from cities or towns.

**badg·er** (baj' ər) *n.* an animal with a heavy body, short legs, long claws, and a short thick tail. It usually lives in holes in the ground.

**ban·is·ter** (ban' is tər) *n.* a handrail and its upright support along the edge of a staircase.

**ban·jo** (ban' jō) *n.* a stringed instrument with a long neck and a round body.

**ba·sin** (bā'sin) *n.* a bowl or sink for washing, as in a bathroom.

**ba·tik** (bə tēk') *n.* a method of hand-printing colored designs on cloth, by putting a wax coating on the parts that are not to be dyed.

**bead·y** (bē' dē) *adj.* small, round, and glittering.

**be·friend** (bi frend') *v.* to act as a friend to; assist or help.

**be·held** (bi held') *v.* past tense of **behold**: to look at, see.

**be·mused** (bi myoozd') *adj.* 1. lost in thought. 2. confused.

**bil·low·y** (bil' ō ē) *adj.* swelling; surging.

**bind·ing** (bīn' ding) *n.* anything that ties things together.

**bit·ter** (bit' ər) *adj.* harsh; biting; sharp.

**bleat** (blēt) *v.* to cry like a sheep, goat, or calf.

**blun·der** (blun' dər) *v.,* **blun·dered, blun·der·ing.** 1. to make a careless or stupid mistake. 2. to act blindly or clumsily.

**boll** (bōl) *n.* a rounded seed pod of a plant, as of cotton or flax.

**bri·dle** (brīd' əl) *n.* the part of a horse's harness that fits over the head, used to guide or control the animal.

**bris·tly** (bris' lē) *adj.* like bristles, the short stiff hairs of a hog. **bristled,** *v.*

**broad·cast** (brôd' kast') *v.,* **broad·cast·ed, broad·cast·ing.** to send out information or entertainment by radio or television.

**buck·le** (buk' əl) *v.,* **buck·led, buck·ling.** to bulge or bend.

**bul·le·tin** (bool'it ən) *n.* a short report of news.

**bush·el** (boosh' əl) *n.* a unit of measure equal to four pecks or thirty-two quarts.

**bus·tle** (bus' əl) *v.* to move about in a quick, excited, or noisy manner.

# C

**cab·bage** (kab' ij) *n.* a plant having thick, green or reddish-purple leaves that are eaten as a vegetable.

**ca·ble** (kā'bəl) *n.* a strong, thick rope, especially one made of wires twisted together.

**cad·dy** (kad' ē) *n.* a person who assists a golfer by carrying his or her golf clubs.

---

**PRONUNCIATION KEY**
at; āpe; cär; end; mē; it; īce; hot; ōld; fôrk; wood; fool; oil; out; up; turn; sing; thin; this, hw in white; zh in treasure; ə stands for a in ago, e in taken, i in pencil, o in lemon, u in circus.

**ca·lam·i·tous** (kə lam′ ə təs) *adj.* disastrous.

**cal·lig·ra·phy** (kə lig′ rə fē) *n.* beautiful handwriting.

**can·non** (kan′ ən) *n.* a large gun that is mounted on a base.

**can·ter** (kan′ tər) *n.* a slow gallop.

**ca·pac·i·ty** (kə pas′ ə tē) *n.* the maximum amount that can be held or contained in a space.

**cas·u·al** (kazh′ yōō əl) *adj.* without serious thought; offhand.—**cas′ u·al·ly,** *adv.*

**cham·ber** (chām′ bər) *n.* a room; an enclosed space.

**chan·nel** (chan′ əl) *n.* the bed of a stream, river, or other waterway.

**chick·weed** (chik′ wēd′) *n.* a common weed with a creeping root, small oval leaves, and tiny white flowers.

**chil·e** (chil′ ē) *n.* a spicy red pepper.

**cho·rus** (kôr′ əs) *n.* 1. a large group of people who sing together. 2. The saying or singing of something by a group of people all at the same time.

**chute** (shōōt) *n.* a passageway through which various things may be carried: *a coal chute.*

**ci·pher** (sī′ fər) *n.* a system of secret writing that cannot be understood without the key; code.

**clas·si·cal** (klas′ i kəl) *adj.* relating to music that follows certain established standards of form and style and is of long-lasting interest.

**clo·ver** (klō′ vər) *n.* a plant with leaves usually made up of three leaflets.

**coarse** (kôrs) *adj.* lacking fineness; crude; thick or rough.

**code** (kōd) *n.* a system of writing used to keep messages secret. Letters, words, numbers, or other symbols stand for the letters and words of the message.

**coil** (koil) *n.* anything made up of many spirals or rings: *a coil of rope.*

**col·lide** (kə līd′) *v.* to come together with force; crash.

**com·mo·tion** (kə mō shən) *n.* noisy disorder; confusion.

**com·pet·i·tive** (kəm pet′ ə tiv) *adj.* wanting to beat others in a contest: *He was very competitive.*; involving competition: *a competitive sport.*

**com·pli·cat·ed** (kom′ plə kā′ tid) *adj.* hard to understand; complex.

**con·di·tion** (kən dish′ ən) *n.* 1. the way that a person or thing is. 2. something needed before something else can take place. 3. something that limits or restricts.

**con·fer·ence** (kon′ fər əns) *n.* a meeting for the purpose of talking about something of common interest.

**con·scious·ness** (kon′ shəs nis) *n.* the state of being aware and knowing.

**con·sent** (kən sent′) *n.* permission to do something.

**con·test·ant** (kən tes′ tənt) *n.* someone who takes part in a contest.

**con·trar·y** (kon′ trer ē) *adj.* entirely different; opposite; tending to contradict.

**con·tri·bu·tion** (kon′ trə byōō′ shən) *n.* the act of giving to others.

**coop** (kōōp) *v.,* to confine in a cage or any small space.

**cor·mo·rant** (kôr′ mər ənt) *n.* a large sea bird with dark feathers, a hooked bill, and a pouch under the beak for holding fish.

**cor·ri·dor** (kôr′ ə dər) *n.* a long hallway in a building, often with rooms opening onto it.

**cove** (kōv) *n.* a small, sheltered inlet or bay in a shoreline.

**cra·ter** (krā′ tər) *n.* a bowl-shaped hollow area at the mouth of a volcano.

**craw·dad** (krô′ dad′) *n.* crayfish, a freshwater shellfish like a lobster.

**cred·it** (kred′ it) *v.,* **cred·it·ed, cred·it·ing.** to consider something as belonging to, produced by, or resulting from.

**crest** (krest) *n.* the highest point of anything: *the crest of a hill.*

**criss·cross·es** (kris′ kros′ z) *n.* a pattern made by crossing lines.

**cross·ties** (krôs′ tīz′) *n.* a railroad tie; a supporting beam that helps keep the rails of a railroad in line.

**cruise** (krōoz) *v.,* **cruised, cruis·ing.** to sail from place to place without any special place in mind.

**cul·prit** (kul′ prit) *n.* a person guilty of some offense or crime.

**cun·ning** (kun′ ing) *adj.* clever or skilled in deceiving; tricky; sly.

# D _____

**de·bris** (də brē′) *n.* scattered remains of something destroyed; rubbish.

**de·fy** (di fī′) *v.,* **de·fied, de·fy·ing.** to resist boldly or openly; challenge; dare.

**de·ject·ed** (di jek′ tid) *adj.* showing low spirits; depressed.

**del·i·ca·cy** (del′ i kə sē) *n., pl.* **del·i·ca·cies.** a rare or choice food.

**de·mol·ished** (di mol′ ishd) *adj.* destroyed; ruined completely.

**dem·on·strate** (dem′ ən strāt′) *v.,* **dem·on·strat·ed, dem·on·strat·ing.** to make clear; to describe, explain, or show by use of examples.

**depths** (depths) *n.* the deepest, lowest, or furthest part.

**de·struc·tion** (di struk′ shən) *n.* the state of being broken into pieces; ruin.

**de·vot·ed** (di vō′ tid) *adj.* loyal; faithful; dedicated.

**di·a·lect** (dī′ ə lekt′) *n.* a form of a language that is spoken in a particular area.

**dig·i·tal** (dij′ it əl) *adj.* having numerals (0 through 9).

**dig·ni·ty** (dig′ nə tē) *n.* nobility of character or manner; stateliness or self-respect. —**dig′ ni·fied,** *adj.*

**dis·a·gree·a·ble** (dis′ ə grē′ ə bəl) *adj.*
1. not to one's liking; unpleasant.
2. having a bad temper; quarrelsome.

**dis·ap·prov·al** (dis′ ə prōo′ vəl) *n.* an unfavorable feeling; dislike.

**dis·in·fect·ant** (dis′ in fek′ tənt) *n.* a substance used to destroy germs.

**dis·mount** (dis mount′) *v.* to get off or down.

**dis·pute** (dis pyōot′) *v.* to debate; quarrel about; discuss; argue.

---

**PRONUNCIATION KEY**
at; āpe; cär; end; mē; it; īce; hot; ōld; fôrk; wood; fōol; oil; out; up; turn; sing; thin; <u>th</u>is, hw in white; zh in treasure; ə stands for a in ago, e in taken, i in pencil, o in lemon, u in circus.

**dis·qual·i·fy** (dis kwol′ ə fī′) *v.*, **dis·qual·i·fied, dis·qual·i·fy·ing.** 1. to declare unfit. 2. to bar from winning a prize or contest.

**doc·u·ment** (dok′ yə mənt) *n.* something written or printed that gives information, support, or proof about a particular object or matter.

**dor·mi·to·ry** (dôr′ mə tôr′ ē) *n.* a building having many bedrooms, for college students to live and sleep in.

**douse** (dous) *v.*, **doused, dous·ing.** to throw water or other liquid over; drench.

**down·pour** (doun′ pôr′) *n.* a heavy fall of rain.

**dra·mat·ic** (drə mat′ ik) *adj.* like a drama; emotional; exciting; striking.

**dra·per·y** (drā′ pər ē) *n. pl.*, **dra·per·ies.** cloth hung or arranged in loose, graceful folds.

**draught** (draft) *n.* a device for regulating the flow of air in a stove.

**draw·bridge** (drô′ brij) *n.* a bridge that can be wholly or partly raised or lowered so as to permit or prevent passage.

# E

**ef·fort·less** (ef′ ərt lis) *adj.* needing little or no effort; easy. —**ef′ fort·less·ly,** *adv.*

**e·las·tic** (i las′ tik) *adj.* capable of returning to its original size after being stretched; stretchable.

**e·merge** (i murj′) *v.*, **e·merged, e·merg·ing.** 1. to come into view. 2. to rise or come out.

**en·dur·ance** (en door′ əns) *n.* the ability to bear up under pain, stress, or fatigue.

**e·rect** (i rekt′) *adj.* in a vertical or upright position.

**es·cort** (es kôrt′) *v.*, **es·cort·ed, es·cort·ing.** to accompany as a courtesy.

**es·teemed** (es tēmd′) *adj.* considered good or important; highly valued.

**ex·pect·ant** (eks pek′ tənt) *adj.* looking forward to; waiting in hope. — **ex·pect′ ant·ly,** *adv.*

**ex·pe·di·tion** (eks′ pə dish′ ən) *n.* a journey made for a specific purpose: *The explorers went on an expedition to Antarctica.*

**ex·tent** (eks tent′) *n.* the degree or limit to which something goes.

**ex·te·ri·or** (eks tēr′ ē ər) *n.* 1. the outer surface or part; outside. 2. an outward look or manner.

**ex·tinct** (eks tingkt′) *adj.* 1. no longer in existence. 2. no longer active.

# F

**fair·way** (fer′ wā′) *n.* the mowed area on a golf course between the tee and putting green.

**fare** (fer) *v.* to get along; do: *He will fare well on his journey.*

**fee·ble** (fē′ bəl) *adj.* lacking strength; weak. —**fee′ bly,** *adv.*

**fe·ro·cious** (fə rō′ shəs) *adj.* savage; fierce.

**fer·ry** (fer′ ē) *n. pl.* **ferries.** a boat used to carry people and goods across a river or other narrow body of water. **fer·ried, fer·ry·ing.** *v.*

**fer·ti·lize** (furt′ əl īz′) *v.* 1. to make fertile or productive. 2. to put fertilizer (manure or chemicals) on.

**fife** (fīf) *n.* a shrill-toned musical instrument of the flute family.

**flank** (flangk) *n.* the part between the ribs and hip on the side of a human being or animal.

**flare** (fler) *v.*, **flared, flar·ing.** to open or spread outward.

**flaw·less** (flô′ lis) *adj.* perfect.

**fleet** (flēt) *adj.* swift; fast.

**fling** (fling) *v.*, **flung, fling·ing.** to throw with force or violence; hurl; thrust.

**floun·der** (floun′ dər) *v.* to move or struggle with stumbling motions.

**flour·ish** (flur′ ish) *v.*, **flour·ished, flour·ish·ing.** 1. to thrive. 2. to wave about with bold or sweeping gestures.

**flush** (flush) *v.* to turn red; blush; glow.

**foot·bridge** (foot′ brij′) *n.* a bridge that can be walked on only.

**forge** (fôrj) *v.*, **forged, forg·ing.** 1. to move forward slowly but steadily. 2. to copy something in order to cheat someone; counterfeit.

**for·lorn** (fôr lôrn′) *adj.* unhappy, as from being lost or lonely. —**for·lorn′ ly,** *adv.*

**foul** (foul) *n.* an unfair action, breaking of the rules.

**fran·tic** (fran′ tik) *adj.* wildly excited by worry, grief, fear, or anger; frenzied. —**fran′ ti·cal·ly,** *adv.;* also **fran′ tic· ly,** *adv.* —**fran′ tic·ness,** *n.*

**froth·y** (frô′ thē) *adj.* covered with bubbles; foamy.

**func·tion** (fungk′ shən) *n.* the natural use of something; purpose.

**fu·ri·ous** (fyoor′ ē əs) *adj.* extremely angry. —**fu′ ri·ous·ly,** *adv.*

**fuse** (fyo͞oz) *v.*, **fused, fus·ing.** to blend or unite by melting together.

# G

**gad·get** (gaj′ it) *n.* a small mechanical device.

**gal·ax·y** (gal′ ək sē) *n.* 1. any of the vast groupings of stars in the universe. 2. a brilliant or splendid group.

**gale** (gāl) *n.* a very strong wind, especially one having a speed of from thirty-two to sixty-three miles per hour.

**gal·lant** (gal′ ənt) *adj.* brave; noble; heroic.

**gap** (gap) *n.* a break, crack, or unfilled space.

**ga·zelle** (gə zel′) *n.* a slender, horned animal, a form of antelope, living mostly on plains of Africa and Asia. It is a grass-eater, and it can run as fast as sixty miles per hour.

**ge·nie** (jē′ nē) *n.* in Arabian folk tales, a spirit having magic powers.

**ge·o·graph·ic** (jē′ ə graf′ ik) *adj.* relating to the physical and cultural features of a region.

**gild** (gild) *v.*, **gild·ed, gild·ing.** 1. to coat with a thin layer of gold. 2. to adorn, especially with a golden light.

**glare** (gler) *v.*, **glared, glar·ing.** 1. to shine with a strong light. 2. to look piercingly and with hostility.

---

**PRONUNCIATION KEY**
at; āpe; cär; end; mē; it; īce; hot; ōld; fôrk; wood; fo͞ol; oil; out; up; turn; sing; thin; <u>th</u>is, hw in white; zh in treasure; ə stands for a in ago, e in taken, i in pencil, o in lemon, u in circus.

**glide** (glīd) *v.*, **glid·ed, glid·ing.** to move smoothly and effortlessly.

**glint** (glint) *v.*, **glint·ed, glint·ing.** to shine; sparkle.

**gloss·y** (glô′ sē) *adj.* having a shiny surface.

**glut·ton** (glut′ ən) *n.* someone who eats too much or enjoys eating excessively.

**gog·gles** (gog′ əls) *n.* large, close-fitting eyeglasses used to protect the eyes, as from wind, dust, or water.

**goods** (goodz) *n. pl.* 1. things that are sold; merchandise; wares. 2. fabric; cloth.

**grate** (grāt) *v.* to rub together so as to produce a harsh, scraping sound.

**grave** (grāv) *adj.* 1. of great importance. 2. dangerous; critical. —**grave′ ly,** *adv.*

**green·house** (grēn′ hous′) *n.* a building with a glass or transparent plastic roof and sides that trap the heat of the sun, where plants can be grown all year.

**gren·a·dier** (gren′ ə dēr′) *n.* a soldier in the British Army who serves the royal household.

**grieve** (grēv) *v.*, **grieved, griev·ing.** to feel very sad.

**grim** (grim) *adj.* having a stern or forbidding quality or look. —**grim′ ly,** *adv.*

**grit** (grit) *v.* to grind together.

**grooved** (groovd) *adj.* having long narrow channels or ruts in a surface.

**grove** (grōv) *n.* a small group of trees without underbrush.

**gruff** (gruf) *adj.* deep and rough.

**gui·tar·ist** (gi tär′ ist) *n.* someone who plays the guitar.

**gust·y** (gus′ tē) *adj.* windy; blustery.

**gut·ter** (gut′ ər) *n.* a trough fixed under or along the edge of a roof to carry off rainwater.

# H

**hair·spring** (her′ spring′) *n.* a fine, coiled spring in a watch or clock that regulates the movement of the balance wheel.

**har·di·ness** (här′ dē nis) *n.* physical strength.

**har·ness** (här′ nis) *v.*, **har·nessed, har·ness·ing.** to put a harness on.

**harp** (härp) *n.* a musical instrument that has strings set in a frame. It is played by plucking the strings with the fingers.

**har·row** (har′ ō) *v.* to break up or level plowed ground by drawing a harrow, a heavy frame with teeth, over it.

**has·ten** (hā′ sən) *v.* to act quickly; hurry.

**haught·y** (hô′ tē) *adj.* having or showing much pride in oneself. —**haugh′ ti·ly,** *adv.*

**haz·ard·ous** (haz′ ər dəs) *adj.* involving danger; risky.

**heart's-ease** (härtz′ ēz) *n.* a kind of flower with violet-colored petals.

**heave** (hēv) *v.* to rise and fall continuously in a rhythmic manner.

**heir·loom** (er′ loom′) *n.* a personal possession handed down in a family from generation to generation.

**herb** (urb) *n.* any plant whose leaves, stems, seeds, or roots are used in cooking for their flavor.

**hes·i·ta·tion** (hez′ ə tā′ shən) *n.* a delay due to fear, uncertainty, or doubt; a pause.

**hew** (hyo͞o) *v.* to make or shape with cutting blows, as from an ax.

**high-rise** (hī′ rīz′) *adj.* having many stories: *a high-rise building.*

**hinge** (hinj) *v.*, **hinged, hing·ing.** to attach something, such as a door, with a metal device so that it can swing or turn.

**hom·i·ny** (hom′ ə nē) *n.* kernels of white corn that have been dried and boiled in water.

**ho·ri·zon** (hə rī′ zən) *n.* the line where the sky and the earth seem to meet.

**hor·i·zon·tal** (hôr′ ə zont′ əl, (hor′ ə zont′ əl) *adj.* parallel to the horizon; level.

**hu·mil·i·ate** (hyo͞o mil′ ē āt′) *v.*, **hu·mil·i·at·ed, hu·mil·i·at·ing.** to lower the pride of; cause to seem foolish; embarrass.

**hustling** (hus′ ling) *adj.* energetic; willing to earn money through energetic action.

# I

**i·bis** (ī′ bis) *n.* a long-legged wading bird that has a long, downward curving bill.

**ill-mannered** (il man′ ərd) *adj.* having bad manners; rude.

**in·ci·den·tal·ly** (in′ sə dent′ lē) *adv.* by the way.

**in·cor·ri·gi·ble** (in kôr′ ə jə bəl) *adj.* that cannot be made better or reformed.

**in·di·cate** (in′ di kāt′) *v.*, **in·di·cat·ed, in·di·cat·ing.** to signal; to show; to point out.

**in·dulge** (in dulj′) *v.* to allow oneself to have, do, or enjoy; to yield to.

**in·her·it·ance** (in her′ it əns) *n.* something that is received from another at his or her death.

**in·no·cent** (in′ ə sənt) *adj.* free from guilt or wrongdoing.

**in·quis·i·tive** (in kwiz′ ə tiv) *adj.* eager for knowledge; curious; nosy.

**in·sert** (in surt′) *v.* to put, set, or place in.

**in·ten·tion** (in ten′ shən) *n.* purpose; plan.

**in·tone** (in tōn′) *v.*, **in·toned, in·ton·ing.** to recite in a singing voice or monotone, flat voice.

**in·trude** (in tro͞od′) *v.*, **in·trud·ed, in·trud·ing.** to come in as a disturbing or unwelcome addition; enter without being asked or wanted.

**in·ves·ti·gate** (in ves′tə gāt′) *v.* to look into carefully in order to uncover facts or gain information.

# J

**jag·ged** (jag′ id) *adj.* having sharp points that stick out or uneven edges.

**jaun·ty** (jôn′ tē) *adj.* lively, carefree, or self-confident in air or manner; sprightly. —**jaunt′ti·ly,** *adv.*

**jeer** (jēr) *v.*, **jeered, jeer·ing.** to speak or shout in a scornful or mocking way; to make fun of.

**jer·sey** (jur′ zē) *n.* a knitted fabric.

**jock·ey** (jok′ ē) *n.* a person who rides horses in races.

**PRONUNCIATION KEY**
at; āpe; cär; end; mē; it; īce; hot; ōld; fôrk; wood; fo͞ol; oil; out; up; turn; sing; thin; <u>th</u>is, **hw** in white; **zh** in treasure; ə stands for a in ago, e in taken, i in pencil, o in lemon, **u** in circus.

# K _____

**kay·ak** (kī′ ak) *n.* a canoe covered with animal skins or other material, with a small opening in the center for the paddler.

**keel** (kēl) *n.* the main piece which extends lengthwise along the center of a boat.

**kin·dling** (kind′ ling) *n.* material for starting a fire, such as small pieces of dry wood or twigs.

**knoll** (nōl) *n.* a small, rounded hill or mound.

# L _____

**lan·guid** (lan′ gwid) *adj.* showing a lack of energy or force; weak; sluggish.

**laugh·ing·stock** (laf′ing stock′) *n.* an object of ridicule or laughter.

**launch** (lônch) *v.*, **launch·ed, launch·ing.** to push or propel by force into the air or water.

**lav·en·der** (lav′ ən dər) *n.* a pale purple color.

**lean-to** (lēn′ tōō′) *n.* 1. a shed or small building that has a sloping roof and leans against a larger buidling. 2. a crude, open shelter with a sloping roof, made of branches and twigs.

**leer·y** (lēr′ ē) *adj.* not having trust in; suspicious.

**loft·y** (lôf′tē) *adj.* 1. towering. 2. too proud; snobbish. —**loft·i·ly,** *adv.*

**loi·ter** (loi′ tər) *v.*, **loi·tered, loi·ter·ing.** to linger idly or aimlessly about a place.

**long·ing** (lông′ ing) *adj.* feeling a strong or restless desire or yearning. —**long′ ing·ly,** *adv.*

**loom** (lōōm) *v.*, **loomed, loom·ing.** to appear indistinctly as a large, threatening shape.

**lope** (lōp) *n.* a long, easy stride.

**lord·ly** (lôrd′ lē) *adj.* of, or suited for, a lord; haughty or domineering.

**lull** (lul) *v.*, **lulled, lull·ing.** to calm with soothing sounds or caresses.

**lum·ber** (lum′ bər) *v.*, **lum·bered, lum·ber·ing.** to move in a clumsy or noisy manner.

**lu·mi·nous** (lōō′ mə nəs) *adj.* sending out light of its own; shining; bright.

**lurk** (lurk) *v.*, to lie hidden; to move about in a sneaky manner.

# M _____

**mack·er·el** (mak′ ər əl) *n.* a fish related to the tuna, having a silvery body that is marked in metallic blue.

**main·land** (mān′ lənd′) *n.* the largest land mass of a region, country, or continent; not an island.

**main·spring** (mān′ spring′) *n.* the principle spring in the mechanism, especially of a watch or clock.

**mane** (mān) *n.* long, heavy hair along the back and neck of certain animals, such as the horse and lion.

**mas·cot** (mas′ kot) *n.* an animal or thing kept to bring good luck.

**mass** (mas) *n. pl.*, **mass·es.** 1. a body of matter sticking together without a particular shape. 2. a large quantity.

**me·di·e·val** (mē′ dē ē′ vəl) *adj.* of the Middle Ages (about 400–1400 A.D.).

**meek** (mēk) *adj.* mild in manner; gentle; lacking spirit. —**meek′ ly,** *adv.*

**meg·a·phone** (meg′ ə fōn′) *n.* a funnel-shaped device used to make a person's voice louder.

**mem·o·ry** (mem′ ər ē) *n.* 1. the ability to remember. 2. the place in a computer where information is stored.

**mid·dlings** (mid′ lings) *n.* a kind of animal feed made from the by-products of flour milling.

**mid·stretch** (mid′ strech′) *adj.* in the middle of stretching.

**mill** (mil) *n.* a building or business containing machinery for grinding grain, sawing wood, or manufacturing metals.

**mim·ic** (mim′ ik) *v.,* **mim·icked, mim·ick·ing.** to imitate the speech, manners, or gestures of, especially so as to make fun of.

**min·now** (min′ō) *n.* a very small fish.

**mi·rac·u·lous** (mi rak′ yə ləs) *adj.* amazing; extraordinary; incredible. —**mi·rac′ u·lous·ly,** *adv.*

**mock** (mok) *adj.* imitating the real thing; not real.

**mod·est** (mod′ ist) *adj.* not boastful; reserved. —**mod′est·ly,** *adj.*

**moor·hen** (moor′ hen) *n.* the female of the red grouse, a kind of game bird.

**moor·ing** (moor′ing) *n.* a device, such as a cable, rope, or anchor, by which something is moored, or held in place.

**moss** (môs) *n.* nonflowering plants that grow in clusters and often form a soft, dense mat.

**mu·nic·i pal** (myoo nis′ ə pəl) *adj.* relating to the local government or affairs of a community.

# N

**no·bil·i·ty** (nō bil′ ə tē) *n.* a class of people having high birth, rank, or title.

**non·cha·lant** (non′ shə länt′) *adj.* showing a lack of interest; casually indifferent. —**non·cha·lant′ ly,** *adv.*

**nui·sance** (noo′ səns) *n.* something that annoys or offends.

# O

**ob·jec·tion·a·ble** (əb jek′ shə nə bəl) *adj.* causing dislike or disapproval; offensive.

**ob·long** (ob′ lông) *adj.* having greater length than width.

**oc·tave** (ok′ tiv) *n.* eight tones on a musical scale.

**of·fend** (ə fend′) *v.,* **of·fend·ed, of·fend·ing.** to cause displeasure; insult.

**off·hand** (ôf′ hand′) *adj.* done without previous thought; informal.

**op·po·si·tion** (op′ ə zish′ ən) *n.* the act of being or struggling against; resistance.

**or·gan·dy** (ôr′ gən dē) *n.* a sheer, lightweight fabric with a crisp finish, usually made of cotton.

**or·i·gin** (ôr′ ə jin) *n.* the source or place from which something comes.

**or·na·ment** (ôr′nə mənt) *n.* anything used to decorate; often a small, brightly colored object.

---

**PRONUNCIATION KEY**
at; āpe; cär; end; mē; it; īce; hot; ōld; fôrk; wood; fool; oil; out; up; turn; sing; thin; this, hw in white; zh in treasure; ə stands for a in ago, e in taken, i in pencil, o in lemon, u in circus.

**out·line** (out′ līn′) *n.* a summary or general description of, especially of a plan.

**outskirts** (out′ skurts′) *n.* the edges of an area or city.

**o·ver·joy** (ō′ vər joi′) *v.*, **o·ver·joyed.** to make very happy.

# P

**pan·sy** (pan′ zē) *n. pl.*, **pan·sies.** a flower with five fat overlapping petals and growing in a variety of colors.

**pan·ther** (pan′ thər) *n.* a large leopard with a black coat; another word for a cougar or jaguar.

**par·af·fin** (par′ə fin) *n.* a white, waxy substance used for making candles, waxed paper, and sealing jars of preserves.

**par·lor** (pär′ lər) *n.* a room in a home where visitors are received and entertained.

**par·ti·tion** (pär tish′ ən) *n.* something that divides, especially a structure that separates parts of a room.

**par·tridge** (pär′ trij) *n.* a plump game bird that has gray, brown, or white feathers.

**pat·tern** (pat′ ərn) *n.* an arrangement; design of colors, shapes, or lines.

**pe·cul·iar** (pi kyool′ yər) *adj.* strange or unusual; odd.

**pel·i·can** (pel′i kən) *n.* a web-footed water bird with a large pouch beneath the bill that is used for storing fish.

**pen·e·trate** (pen′ ə trāt′) *v.* to pass into or through, especially by force or with difficulty.

**pen·guin** (pen′ gwin) *n.* a sea bird that cannot fly, native to Antarctica and to the coastlines of southern continents. *Penguins* have feathers that are black on the back and white on the chest.

**per·son·al** (pur′sən əl) *adj.* private; relating to a particular person.

**pert** (purt) *adj.* 1. showing disrespect in speech or behavior. 2. spirited; lively.

**pheas·ant** (fez′ ənt) *n.* a long-tailed bird. The male often has brilliantly colored feathers.

**phoe·nix** (fē′ niks) *n.* a miraculous bird thought to live for 500 years and to die in the flames of a funeral pyre, and then to rise again from its own ashes.

**phos·pho·res·cence** (fos′ fa res′ əns) *n.* the giving off of light from a substance that has absorbed radiant energy.

**pig·weed** (pig′ wēd′) *n.* a strongly growing weedy plant.

**pil·lar** (pil′ ər) *n.* an upright structure that serves as a support for a building.

**pit·i·ful** (pit′ i fəl) *adj.* causing a feeling of sorrow or sympathy for the suffering of another.

**piv·ot** (piv′ ət) *n.* a point, shaft, or pin that something turns on.

**plague** (plāg) *v.* to trouble or annoy.

**plaid** (plad) *n.* a pattern that has narrow and wide stripes of different colors crossing one another at right angles.

**pod** (pod) *n.* the part of certain plants, such as a pea or bean, that carries the seeds.

**point·ed** (poin′ tid) *adj.* clearly aimed at or referring to a person or thing. —**point′ed·ly,** *adv.*

**pole·cat** (pōl′ kat′) *n.* a small, meat-eating animal closely related to the weasel, having long, soft, gray fur.

**poll** (pōl) *n.* a survey of public opinion on a subject.

**pom·pous** (pom′ pəs) *adj.* showing too much dignity or self-importance; pretentious.

**pop·lar** (pop′ lər) *n.* a kind of fast-growing tree, with pale ridged bark and broad leaves.

**pop·u·la·tion** (pop′ yə lā′ shən) *n.* the number of people living in an area or place.

**por·ce·lain** (pôr′ sə lin) *n.* a fine material made from clay that is hard and white.

**port·a·ble** (pôr′ tə bəl) *adj.* that can be carried easily, especially by hand.

**pos·i·tive** (poz′ ə tiv) *adj.* admitting of no question or doubt; certain, convinced. —**pos′ i·tive·ly,** *adv.*

**pouch** (pouch) *n.* 1. a bag or sack. 2. any baglike part of an animal, such as under the bill of a pelican.

**prick** (prik) *v.,* **pricked, prick·ing.** to raise the ears to an erect position.

**pri·ma·ri·ly** (prī mer′ ə lē) *adv.* chiefly; mostly.

**pro** (prō) *n.* short for professional; in golf, an expert golfer employed by a golf course.

**pro·ces·sion** (prə sesh′ ən) *n.* a group of persons moving along in an orderly manner, often in a long line.

**proc·la·ma·tion** (prok′lə mā′shən) *n.* an official announcement.

**pro·fes·sion** (prə fesh′ən) *n.* an occupation that requires special education or training.

**prune** (prōōn) *v.* 1. to cut off. 2. to remove unnecessary or unwanted parts from.

**pros·pect** (pros′ pekt) *n.* something looked forward to or expected.

**prov·en·der** (prov′ ən dər) *n.* dry food for livestock.

**prowl** (proul) *v.* to move about quietly or secretly, as in search of prey.

**pul·ley** (pool′ ē) *n.* a grooved wheel on which a rope or chain is pulled, usually used to lift heavy loads.

**pur·sue** (pər sōō′) *v.* 1. to follow in order to capture or kill. 2. to go along; follow. 3. to strive for; seek.

**pur·suit** (pər sōōt′) *n.* the act of following in order to overtake.

# Q

**quail** (kwāl) *n.* a game bird that has gray or brown feathers that are often speckled with white.

**qual·i·fy** (kwol′ə fī) *v.,* **qual·i·fied, qual·i·fy·ing.** to make fit, as for a certain job or task.

**quill** (kwil) *n.* a large, stiff feather.

**quiv·er** (kwiv′ər) *v.,* **quiv·ered, quiv·er·ing.** to shake slightly; tremble.

---

**PRONUNCIATION KEY**
at; āpe; cär; end; mē; it; īce; hot; ōld; fôrk; wood; fōōl; oil; out; up; turn; sing; thin; this, hw in white; zh in treasure; ə stands for a in ago, e in taken, i in pencil, o in lemon, u in circus.

# R _____

**ram·ble** (ram′ bəl) *v.*, **ram·bled,**
**ram·bling.** to go about or move about
aimlessly; roam.

**re·as·sur·ing** (rē′ ə shoor′ ing) *adj.* giving
confidence or courage in.

**re·cov·er** (rē′ kuv′ ər) *v.*, **re·cov·ered,**
**re·cov·er·ing.** to get back something
lost or stolen.

**re·cre·a·tion·al** (rek′ rē ā′ shə nəl) *adj.*
relating to any form of amusement
or relaxation.

**red·wood** (red′ wood) *n.* the soft, light
wood from a tall evergreen tree having a thick reddish-brown bark,
found only along the western coast of
North America.

**reef** (rēf) *n.* a ridge of sand, rock, or coral
that lies near the surface of the sea.

**re·flect** (ri flekt′) *v.*, **re·flect·ed, re·flect·ing.**
to give back an image of; mirror.

**re·frain** (ri frān′) *n.* phrase or verse in a
song or poem that is repeated reg-
ularly, especially at the end of each
stanza.

**ref·uge** (ref′ yōōj) *n.* a shelter or protection as from danger or trouble; safe
place.

**re·gain** (rē gān′) *v.* to get back; recover;
reach again.

**rein** (rān) *n.* the long, narrow straps attached at either side of a horse's
mouth and used to control the movement of the horse.

**re·late** (ri lāt′) *v.* to report the events of; tell.

**re·lease** (ri lēs′) *v.*, **re·leased, re·leas·ing.** to
set free.

**re·luc·tant** (ri luk′ tənt) *adj.* feeling
hesitation or unwillingness.
—**re·luc′ tant·ly,** *adv.*

**re·spect·a·ble** (ri spek′tə bəl) *adj.* showing
proper standards of conduct; honest
and decent.

**re·store** (ri stôr′) *v.*, **re·stored, re·stor·ing.**
to bring back; reestablish.

**rhyth·mi·cal** (rith′ mi kəl) *adj.* char-
acterized by a regular or orderly
repetition of sound or movement.
—**rhyth′ mi·cal·ly,** *adv.*

**ri·dic·u·lous** (ri dik′ yə ləs) *adj.* laughable;
silly. —**ri·dic′u·lous·ly,** *adv.*

**rig** (rig) *v.*, **rigged, rig·ging.** to make or
build in a makeshift way.

**roe** (rō) *n.* the eggs of fish.

**rough** (ruf) *n.* the unmowed part of a
golf course surrounding the fairways
and greens.

**ru·ral** (roor′ əl) *adj.* relating to the
country.

**rush** (rush) *n.* a plant resembling reeds or
grass, found in marshy areas, having
thin, often hollow stems.

**rut** (rut) *v.*, **rut·ted, rut·ting.** to make a
groove or track in the road by contin-
uous wear.

# S _____

**sa·la·mi** (sə lä′ mē) *n.* a sausage made of
pork or beef and spices.

**sanc·tu·a·ry** (sangk′ chōō er′ē) *n.* 1. any
place of refuge or protection. 2. an
area where birds and animals are protected from hunters.

**scamp** (skamp) *n.* 1. a worthless, dishon-
est person. 2. a mischevious or
playful person, especially a youngster.

**scam·per** (skam′ pər) *v.* to run quickly; to
move about playfully.

**scheme** (skēm) *v.*, **schemed, schem·ing.** to

plan something, especially in a secret way; plot.

**scoff** (skof) *v.*, **scoffed, scoff·ing.** to mock; jeer.

**scorn·ful** (skôrn′ fəl) *adj.* showing or feeling hatred or contempt for someone or something considered bad.

**scrag·gly** (skrag′lē) *adj.* having a ragged or rough appearance.

**sculp·ture** (skulp′ chər) *n.* a figure or design made by carving stone or marble, modeling clay or wax, or casting a metal.

**scur·ry** (skur′ ē) *v.*, **scur·ried, scur·ry·ing.** to move hurriedly.

**sec·tor** (sek′ tər) *n.* a particular division or part.

**se·cure** (si kyoor′) *adj.* 1. not likely to be taken away; guaranteed. 2. safe from danger. 3. free from worry. —*v.*, **se·cured.** 1. to get. 2. to fasten firmly. —**se·cure′ly,** *adv.*

**sedge** (sej) *n.* a grassy plant that grows in marshes.

**seize** (sēz) *v.*, **seized, seiz·ing.** to take hold of suddenly and forcibly; grab on to; to capture or arrest.

**sel·dom** (sel′ dəm) *adv.* not often; on a few occasions; rarely.

**sem·i·au·to·mat·ic** (sem′ ē ô′ tə mat′ik) *adj.* partly automatic, or acting by itself.

**se·rene** (sə rēn′) *adj.* peaceful; calm.

**shaft** (shaft) *n.* the long, straight handle of a tool, or piece of sports equipment, such as in a hammer or golf club.

**sheaf** (shēf) *n.* any bundle of things of the same kind.

**shell·fish** (shel′ fish′) *n.* any animal having a shell and living in water. *Shrimps,*

*lobsters, clams, and oysters are shellfish.*

**shin·gle** (shing′ gəl) *v.*, **shin·gled, shin·gling.** to cover with thin pieces of wood or other material.

**ship·wreck** (ship′ rek′) *n.* the remains of a wrecked ship.

**shut·ter** (shut′ər) *n.* a moveable panel for a door or window, used to shut out light or to give protection or privacy.

**siege** (sēj) *n.* the surrounding of an enemy for a long period of time in order to cut off supplies and force surrender.

**sift** (sift) *v.*, **sift·ed, sift·ing.** 1. to separate. 2. to examine closely.

**sit·u·a·tion** (sich′ oo ā′shən) *n.* a condition or state of affairs; a position.

**slab** (slab) *n.* a broad, flat, and usually thick piece of some material.

**sloop** (sloop) *n.* a sailboat.

**smug** (smug) *adj.* too highly pleased with oneself; self-satisfied. —**smug′ ly,** *adv.*

**snooze** (snooz) *n.* a nap; doze.

**snow·shoe** (snō′ shoo′) *n.* a light wooden frame strung with a webbing of rawhide, fastened to the foot. Used for walking over deep snow without sinking in.

**soothe** (sooth) *v.* to make quiet or calm; comfort.

**sor·rel** (sôr′ əl) *n.* a reddish-brown colored horse.

---

**PRONUNCIATION KEY**
at; āpe; cär; end; mē; it; īce; hot; ōld; fôrk; wood; fool; oil; out; up; turn; sing; thin; this, hw in white; zh in treasure; ə stands for a in ago, e in taken, i in pencil, o in lemon, u in circus.

**sou·ve·nir** (sōō′ və nēr′) *n.* something that is kept as a reminder of a person, place or event; memento.

**span** (span) *n.* a part or section between two supports.

**spe·cif·i·cal·ly** (spi sif′ ik ə lē) *adv.* definitely; explicitly.

**spec·ta·cles** (spek′ tə kəls) *n.* a pair of eyeglasses.

**spike** (spīk) *n.* a large, heavy nail.

**spin·dly** (spind′lē) *adj.* having a tall and thin shape.

**spi·ral** (spī′ rəl) *n.* a three-dimensional curve that winds around a cylinder or cone.

**spire** (spīr) *n.* a tall, pointed structure built on the top of a tower.

**spit** (spit) *n.* a thin, pointed rod on which meat is roasted over a fire.

**sprawl** (sprôl) *v.* to spread out in a straggling manner.

**sprout** (sprout) *n.* a bean pod, used when very young, as a vegetable.

**squad** (skwod) *n.* a military unit, usually composed of ten men.

**stam·mer** (stam′ər) *v.* **stam·mered, stam·mer·ing.** to speak haltingly, especially by repeating a letter or sound.

**stash** (stash) *v.* to store or hide for safekeeping or future use.

**sta·tion·er·y** (stā′shə ner′ē) *n.* writing paper and envelopes.

**stealth·y** (stel′thē) *adj.* moving or acting in a secret manner. —**stealth′ i·ly,** *adv.*

**stern¹** (sturn) *adj.* severe or strict; harsh. —**stern′ly,** *adv.*

**stern²** (sturn) *n.* the rear part of a boat.

**stilt** (stilt) *n. pl.,* **stilts.** a long pole with a footrest which allows the wearer to walk above the ground.

**stodg·y** (stoj′ē) *adj.* 1. very old-fashioned and stuffy; dull. 2. (of food) heavy and thick; hard to digest.

**stow** (stō) *v.,* **stowed, stow·ing.** to put or pack away, especially in a neat manner.

**strad·dle** (strad′əl) *v.,* **strad·dled, strad·dling.** to sit, stand, or walk with one leg on each side of.

**strained** (strānd) *adj.* not natural; forced.

**strand·ed** (strand′ əd) *adj.* left in a difficult or helpless position.

**struc·ture** (struk′ chər) *n.* anything that is built, arranged, or organized, such as a building or bridge.

**strut** (strut) *v.,* **strut·ted, strut·ting.** to walk in a vain or conceited manner.

**stud** (stud) *v.,* **stud·ded, stud·ding.** to be scattered or spread over.

**sub·urb** (sub′ urb) *n.* an area where people live on the outer edge of a city.

**sun·flow·er** (sun′ flou′ər) *n.* a large plant with rays of petals surrounding a yellow or purplish-brown disk, usually with seeds in it.

**su·pe·ri·or** (sə pēr′ē ər) *adj.* 1. higher than the average in quality. 2. haughty; like a snob.

**surf·board** (surf′ bôrd′) *n.* a long, flat board used to ride on waves.

**sus·pi·cious** (sə spish′ əs) *adj.* tending to arouse distrust or uncertainty; questionable.

**swerve** (swurv) *v.,* **swerved, swerv·ing.** to turn aside suddenly.

**swollen** (swō′ lən) *adj.* made larger by swelling.

# T

**tam·a·rind** (tam′ə rind) *n.* a tropical tree that bears small yellow flowers and juicy fruit.

**tap·es·try** (tap′ is trē) *n.* a heavy woven fabric decorated with design or pictures often showing historical events.

**tar** (tär) *n.* a thick, dark, sticky substance often used to waterproof.

**tech·no·log·i·cal** (tek′ nə loj′i kəl) *adj.* relating to the use of specific knowledge for practical purposes.

**temp·ta·tion** (temp tā′shən) *n.* something that persuades someone to do something wrong.

**ten·e·ment** (ten′ ə mənt) *n.* an apartment building, often located in a slum.

**tense** (tens) *v.* **tensed, tens·ing.** to become stretched or strained.

**tet·a·nus** (tet′ən əs) *n.* an often death-causing disease caused by a germ that usually enters the body through a puncture wound or cut.

**thick·et** (thik′ it) *n.* a dense growth of shrubs or bushes.

**this·tle** (this′ əl) *n.* a prickly plant that has red or purple flowers.

**til·ing** (tī′ ling) *n.* a group of tiles, or thin porcelain slabs used to cover floors and walls.

**tim·ber** (tim′ bər) *n.* a single piece of wood used in construction; beam.

**to·bog·gan** (tə bog′ən) *v.*, **to·bog·ganed, to·bog·gan·ing.** to coast or ride, as on a toboggan or sled.

**ton·sil** (ton′ səl) *n.* either of a pair of oval masses of spongy tissue on each side of the tongue at the back of the mouth.

**trek** (trek) *n.* a journey, especially one that is slow or difficult.

**trod·den** (trod′ən) a past participle of **tread**: to walk on; trample; crush.

**trough** (trôf) *n.* a long, deep, narrow container, used especially for holding water.

**trudge** (truj) *v.*, **trudged, trudg·ing.** to walk in a steady, slow manner; plod.

**tur·ret** (tur′ it) *n.* a small tower.

# U

**un·grat·i·fied** (un grat′ə fīd′) *adj.* not satisfied; discontented.

**un·heed·ed** (un hēd′ əd) *adj.* unnoticed.

**u·ni·son** (yōō′nə sən) *n.* perfect agreement; said or sung at the same time.

**up·heav·al** (up hē′ vəl) *n.* violent disturbance or change.

**up·roar** (up′ rôr′) *n.* a state of noisy or confused excitement or disorder.

**urn** (urn) *n.* a vase with a foot or base; a container.

# V

**va·cant** (vā′ kənt) *adj.* containing no one or nothing; empty.

**vain** (vān) *adj.* overly proud of one's appearance and abilities; conceited.

**ven·dor** (ven′ dər) *n.* a person who sells goods.

---

**PRONUNCIATION KEY**
at; āpe; cär; end; mē; it; īce; hot; ōld; fôrk; wood; fōōl; oil; out; up; turn; sing; thin; this, hw in white; zh in treasure; ə stands for a in ago, e in taken, i in pencil, o in lemon, u in circus.

**ven·i·son** (ven'ə sən) *n.* the flesh of a deer, used as food.

**ver·sion** (vur' zhən) *n.* a different or changed form of something.

**ver·ti·cal** (vur' ti kəl) *adj.* upright; not horizontal.

**vi·brate** (vī' brāt) *v.* to move back and forth or up and down rapidly.

**vow** (vou) *v.*, **vowed, vow·ing.** to promise or pledge seriously.

# W _____

**waist·coat** (wes' kət) *n.* vest.

**wal·low** (wol' ō) *v.*, **wal·lowed, wal·low·ing.** to toss or roll about in something.

**wa·ry** (wer' ē) *adj.* always on the alert; watchful; cautious.

**wea·ry** (wēr' ē) *adj.* extremely tired. —**wea' ri·ly,** *adv.*

**wharf** (hwôrf) *n. pl.*, **wharves.** a structure built along a shore to be used as a landing place for boats and ships; dock.

**whelk** (hwelk) *n.* a large snail that lives in saltwater.

**wheel·house** (hwēl' hous') *n.* a deck of a ship that shelters the steering wheel and the pilot.

**wick·er·work** (wik'ər wurk') *n.* something made of twigs woven together, as in furniture or a basket.

**wil·low** (wil' ō) *n.* a tree or shrub with slender leaves and branches, that often droop to the ground.

**with·er·ing** (with' ər ing) *adj.* scornful; causing something to shrivel up, figuratively.

**woe·be·gone** (wō' bi gôn') *adj.* showing great sorrow or grief; mournful.

**wrench** (rench) *v.*, **wrenches.** to twist, turn, or pull with a sudden, sharp motion.

# XYZ _____

**zin·ni·a** (zin' ē ə) *n.* a plant with colorful flowers.

(Acknowledgments continued)

"The Deer, the Deer" is from Bureau of American Ethnology Bulletin 165, *Music of Acoma, Isleta, Cochiti, and Zuni Pueblos* by Frances Densmore, Smithsonian Institution, Washington, D.C. 1957. Reprinted by permission of the Smithsonian Institution Press.

"Defining Delicious" is adapted from THE SEARCH FOR DELICIOUS by Natalie Babbitt. © 1969 by Natalie Babbitt. Reprinted by permission of Farrar, Straus and Giroux, Inc. and Chatto & Windus, Ltd., London.

"Diving Class" is from YOURS TILL NIAGARA FALLS, ABBY by Jane O'Connor. Copyright © 1979 by Jane O'Connor. Reprinted by permission of Scholastic Inc.

"For Mugs" is from 4-WAY STOP AND OTHER POEMS by Myra Cohn Livingston. Copyright © 1976 by Myra Cohn Livingston. Reprinted by permission of Marian Reiner for the author.

"Fox!" is from THE MIDNIGHT FOX by Betsy Byars. Copyright © 1968 by Betsy Byars. Reprinted by permission of Viking Penguin, Inc.

"The Fun They Had" is from "The Fun They Had" by Isaac Asimov. © 1954 by Mercury Press, Inc. Reprinted from *The Magazine of Fantasy and Science Fiction* by permission of the author.

"The Girl Who Saved a Train" by John Loveland from *Golden Magazine* copyright © 1970 by Review Publishing Company, Indianapolis, Ind. Adapted by permission of the publisher.

"A Hike in New York City" is from IN ONE ERA AND OUT THE OTHER by Sam Levenson. Copyright © 1973 by Sam Levenson. Reprinted by permission of Simon & Schuster, Inc. and Harold Matson Literary Agency.

"How Will Computers Affect Our Future?" is from "How Will Computers Affect Our Future?" by Nancy Barton which appeared in *Cobblestone's* June 1984 issue: *Computers*. Copyright © 1984 Cobblestone Publishing, Inc., Peterborough, NH 03458. Reprinted by permission of the publisher.

"I Never Had a Lesson" is from "I Never Had A Lesson" by Lee Trevino and Sam Blair which appeared originally in *Boys' Life,* March 1985. Copyright 1985 Lee Trevino and Sam Blair. Reprinted by permission of the authors.

"If Once You Have Slept On An Island" is from TAXIS AND TOADSTOOLS by Rachel Field. Copyright 1926 by the Century Company. Reprinted by permission of Doubleday & Company, Inc. and World's Work Ltd., London.   .

"If You Dare" is from "If You Dare" by Roxie and Andy Shirk and appeared originally in *Cricket* Magazine. Copyright © 1983 by Roxie and Andy Shirk and reprinted by permission.

"The Indianapolis Ten-Mile Bicycle Race" is abridged and adapted from BICYCLE RIDER by Mary Scioscia. Copyright © 1983 by Mary Scioscia. Reprinted by permission of Harper & Row, Publishers, Inc.

"Keplik, the Match Man" is abridged and adapted from THE WITCH OF FOURTH STREET AND OTHER STORIES by Myron Levoy. Copyright © 1972 by Myron Levoy. Reprinted by permission of Harper & Row, Publishers, Inc.

"Loneliness" is adapted from pp. 25-41 in CHARLOTTE'S WEB by E. B. White with illustrations by Garth Williams. Text Copyright 1952, renewed 1980 by E. B. White, illustrations Copyright 1952, renewed 1980 by Garth Williams. Reprinted by permission of Harper & Row, Publishers, Inc. Text also by permission of Hamish Hamilton Ltd., London.

"maggie and milly and molly and may" from COMPLETE POEMS 1913-1962 by e. e. cummings. Copyright © 1956 by e. e. cummings. Reprinted by permission of Harcourt Brace Jovanovich, Inc. and Granada Publishing Ltd.